TOWER BIBLIOGRAPHICAL SERIES
NUMBER NINE

The T. S. Eliot Collection

of

The University of Texas at Austin

Compiled by

ALEXANDER SACKTON

Humanities Research Center

THE UNIVERSITY OF TEXAS AT AUSTIN

Frontispiece drawing by Wyndham Lewis, 1949

CONTENTS

ILLUSTRATIONS

PREFACE

This catalogue describes materials at The University of Texas at Austin which will be of interest and use to students of T. S. Eliot and his work. Published materials are numbered as in the revised edition of Donald Gallup's *T. S. Eliot: A Bibliography* (1969). Items unnumbered by Gallup are designated by a related Gallup number followed by a decimal addition. The aim is to describe distinctive features of the items held at Austin. Full bibliographical descriptions found in Gallup are not repeated. When more than one copy of a title is held, the duplicate is listed if it has a markedly unique feature. Exact duplicates are not listed. Manuscripts and other original materials are designated with letters unused in Gallup.

The T. S. Eliot Collection at the Humanities Research Center and in the Mirabeau B. Lamar Library has grown from the interests and efforts of many persons. Professor Leonidas W. Payne, who took an early interest in reading Eliot with his students at Austin, bought the books in the collection which have been in Austin the longest time. Major additions came from the private libraries of Philip Mairet, Alfred A. Knopf, Frederic Prokosch, Mary Trevelyan, and others. Eliot made some gifts directly to the library at Austin where the exhibition of his work in 1961 evoked his interest and cooperation.

I was helped by several persons to whom I would like to express my thanks. Mrs. Valerie Eliot was kind in answering inquiries and in granting permission to quote from some materials under copyright. Professor Donald Gallup permitted me to examine the revised edition of his bibliography when it was still in manuscript. Professor Warren Roberts, Director of the Humanities Research Center, invited me to undertake the project. The staff of the Humanities Research Center Library made arrangements to ease my work from day to day, and I remember the special helpfulness of Mrs. Mary Hirth, Mrs. Lois Garcia, and Mrs. Henriette Cline. I am grateful to Miss Letitia Blalock for her meticulous care in helping to prepare the final copy for the press. To my wife, Ivria, I can never adequately express my gratitude for her support in this as in all my undertakings.

ALEXANDER SACKTON

A

BOOKS AND PAMPHLETS

BY

T. S. ELIOT

Numbered as in Gallup, with the addition of subordinate numbers, in parenthesis, for listing more than one copy. Items unnumbered by Gallup are given a related number with decimal addition.

BOOKS AND PAMPHLETS

A1 PRUFROCK AND OTHER OBSERVATIONS London The Egoist 1917

First edition

(1) In original paper covers. In a black cloth folder and slipcase with leather spine. Inscribed on half title: "I have no doubt that this is the copy that Rodker used. The two quotations, from Lucian & Virgil, are certainly in my hand. With cordial wishes, to Frederic Prokosch, T. S. Eliot 15.v.33". The Greek quotation from Lucian is added in autograph on page 35 under the title "Mr. Apollinax," which is rewritten in block letters at the top of the page. The Latin quotation from Virgil is added in autograph on page 39 under the title "La Figlia che Piange." These additions to the text appear first in *Ara Vos Prec* (1920), published by John Rodker, but not in other editions before the American edition of *Poems 1909–1925* (1932). Prokosch (1908–) is the American poet and novelist who published Eliot's *Words for Music* (1934) and *Two Poems* (1935) in small private editions.

This is a review copy, with the publisher's slip completed in autograph. "The Egoist Press Ltd. have the pleasure of enclosing herewith a copy of *Prufrock and other Observations* for a favour of a review and would be grateful for a copy of your publication containing any notice which may appear. Size *7 x 5*; pp. *40* Prices *1/-net*. Date of publication *ready now.*"

(2) In original paper covers. In a blue cloth folder and slipcase. Signed on title page: "T. S. Eliot".

(3) In original paper covers. In a gray cloth folder and slipcase with leather spine. Enclosed loosely is "The Egoist Subscription Form." With bookplates of John Quinn, the American collector, and Alfred A. Knopf.

(4) In original paper covers. In a blue slipcase. With bookplate of L. W. Payne.

(5) In original paper covers. Signed on title page: "T. S. Eliot Austin: 23.iv.58".

(6) In original paper covers. In autograph on the title page: "Inscribed

for William Turner Levy by T. S. Eliot 15.xi.59". Levy (1922–) is the American teacher and Episcopal priest who was befriended by Eliot.

A2 EZRA POUND   HIS METRIC AND POETRY   New York   Alfred A. Knopf   1917

(1) In original paper boards. With bookplate of John Johnson.

(2) In original paper boards and dustwrapper. In autograph on title page: "Inscribed for William Turner Levy by his friend the author T. S. Eliot".

A3 POEMS   Richmond, Surrey   The Hogarth Press   1919

In original batik paper covers and a cloth folder. In "Lune de Miel," line 11, "capitaux" is printed for "chapiteaux." With bookplates of Oliver Brett and John Johnson.

A4a ARA VOS PREC   London   The Ovid Press   1920

First edition, limited to 264 copies

(1) In original black paper boards and yellow cloth spine; with a white paper label on spine printed with the corrected title, *Ara Vos Prec*, for *Ara Vus Prec* on title page. Number 76. With bookplate of Alfred A. Knopf.

(2) In original cloth boards; yellow spine with paper label as in (1). Number 142. With bookplate of John Johnson.

(3) In original cloth boards; yellow spine with paper label as in (1). Number 8 of 30 copies signed "T. S. Eliot". From the library of Holbrook Jackson. Enclosed loosely is an early photograph of T. S. Eliot clipped from a magazine.

A4b POEMS   New York   Alfred A. Knopf   1920

First American edition

(1) In original paper boards; in a blue cloth slipcase. With bookplate of John Johnson. Signed on flyleaf: "Edward J. O'Brien."

(2) In original paper boards. With bookplate of "F. R."

A4.1 POEMS   New York   Alfred A. Knopf   1927

In original paper boards with cloth spine and dustwrapper. With penciled notes by Leonidas W. Payne (1873–1945), formerly Professor of English at the University of Texas.

A5a THE SACRED WOOD   ESSAYS ON POETRY AND CRITICISM   London   Methuen & Co.   1920

First edition

(1) In original cloth and dustwrapper. "Methuen" on spine measures 3 mm., as in the earlier issue.

(2) In original cloth. Signed on title page: "T. S. Eliot Austin: 23.iv.58". With bookplate of G. Dudley Harbron.

(3) In original cloth; in a blue cloth slipcase. With bookplate of John Johnson.

(4) In original cloth. With bookplate of Oliver Brett. From the collection of Alfred A. Knopf.

A5b THE SACRED WOOD   ESSAYS ON POETRY AND CRITICISM   New York   Alfred A. Knopf   1921

American issue

In original cloth.

A5c THE SACRED WOOD   ESSAYS ON POETRY AND CRITICISM   London   Methuen & Co.   1928

Second edition

(1) In original cloth and dustwrapper. Pages unopened.

(2) In original cloth and dustwrapper. With bookplate of Alfred A. Knopf.

(3) In original cloth. With bookplate of John Johnson.

A6a THE WASTE LAND   New York   Boni and Liveright   1922

First edition

(1) In original flexible cloth. "Number 385" is stamped in type 5 mm.

high. On page 41 "mountain" is printed correctly, as in first copies. Signed on flyleaf: "Nicholas Moore".

(2) In original flexible cloth. "Number 466" is stamped in type 5 mm. high. On page 41 "mountain" is printed correctly. With bookplate of John Johnson.

(3) In original stiff cloth. "Number 629" is stamped in type 2 mm. high. On page 41 "a" has been dropped from the word "mountain." Signed on flyleaf: "S. T. Foote 1932".

(4) In original stiff cloth. "Number 735" is stamped in type 2 mm. high. On page 41 "a" has been dropped from the word "mountain." Signed on front paste-down: "C. E. Blake   Dartmouth".

A6c THE WASTE LAND   Richmond, Surrey   The Hogarth Press 1923

First English edition

(1) In original marbled paper boards, with the paper label in state 1. Pages unopened. Inscribed on flyleaf: "For Charles Whibley, Esq. with the author's humble respects. T. S. Eliot. 14.ix.23". With the following corrections of the text in Eliot's hand: "under" corrected to "over" (p. 7, l. 21); "coloured" corrected to "carven" (p. 9, l. 21), not "carvèd" as in the American edition; "MacMillan" corrected to "Cambridge" (p. 29, l. 5).

(2) In original marbled paper boards, with paper label in state 1. Inscribed on flyleaf: "To Edith Sitwell with the humble & sincere compliments of T. S. Eliot 3.iv.24". With autograph corrections as in copy (1).

(3) In original marbled paper boards, with paper label in state 1. In a blue cloth slipcase, with bookplate of John Johnson.

(4) In original marbled paper boards, with the paper label in state 2. Pages unopened.

A6d THE WASTE LAND   London   Faber & Faber   1961

Mardersteig edition, limited to 300 copies

In original marbled paper boards with parchment spine. Number 233. Signed: "T. S. Eliot".

A7 HOMAGE TO JOHN DRYDEN   THREE ESSAYS ON POETRY

OF THE SEVENTEENTH CENTURY   London   The Hogarth Press
1924

First edition

(1) In original paper wrappers. Signed on title page: "T. S. Eliot".

(2) In original paper wrappers. Signed on flyleaf: "Cecil Day Lewis
November/26".

A8a POEMS 1909–1925   London   Faber & Gwyer   1925

First edition, ordinary copies

(1) In original cloth and dustwrapper. Inscribed on flyleaf: "for Edith
Sitwell with the homage and regards of T. S. Eliot. 10.12.25".

(2) In original cloth and dustwrapper. Inscribed on flyleaf: "for my
dearest Vivien this book, which no one else will quite understand. T. S.
Eliot 25.xii.25".

(3) In original cloth, stamped on the cover in gold with the seal of
Marlborough College. Signed: "Louis MacNeice".

A8b   POEMS 1909–1925   London   Faber & Gwyer   1925

Signed copies, limited to 85, issued in 1926

(1) In original cloth. Number 48. Signed: "T. S. Eliot". With bookplate
of Alfred A. Knopf.

(2) In original cloth. Number 55. Signed: "T. S. Eliot". Pages unopened.

(3) In original cloth. Number 55, written in a different hand from that
of (2) above. Signed: "T. S. Eliot".

A8b.1 POEMS 1909–1925   London   Faber & Gwyer   1928

Third impression

In original cloth. From the library of W. Somerset Maugham.

A8c POEMS 1909–1925   New York   Chicago   Harcourt, Brace and
Company

First American edition

In original cloth and dustwrapper.

A9a JOURNEY OF THE MAGI   Drawings by E. McKnight Kauffer
London   Faber & Gwyer   1927

First edition, ordinary copies

In original paper wrappers. Inscribed "James Stephens from T. S. Eliot".

A9b JOURNEY OF THE MAGI   Drawings by E. McKnight Kauffer
London   Faber & Gwyer   1927

Signed copies, limited to 350

(1–5) In original paper boards. Numbers 34, 73, 111, 141, 151. Signed: "T. S. Eliot".

A9c JOURNEY OF THE MAGI   New York   William Edwin Rudge
1927

First American edition of 27 copies

In original paper wrappers and, together with seven other Ariel poems, the first year's series, in a brown cloth folder and slipcase with leather spine.

A10 SHAKESPEARE AND THE STOICISM OF SENECA   London
Oxford University Press   1927

First edition

In original paper wrappers. Inscribed: "J[ohn]. M[iddleton]. M[urry]. from T. S. E. I dare say I am altogether wrong."

A11a A SONG FOR SIMEON   Drawings by E. McKnight Kauffer
London   Faber & Gwyer   1928

First edition

In original paper wrappers. Inscribed: "For W. Rothenstein Esq. from T. S. Eliot 14.xii.28". Sir William Rothenstein had drawn a portrait of Eliot reproduced in *Twelve Portraits by William Rothenstein* (London: Faber & Faber, 1929).

A11b A SONG FOR SIMEON   Drawings by E. McKnight Kauffer
London   Faber & Gwyer   1928

Signed edition of 500 copies

(1–3) In original paper boards. Numbers 42, 49, 230. Signed: "T. S. Eliot".

(4) In original paper boards. Number 174. Signed: "T. S. Eliot". Inscribed on flyleaf: "For Alfred Knopf with friendship from E. McKnight Kauffer." With bookplate of Alfred A. Knopf.

(5) In original paper boards. Number 415. Signed: "T. S. Eliot". Inscribed on flyleaf: "With best wishes, E. McKnight Kauffer 1928–29".

A12a FOR LANCELOT ANDREWES   ESSAYS ON STYLE AND ORDER   London   Faber & Gwyer   1928

First edition

(1) In original cloth and dustwrapper. With bookplate of John Johnson.

(2) In original cloth and dustwrapper. With bookplate of Alfred A. Knopf.

A12b FOR LANCELOT ANDREWES   ESSAYS ON STYLE AND ORDER   Garden City, N. Y.   Doubleday, Doran and Company   1929

First American edition

(1) In original cloth and dustwrapper.

(2) In original cloth. With bookplate of Mitchell Kennerley.

A13a DANTE   London   Faber & Faber   1929

First edition, ordinary copies

In original paper boards and dustwrapper. With bookplate of Alfred A. Knopf.

A13b DANTE   London   Faber & Faber   1929

Signed copies, limited to 125

(1) In original cloth. Number 59. Signed: "T. S. Eliot". With bookplate of Alfred A. Knopf.

(2–5) In original cloth. Numbers 9, 94, 114, 121. Signed: "T. S. Eliot".

A14a ANIMULA   London   Faber & Faber   1929

First edition

In original paper wrappers.

A14b ANIMULA   London   Faber & Faber   1929

Signed edition of 400 copies

(1–4) In original paper boards. Numbers 44, 275, 302, 337. Signed: "T. S. Eliot".

A15a ASH-WEDNESDAY   New York   The Fountain Press   London
Faber & Faber   1930

First edition, limited to 600 copies

(1) In original cloth. Number 49. Signed: "T. S. Eliot". With bookplate of John Johnson.

(2) In original cloth. Number 408. Signed: "T. S. Eliot".

(3) In original cloth. Number 88. Signed: "T. S. Eliot". Signed on title page: "Hugh Scott Charles".

A15b ASH-WEDNESDAY   London   Faber & Faber   1930

First ordinary edition

(1) In original cloth and dustwrapper.

(2) In original cloth. Signed on flyleaf: "George Bowles Esqre."

(3) In original cloth. With bookplate of John Johnson.

A15c ASH-WEDNESDAY   New York   London   G. P. Putnam's Sons
1930

First American ordinary edition

In original cloth. With penciled notes in margins.

A16a ANABASIS   A POEM   by St.-J. Perse   with a translation into
English by T. S. Eliot   London   Faber & Faber   1930

First edition, first ordinary issue

In original cloth and dustwrapper.

A16b ANABASIS   A POEM   by St.-J. Perse   with a translation into
English by T. S. Eliot   London   Faber & Faber   1930

Signed copies, limited to 350

(1) In original cloth. Number 38. Signed: "T. S. Eliot". With bookplate
of John Johnson.

(2) In original cloth. "Out of Series." Signed: "T. S. Eliot".

A16c ANABASIS   A POEM   by St.-J. Perse   with a translation into
English by T. S. Eliot   London   Faber & Faber   1930

Second ordinary issue [1937]

Rebound in blue cloth.

A16d ANABASIS   A POEM   by St.-J. Perse   with a translation into
English by T. S. Eliot   New York   Harcourt, Brace and Company
1938

Second edition (first American edition)

In original cloth and dustwrapper. Inside flap of the dustwrapper
stamped "February 21 1938". Publication date was March 3. The flyleaf
has been cut out.

A16e ANABASIS   A POEM   by St.-J. Perse   translated by T. S.
Eliot   New York   Harcourt, Brace and Company   1949

Third edition, revised and corrected

In original cloth and dustwrapper. Signed on flyleaf: "Edith Sitwell".

A16e.1   ANABASIS   A POEM   by St.-J. Perse   translated by T. S.
Eliot   London   Faber & Faber   1959

English edition, revised and corrected

In original cloth and dustwrapper.

A17a MARINA   London   Faber & Faber   1930

First edition

(1) Proof copy. In original paper covers; in a blue cloth folder. With

"Datta Dayadhvam Damyata" in the drawing by E. McKnight Kauffer, and textual variations in lines 5 and 19, and with an extra line between lines 21 and 22. With bookplate of John Johnson.

(2) In original paper wrappers. Inscribed: "For the Master of University [College, Oxford?] from T. S. Eliot".

(3) In original paper wrappers. Signed: "T. S. Eliot".

A17b MARINA   London   Faber & Faber   1930

Limited edition of 400 copies

(1–4) In original paper boards. Numbers 156, 164, 244, 398. Signed: "T. S. Eliot".

A18a THOUGHTS AFTER LAMBETH   London   Faber & Faber 1931

First edition, ordinary copies

(1) In original paper wrappers. "Proof Copy Only" written in block letters on front.

(2) In original paper wrappers. Inscribed on wrappers: "J[ohn]. M[iddleton]. Murry from Tom".

(3) In original paper wrappers. Inscribed on wrappers: "to Sir Michael Sadler from T. S. Eliot". With bookplate of John Johnson.

(4) In original paper wrappers. Signed on title page: "T. S. Eliot".

A18b THOUGHTS AFTER LAMBETH   London   Faber & Faber 1931

Bound copies, limited to 300

In original cloth. Pages unopened.

A19a TRIUMPHAL MARCH   London   Faber & Faber   1931

First edition

(1) In original paper cover-title. Inscribed: "to I. A. Richards from T. S. Eliot".

(2) In original paper cover-title. Inscribed: "to Wystan Auden from T. S. Eliot".

A19b TRIUMPHAL MARCH   London   Faber & Faber   1931

Limited edition of 300 copies

(1) In original paper boards. Number 55. Signed: "T. S. Eliot".

(2) In original paper boards. Number 262. Signed: "T. S. Eliot". From the collection of Alfred A. Knopf.

(3) In original paper boards. Number 48. Signed: "T. S. Eliot". With an inscription on verso of flyleaf: "for Lady Ross—with love from Ted. E. McKnight Kauffer 1931–32". The poem is illustrated with drawings by Kauffer.

A20 CHARLES WHIBLEY   A MEMOIR   London   Oxford University Press   1931

First edition

In original paper covers.

A21a SELECTED ESSAYS   1917–1932   London   Faber & Faber   1932

First edition (English), ordinary copies

(1) In original cloth. Pages unopened.

(2) In original cloth and dustwrapper.

(3) In original cloth. With bookplate of John Johnson.

A21b SELECTED ESSAYS   1917–1932   London   Faber & Faber   1932

Signed copies, limited to 115

(1) In original blue vellum. Number 96. Pages unopened. Signed: "T. S. Eliot". With bookplate of Alfred A. Knopf.

(2) In original blue vellum. Number 29. Pages unopened. Signed: "T. S. Eliot". Signed on flyleaf: "Dorothy G. Gianetti".

A21c SELECTED ESSAYS   1917–1932   New York   Harcourt, Brace and Company   1932

First edition (American)

In original cloth and dustwrapper. "Advance Copy" slip pasted on dust-wrapper, with the release date "September 15."

A21d SELECTED ESSAYS   New York   Harcourt, Brace and Company   1950

Second American edition

In original cloth.

A22a JOHN DRYDEN   THE POET THE DRAMATIST THE CRITIC   New York   Terence & Elsa Holliday   1932

First edition, ordinary copies

In original paper boards. With bookplate of John Johnson.

A22b JOHN DRYDEN   THE POET THE DRAMATIST THE CRITIC   New York   Terence & Elsa Holliday   1932

Signed copies, limited to 110

(1) In original marbled paper boards with cloth spine. Number 24. Signed: "T. S. Eliot". With bookplate of Alfred A. Knopf.

(2) In original marbled paper boards with cloth spine. Number 98. Signed: "T. S. Eliot".

A23 SWEENEY AGONISTES FRAGMENTS OF AN ARISTO-PHANIC MELODRAMA   London   Faber & Faber   1932

First edition

In original paper boards and dustwrapper. With bookplate of Alfred A. Knopf.

A24a THE USE OF POETRY AND THE USE OF CRITICISM   London   Faber & Faber   1933

First edition (English)

(1) In original cloth and dustwrapper.

(2) In original cloth. With bookplate of John Johnson.

A24c THE USE OF POETRY AND THE USE OF CRITICISM   London   Faber & Faber   1964

Faber paper covered editions

In original paper covers. With a new preface dated 1963.

A25a AFTER STRANGE GODS   A PRIMER OF MODERN HERESY   London   Faber & Faber   1934

First edition

(1) In original cloth and dustwrapper.

(2) In original cloth. With bookplate of John Johnson.

(3) In original cloth. Signed "Daniel Cory" on flyleaf. Autograph notes throughout by George Santayana (pp. 24, 46, 53, 54, 55, 59, 60, 63, 67, 68).

A25b AFTER STRANGE GODS   A PRIMER OF MODERN HERESY   New York   Harcourt, Brace and Company   1934

First American edition

In original cloth and dustwrapper. With signature on flyleaf: "R. M. Leveridge   Nov. 1940   New York."

A26a THE ROCK   A PAGEANT PLAY   London   Faber & Faber   1934

First edition

(1) In original paper wrappers.

(2) In original paper boards and dustwrapper. With bookplate of John Kopler.

A26b THE ROCK   A PAGEANT PLAY   New York   Harcourt, Brace and Company   1934

First American edition

In original cloth and dustwrapper. "Advance Copy" slip pasted on dustwrapper, with the date for release "August 23, 1934."

A27 ELIZABETHAN ESSAYS London Faber & Faber 1934

First edition

State 2. On the half title the series number is printed correctly as "24".
In original cloth and dustwrapper. With bookplate of John Johnson.

A28.1 WORDS FOR MUSIC New Haven, Connecticut Privately
Published 1934

Trial copies

(1) Original proof for this edition, containing the entire text except
title. With penciled corrections, and with autograph note by Frederic
Prokosch on a separate loose sheet: " 'Words for Music' printed and
bound by me in New Haven in 1934." According to Gallup this edition
was printed "for Frederic Prokosch at the 'Bryn Mawr Press,' Bryn
Mawr, Pennsylvania."

(2) In original marbled paper wrappers. With a white paper label
(3½ x 5 cm.) printed in Garamond. The word "number" in the colophon
is canceled, and the following in autograph is signed F[rederic]. P[ro-
kosch].: "one of four preliminary trial copies in Garamond (which was
then discarded in favor of Sans-Serif)." This copy has a title page, also
in Garamond, with the word "Christmas", which was dropped in the
regular issue.

(3) Like copy (2), with the autograph note signed, "F. P.", but with a
white paper label (3 x 5 cm.) printed in sans-serif. Signed on title page:
"T. S. Eliot".

A28 WORDS FOR MUSIC New Haven, Connecticut Privately
Published 1934

First separate edition, "twenty copies . . . printed for author"

(1) In original marbled paper wrappers with a white paper label. Number 5 of six copies printed on Oxhead.

(2) In original marbled paper wrappers with a white paper label. Number 6 of six copies printed on Oxhead. Inscribed: "Marianne Moore
from T. S. E." In the last line of "Virginia" a line is drawn through the
word "red", and, in Eliot's autograph, the word "river" is written in the
margin, correcting "Red river, red river" to "Red river, river, river".

(3) In decorated paper wrappers with a silver paper label. Number IV of six copies printed on Leipsig.

(4) In gold paper wrappers with a white paper label. Number e of six copies printed on Rives.

(5) In red and gold paper wrappers with a gold paper label; and a cellophane dustwrapper with a paper label. Number A of two copies printed on Imperial vellum. With bookplate of Frederic Prokosch. Copies (1), (3), (4), and (5) are in a black cloth folder and slipcase with leather spine.

A29a MURDER IN THE CATHEDRAL   Canterbury   H. J. Golden 1935

First (acting) edition

(1) In original paper covers. With the signature of Charles C. Elam, the Cathedral Banner bearer, and, on the verso of flyleaf, signatures of the players, the stage managers, and the producer. Signed by T. S. Eliot on page [1].

(2) In original paper covers. From the collection of Alfred A. Knopf.

(3) In original paper covers. With bookplate of John Johnson.

A29b MURDER IN THE CATHEDRAL   London   Faber & Faber 1935

First complete edition

In original cloth and dustwrapper. Signed on flyleaf: "Constance Palmer".

A29d MURDER IN THE CATHEDRAL   London   Faber & Faber 1937

Third edition

(1) In original cloth. Autograph note signed on flyleaf: "Text for 4th Edition May I see proof, & this copy with it? TSE[liot]". With revisions throughout.

(2) Fifth reprint, August 1943. In original cloth and dustwrapper. Inscribed: "To Miss Mary Trevelyan (Warden) with the compliments of Old Possum (Bard) 25.xii.43". Loosely enclosed is a program for the performance at the Lyric Theater.

A29f.1 MURDER IN THE CATHEDRAL New York Harcourt, Brace and Company 1935

In original cloth and dustwrapper. From the Florence Hamilton Collection. Like the first edition, except for absence of "first edition" on verso of title leaf.

A29i THE FILM OF MURDER IN THE CATHEDRAL by T. S. Eliot and George Hoellering London Faber & Faber 1952

First Faber edition

(1) In original cloth and dustwrapper. Signed on flyleaf: "J. Clifford Gill 1953".

(2) In original cloth. With bookplate of John Johnson.

A29j THE FILM OF MURDER IN THE CATHEDRAL by T. S. Eliot and George Hoellering New York Harcourt, Brace and Company 1952

First American edition

In original paper boards, cloth spine, and dustwrapper.

A30 TWO POEMS Cambridge, England Privately Published 1935

First edition

(1) Original proof containing the entire text except title and colophon. With the stamp of the University Press, Cambridge, dated 25 October 1935. And with an autograph note by Frederic Prokosch: "Proof in Centaur type. One of two copies." Also with autograph note by Frederic Prokosch on a separate loose sheet: " 'Two Poems,' printed at the Cambridge University Press (England) and bound by me in 1935."

(2) In decorated paper wrappers with a gray paper label. Number 2 of five copies printed on Arches.

(3) In yellow paper wrappers with a silver paper label. Number I of five copies printed on Normandie.

(4) In tan paper wrappers with a gray paper label. This binding is not described in Gallup. Number c of five copies printed on Bremen.

(5) In marbled paper wrappers with a white paper label. Number B of five copies printed on Brussels parchment.

(6) In silver paper wrappers with a red paper label. Number X, one of two copies, printed on red Florentine. Copies (1–6) are in a black cloth folder and slipcase with leather spine.

A31a ESSAYS ANCIENT & MODERN London Faber & Faber 1936

First edition

(1) In original cloth and dustwrapper.

(2) In original cloth. With bookplate of John Johnson.

A31b ESSAYS ANCIENT AND MODERN New York Harcourt, Brace and Company 1936

First American edition

In original cloth and dustwrapper.

A32a COLLECTED POEMS 1909–1935 London Faber & Faber 1936

First edition

(1) In original cloth and dustwrapper. With penciled notes by Professor Leonidas W. Payne in margins and on loose slips.

(2) In original cloth. With bookplate of John Johnson and, loosely inserted, a photograph cut from a newspaper of Wyndham Lewis standing beside a portrait of Eliot.

A32b COLLECTED POEMS 1909–1935 New York Harcourt, Brace and Company 1936

First American edition

In original cloth and parts of the dustwrapper loosely inserted.

A32b.1 COLLECTED POEMS 1909–1935 London Faber & Faber 1942

Fifth impression

In original cloth and dustwrapper. From the library of Edith Sitwell, with her autograph notes on flyleaf.

A32b.2 COLLECTED POEMS   1909–1935   London   Faber & Faber
1944

Seventh impression

In original cloth. Inscribed: "to Mary Trevelyan for use in Belgium T S
Eliot 22.iii.45".

A32b.3 COLLECTED POEMS   1909–1935   London   Faber & Faber
1954

Fifteenth impression

In original cloth. From the library of W. Somerset Maugham.

A33a THE FAMILY REUNION   London   Faber and Faber   1939

First edition

(1) Proof copy. In original yellow paper covers. With bookplate of John
Johnson.

(2) In original cloth and dustwrapper. Inscribed on flyleaf: "to J. B.
Priestly with the author's homage. T. S. Eliot 11.v.39".

(3) In original cloth and dustwrapper. Signed on title page: "T. S. Eliot".

(4) In original cloth and dustwrapper. Inscribed: "to S/sgt. Mary Trevelyan from T. S. Eliot. And don't lose this one." With autograph note
by Mary Trevelyan on page [10].

(5) In original cloth and dustwrapper. Inscribed on title page: "T. S.
Eliot Austin 23.iv.58".

(6) In original cloth and dustwrapper. With signature on flyleaf of Una
Ellis-Fermor, and notes throughout in her hand, with an extra sheet,
loosely inserted, of notes on "T. S. Eliot. The Developing Dramatist."

(7) In original cloth and dustwrapper. Autograph note on title page
under the canceled name of the author: "Inscribed for William Turner
Levy by T. S. Eliot July 26, 1948".

A33b THE FAMILY REUNION   New York   Harcourt, Brace and
Company   1939

First American edition

In original cloth. With bookplate of Nelson Wylie.

A34a OLD POSSUM'S BOOK OF PRACTICAL CATS   London
Faber & Faber   1939

First edition

(1) Proof copy. In original yellow paper covers.

(2) In original cloth and dustwrapper. Pages unopened.

(3) In original cloth. With bookplate of John Johnson.

(4) In original cloth and dustwrapper.
Inscribed on half title:
> to Miss Mary Trevelyan
> Thanks a million
> > O[ld]. P[ossum].

On a card (9 x 11½ cm.) pasted below this signature are the following
lines in Eliot's autograph:
> Miss Mary Trevelyan
> Is like Godfrey of Bouillon
> For *his* name means *pottage*
> And *her* name means *cottage.*
> (Remove if you will
> The elegant varnish
> Provided by Cornish,
> It means 'public house
> > under the hill.')

A34b OLD POSSUM'S BOOK OF PRACTICAL CATS   New York
Harcourt, Brace and Company   1939

First American edition

In original cloth and dustwrapper.

A34c OLD POSSUM'S BOOK OF PRACTICAL CATS   London   Faber
& Faber   1940

First illustrated edition

In original cloth and dustwrapper.

A34d.1 OLD POSSUM'S BOOK OF PRACTICAL CATS   London
Faber & Faber   1964

In original cloth.

A35a THE IDEA OF A CHRISTIAN SOCIETY   London   Faber &
Faber   1939

First edition

(1) In original cloth and dustwrapper. Pages unopened.

(2) In original cloth. With bookplate of John Johnson.

A35b THE IDEA OF A CHRISTIAN SOCIETY   New York   Harcourt,
Brace and Company   1940

First American edition

(1) In original cloth and dustwrapper.

(2) In original cloth. Signed on flyleaf: "Rosa Sherrod Penman".

A35xa THE WASTE LAND AND OTHER POEMS   London   Faber
& Faber   1940

First edition of this selection, made by the author

Proof copy. With original yellow paper covers bound in red cloth.

A35xb.1   THE WASTE LAND AND OTHER POEMS   New York
Harcourt, Brace and Company   1958

American edition

In original paper covers. The first American edition had been issued
in 1955.

A36a EAST COKER   London   The New English Weekly   1940

First edition

Unbound, as issued.

A36c EAST COKER   London   Faber & Faber   1940

Third (first Faber) edition

In original paper wrappers.

A36c.1 EAST COKER   London   Faber & Faber   1941

Fifth impression

In original paper wrappers. With marginal notes in the autograph of
A. E. Coppard.

A37a. BURNT NORTON   London   Faber & Faber   1941

First separate edition

(1) In original paper wrappers. Pages unopened.

(2) In original paper wrappers.

A37a.1 BURNT NORTON   London   Faber & Faber   1941

Second impression

(1) In original paper wrappers. With marginal notes in the autograph
of A. E. Coppard.

(2) In original paper wrappers. Signed on flyleaf: "Anne Hodgson".

A38 POINTS OF VIEW   London   Faber & Faber   1941

First edition

(1) In original cloth and dustwrapper. Signed on title page: "T. S.
Eliot".

(2) In original cloth. With bookplate of John Johnson.

A39 THE DRY SALVAGES   London   Faber & Faber   1941

First edition

(1) In original blue wrappers folded over stiff tan paper. Review copy
with publisher's note tipped in announcing date of publication, September 4, 1941.

(2) In original blue wrappers folded over stiff cream paper, the first
issue.

(3) In original blue wrappers folded over stiff gray paper. Inscribed
on half title: "for Philip Mairet from T. S. Eliot".

(4) In original blue wrappers folded over stiff blue paper. Autograph
correction, p. 7, signed "T. S. E.", changes "hermit [crab]" to "horseshoe [crab]".

(5) In original blue wrappers folded over stiff white paper. Pages un-opened.

(6) In original blue wrappers folded over stiff white paper. Signed on half title: "Ann Hodgson".

A40 THE CLASSICS AND THE MAN OF LETTERS London New York Toronto Oxford University Press 1942

First edition

(1) Page proof, with untrimmed margins. Two gatherings, each of 16 pages, are sewn together.

(2) In original paper wrappers. Inscribed on half title: "Philip Mairet from T. S. Eliot".

(3) In original paper wrappers. Inscribed on half title: "M[ary]. T[revelyan]. from T. S. E."

A41 THE MUSIC OF POETRY Glasgow Jackson, Son & Company 1942

First edition

(1) In original paper covers. Inscribed on cover: "P[hilip]. M[airet]. from T. S. E."

(2) In original paper covers. Signed on half title: "John Bale", with some pencil markings.

(3) In original paper covers. From the collection of Alfred A. Knopf.

A42 LITTLE GIDDING London Faber & Faber 1942

First edition

(1) In original paper covers; sewn, the earlier issue. Inscribed on cover: "Philip Mairet from T. S. Eliot".

(2) In original paper covers; stapled, the later issue. Signed on flyleaf: "Anne Hodgson".

(3)In original paper covers; sewn. Inscribed on front cover: "to Mary Trevelyan from T. S. Eliot". Autograph notes throughout by Mary Trevelyan.

A43a FOUR QUARTETS New York Harcourt, Brace and Company

1943

First edition

In original cloth and dustwrapper. Signed: "Rose Macaulay".

A43b FOUR QUARTETS   London   Faber & Faber   1944

First English edition

(1) In original cloth and dustwrapper.

(2) In original cloth and dustwrapper. With the book-prize plate of Mile End Hospital: "Joan M. Embleton. Dec. 20, 1944. Prize for Anatomy and Physiology".

(3) In original cloth. With bookplate of John Johnson.

A43c FOUR QUARTETS   London   Faber & Faber   1960

Limited edition of 290 copies

(1-2) In original marbled paper boards, and vellum spine, in marbled paper slipcase. Numbers 80, 204. Signed: "T. S. Eliot".

A44 REUNION BY DESTRUCTION REFLECTIONS ON A SCHEME FOR CHURCH UNION IN SOUTH INDIA   London The Pax House   1943

First edition

(1) In original brown covers, the earlier issue.

(2) In original tan covers, the later issue. Inscribed on front cover: "to M[ary]. T[revelyn]. from T. S. E."

A45a WHAT IS A CLASSIC?   London   Faber & Faber   1945

First edition, Virgil Society issue

(1) Page proof with autograph corrections, signed "T. S. E." and dated 27 October 1944.

(2) In original paper cover-title.

A45b WHAT IS A CLASSIC?   London   Faber & Faber   1945

First edition, ordinary issue

(1) In original cloth and dustwrapper. With autograph correction on title page signed: "TSE", changing the reported date of the address from the 16th of October to the 14th. Signed also, on title page under the canceled name of the author: "T. S. Eliot".

(2) In original cloth. Inscribed on flyleaf: "Philip Mairet from T. S. Eliot 7.ii.45".

(3) In original cloth and dustwrapper. Inscribed on flyleaf: "to Mary Trevelyan from T. S. Eliot 7.ii.45".

(4) In original cloth. With bookplate of John Johnson.

(5) In original cloth and dustwrapper. From the Alfred A. Knopf collection.

A46 DIE EINHEIT DER EUROPAISCHEN KULTUR   Berlin Carl Habel   1946

First edition

In original paper covers. "The Unity of European Culture" is printed opposite the German translation.

A47 A PRACTICAL POSSUM Cambridge, Massachusetts   Privately Published   1947

First edition of 80 copies

(1-2) In original paper covers. Numbers 39, 41.

A48 ON POETRY Concord, Massachusetts   Privately Published 1947

First edition of 750 copies

(1-2) In original paper covers. Numbers 7, 555.

A49 MILTON   Proceedings of the British Academy   London   Geoffrey Cumberledge   1947

First edition

In original paper cover-title. Inscribed on cover: "to Mary Trevelyan with the author's compliments. (This essay is serious). T. S. Eliot 10. xi. 47".

A50 A SERMON PREACHED IN MAGDALENE COLLEGE CHAPEL Cambridge, England 1948

First edition of 500 copies

In original paper cover-title. Signed under the canceled name of the author: "T. S. Eliot".

A50xa SELECTED POEMS London Penguin Books 1948

First edition of this selection, made by the author

In original paper covers. Inscribed by T. S. Eliot: "To Miss M. Trevelyan Miau! Miau! Old Possum Ste. Valérie [December 9]: 1953".

A50xa.1 SELECTED POEMS London Faber & Faber 1954

First Faber edition

In original cloth and dustwrapper.

A50xb SELECTED POEMS New York Harcourt, Brace & World 1967

First American edition of this selection, made by the author

In original paper covers.

A51a NOTES TOWARDS THE DEFINITION OF CULTURE London Faber & Faber 1948

First edition

(1) In original cloth and dustwrapper. Inscribed on flyleaf: "to Mary Trevelyan in all simplicity: T. S. Eliot 5.xi.48". The blurb on the inside front panel of the dustwrapper is signed: "T. S. E." With a typed note (14 x 10.2 cm., Faber and Faber letterhead): "With Mr. Eliot's compliments."

(2) In original cloth. One of eighteen copies with the error "a" for "the" in the title on the spine.

A51b NOTES TOWARDS THE DEFINITION OF CULTURE   New York   Harcourt, Brace and Company   1949

First American edition

In original cloth and dustwrapper.

A51c NOTES TOWARDS THE DEFINITION OF CULTURE   London   Faber & Faber   1962

Faber paper covered edition, with a new preface

In original paper covers.

A52a FROM POE TO VALÉRY   New York   Harcourt, Brace and Company   1948

First edition of 1500 copies

(1) In original paper boards. Inscribed on flyleaf in Eliot's autograph: "A Christmas greeting to Mary Trevelyan from Harcourt Brace & Co. Inc. 383 Madison Avenue per T. S. Eliot 1.i.49".

(2) In original paper boards. From the collection of Alfred A. Knopf.

A52b FROM POE TO VALÉRY   Washington   Library of Congress   1949

Second edition

In original paper cover-title.

A53 THE UNDERGRADUATE POEMS OF T. S. ELIOT   Cambridge, Massachusetts   The Harvard Advocate   1949

First edition

In original paper cover-title.

A54 THE AIMS OF POETIC DRAMA   London   Poets' Theatre Guild   1949

First edition

Unbound, wire-stitched, as issued.

A55a THE COCKTAIL PARTY A COMEDY London Faber & Faber 1950

First edition

(1) Proof copy. In original gray paper covers. On page 29 "here" is printed for "her" (first state).

(2) Proof copy. Bound in gray cloth with a black leather spine; with original gray paper covers and the publisher's slip, price and date of publication in typescript: "ADVANCE PROOF OF NEW BOOK Probable publication date March 9th   Price: 10/6 net. With the Compliments of the Sales Manager." On page 29, "her" is printed correctly (second state).

(3) Dummy copy. In green cloth as later published. First state. All pages after 64 are blank.

(4) In original cloth and dustwrapper. First state. Inscribed on flyleaf: "Philip Mairet from T. S. Eliot".

(5) In original cloth and dustwrapper. Second state. Inscribed on flyleaf: "to Miss Mary Trevelyan with the author's compliments. T. S. Eliot. See Appendix and with thanks for her contribution to the character of Julia. E.g. p. 151." The tune of *One-eyed Riley*, as published in the Appendix, was "scored from the author's dictation by Miss Mary Trevelyan."

(6) In original cloth and dustwrapper. First state. Inscribed on flyleaf: "Ashley Dukes from T. S. Eliot".

(7) In original cloth and dustwrapper. First state. Inscribed: "To Edith Sitwell with the author's homage T. S. Eliot".

(8) In original cloth and dustwrapper. On page 29 "here" is corrected to "her" in autograph signed "T. S. E." On title page the author's name is canceled and the following note added: "Inscribed for Tennessee Williams by T. S. Eliot 24.8.51".

(9) In original cloth and dustwrapper. First state. Signed on flyleaf: "Charles and Elizabeth Beazley".

(10) In original cloth. First state. Signed on flyleaf: "J. C. Hall".

(11) In original cloth. First state. With bookplate of John Johnson.

(12) In original cloth and dustwrapper. Autograph note on title page after the canceled name of the author: "Inscribed, with my best wishes, to William Turner Levy by T. S. Eliot New York: 2.xii.50".

(13) In original cloth and dustwrapper. First state. Inscribed on fly-leaf: "to Dorothy Bussy from Tom Eliot   6.iii.50".

A55b THE COCKTAIL PARTY A COMEDY New York Harcourt, Brace and Company 1950

First American edition

In original cloth and dustwrapper.

A55c THE COCKTAIL PARTY A COMEDY London Faber & Faber 1950

Fourth impression (revised)

In original cloth.

A56a POEMS WRITTEN IN EARLY YOUTH Stockholm Privately Printed 1950

First edition of 12 copies

A photocopy of Number 6.

A56b POEMS WRITTEN IN EARLY YOUTH London Faber & Faber 1967

Second (trade) edition

(1) Page proofs with autograph corrections.

(2) In original cloth and dustwrapper.

A56c POEMS WRITTEN IN EARLY YOUTH New York Farrar, Straus and Giroux 1967

American edition

In original cloth and dustwrapper.

A57a POETRY AND DRAMA Cambridge, Massachusetts Harvard University Press 1951

First edition

In original cloth and dustwrapper.

A57b POETRY AND DRAMA   London   Faber & Faber   1951

First English edition

(1) In original cloth and dustwrapper. Inscribed on flyleaf: "Ashley Dukes from Tom Eliot 21.ix.51". Publication date was 28 September 1951.

(2) In original cloth and dustwrapper. Inscribed on flyleaf: "for Mary Trevelyan from T. S. Eliot 21.ix.51".

(3) In original cloth and dustwrapper. Inscribed on flyleaf: "to Philip Mairet with the humble regards of T. S. Eliot 1.x.51".

(4) In original cloth and dustwrapper. Inscribed on flyleaf: "to Edith Sitwell with the author's homage T. S. Eliot 2.x.51".

(5) In original cloth. With bookplate of John Johnson.

(6) In original cloth and dustwrapper. Inscribed on flyleaf: "for Dorothy Bussy with the affectionate homage of T. S. Eliot 10.x.51".

A58 THE VALUE AND USE OF CATHEDRALS IN ENGLAND TO-DAY   Chichester   Friend of Chichester Cathedral   1952

First edition

(1) In original paper cover-title. Signed, under the canceled name of the author, "T. S. Eliot", with inscription in T. S. Eliot's autograph, "William Levy's copy".

(2) In original paper cover-title. Signed on cover, "T. S. Eliot".

A59a A PRESIDENTIAL ADDRESS TO MEMBERS OF THE LONDON LIBRARY   London   The London Library   1952

First edition

In original paper covers. Signed on cover above the canceled name of the author: "T. S. Eliot".

A60a THE COMPLETE POEMS AND PLAYS 1909–1950   New York   Harcourt, Brace and Company   1952

First collected edition

In original cloth and dustwrapper.

A60b THE COMPLETE POEMS AND PLAYS 1909–1950 New York Harcourt, Brace and Company 1952

American edition

In original cloth and dustwrapper.

A61 SELECTED PROSE edited by John Hayward London Penguin Books 1953

First edition

(1) In original paper covers. Inscribed on half title: "to William Turner Levy from T. S. Eliot".

(2) In original paper covers. Inscribed on half title: "To Miss M. Trevelyan Miau! Miau! Old Possum. Ste. Valérie [December 9]: 1953".

(3) In original paper covers. With Hayward's autograph inscription on title page after the name of the editor: "and given with love to Graham John Hayward. 17.4.1953". With signature on half title: "Graham Greene", and in Greene's autograph, page numbers referring to markings in ink throughout.

A61.1 SELECTED PROSE edited by John Hayward London Penguin Books In Association With Faber & Faber 1955

Second reprint

In original paper covers. Inscribed on half title: "for Graham Greene with love John Hayward. This copy has no connection with the copy similarly inscribed in the University of Texas." Hayward alludes to A 61 (3) above.

A62 AMERICAN LITERATURE AND THE AMERICAN LANGUAGE St. Louis, Missouri Washington University 1953

First edition

(1) In original paper covers. Signed on title page, under the canceled name of the author, "T. S. Eliot". With a correction on page 12 in Eliot's autograph. From the library of Mary Trevelyan.

(2) In original paper covers. With bookplate of John Johnson.

A63a THE THREE VOICES OF POETRY London for the National Book League Cambridge University Press 1953

First edition

(1) In original paper covers. Inscribed on cover: "for Mary Trevelyan Christmas greetings 1953 from T. S. E."

(2) In original paper covers. In autograph on cover: "Inscribed for R. F. Strudwick by T. S. Eliot".

(3) In original paper covers. Inscribed on cover: "for William Turner Levy greetings T. S. E. Christmas 1953".

A63b THE THREE VOICES OF POETRY New York Cambridge University Press 1954

First American edition

In original cloth and dustwrapper.

A64a THE CONFIDENTIAL CLERK A PLAY London Faber & Faber 1954

First edition

(1) Proof copy. In dark brown paper covers. In autograph on cover, "Mr. Kennerley".

(2) In original cloth and dustwrapper. Inscribed on flyleaf: "to Wm. Turner Levy from his friend T. S. Eliot 18.iii.54". The occasion of this gift is referred to in *Affectionately, T. S. Eliot,* by William Turner Levy and Victor Scherle (Philadelphia and New York: J. B. Lippincott Company, 1968), p. 48.

(3) In original cloth and dustwrapper. Inscribed on flyleaf: "to Mary Trevelyan from T. S. Eliot 22.iii.54".

(4) In original cloth and dustwrapper. Inscribed on flyleaf: "To Ashley Dukes with humble respects T. S. Eliot 23.iii.54".

(5) In original cloth and dustwrapper. Inscribed on flyleaf: "to Edith Sitwell with the homage of T. S. Eliot 23.iii.54".

A64b THE CONFIDENTIAL CLERK A PLAY New York Harcourt, Brace and Company 1954

First American edition

In original cloth and dustwrapper.

A65 RELIGIOUS DRAMA: MEDIAEVAL AND MODERN New York House of Books 1954

First edition of 300 copies

(1) In original cloth and glacine dustwrapper. Number I. Signed: "T. S. Eliot", and with the following inscription signed by Marguerite A. Cohn: "In souvenir of lovely days in Austin at the dedication of the Academic Center. May it continue to grow."

(2–5) In original cloth and dustwrapper. Numbers 9, 52, 228, 263. Signed: "T. S. Eliot".

(6) In original cloth and dustwrapper. Number 22. Signed: "T. S. Eliot". With bookplate of Alfred A. Knopf.

A66a THE CULTIVATION OF CHRISTMAS TREES illustrated by David Jones London Faber & Faber 1954

First edition

In original paper covers. Inscribed on title page: "for William Turner Levy with affectionate wishes for Christmas 1954 from T. S. Eliot". Enclosed in the publisher's envelope, stamped and posted; addressed in Eliot's autograph: "The Revd. William Turner Levy", and completed in the autograph of Valerie Eliot.

A66b THE CULTIVATION OF CHRISTMAS TREES New York Farrar, Straus and Cudahy 1956

First American edition

In original paper boards.

A67 THE LITERATURE OF POLITICS London 1955

First edition

(1) In original paper covers.

(2) In original paper covers. Inscribed: "for Mary Trevelyan with compliments and respects. T. S. Eliot".

A68 THE FRONTIERS OF CRITICISM Minneapolis University of Minnesota Press 1956

First edition

(1) In original paper covers. Inscribed on title page: "for Philip Mairet from T. S. E." Autograph corrections by Eliot on pages 5 and 11.

(2) In original paper covers. Inscribed on title page: "Mary Trevelyan T. S. Eliot with compliments."

(3) In original paper covers. Inscribed on title page: "for William Turner Levy with affectionate good wishes T. S. Eliot". The occasion of the gift is described in *Affectionately, T. S. Eliot*, pp. 100–4.

A69a ON POETRY AND POETS London Faber & Faber 1957

First edition

(1) Proof copy. In original blue paper wrappers. In autograph on front cover: *"New Statesman"*.

(2) In original cloth and dustwrapper. Inscribed on flyleaf: "for Philip Mairet from T. S. Eliot".

(3) In original cloth and dustwrapper. Inscribed on flyleaf: "for William Turner Levy with much affection from T. S. Eliot". The occasion of this gift is referred to in *Affectionately, T. S. Eliot*, p. 100.

A69b ON POETRY AND POETS New York Farrar, Straus, and Cudahy 1957

First American edition

(1) Galley proof with publication date in autograph, "September 16."

(2) In original cloth and dustwrapper.

A70a THE ELDER STATESMAN A PLAY London Faber & Faber 1959

First edition

(1) Proof copy. In original blue paper covers, on which the author's name is printed: "T. S. Elliot".

(2) In original cloth and dustwrapper. With bookplate of John Johnson.

A70b THE ELDER STATESMAN A PLAY New York Farrar, Straus, and Cudahy 1959

First American edition

In original cloth and dustwrapper.

A71 GEOFFREY FABER 1889–1961 London Faber & Faber 1961

First edition of 100 copies

In original paper boards and dustwrapper. Pages unopened. Copy 9. Signed: "T. S. Eliot."

A72 COLLECTED PLAYS London Faber & Faber 1962

First edition of this collection

In original cloth and dustwrapper.

A73a GEORGE HERBERT London for the British Council and the National Book League Longmans, Green & Company 1962

First edition

In original paper covers.

A74a COLLECTED POEMS 1909–1962 London Faber & Faber 1963

First edition

(1) Uncorrected proof copy. In original cream paper covers.

(2) In original cloth and dustwrapper. Signed "Valerie Eliot" on page 235 after the poem "A Dedication to my Wife," followed by the inscription in T. S. Eliot's autograph: "and T. S. Eliot who meant every word of it."

A74b COLLECTED POEMS 1909–1962 New York Harcourt Brace and World 1963

First American edition

In original cloth and dustwrapper.

A75b KNOWLEDGE AND EXPERIENCE IN THE PHILOSOPHY
OF F. H. BRADLEY London Faber & Faber 1964

First published edition

In original cloth and dustwrapper.

A76a TO CRITICIZE THE CRITIC AND OTHER WRITINGS
London Faber & Faber 1965

First edition

In original cloth and dustwrapper.

A76b TO CRITICIZE THE CRITIC AND OTHER WRITINGS
New York Farrar, Straus & Giroux 1965

First American edition, first issue

In original cloth and dustwrapper.

A76c TO CRITICIZE THE CRITIC AND OTHER WRITINGS
New York Noonday Press 1967

First American edition, second issue

In original paper covers.

B

BOOKS AND PAMPHLETS EDITED

OR WITH CONTRIBUTIONS

BY T. S. ELIOT

Numbered as in Gallup, with the addition of subordinate numbers, in parenthesis, for listing more than one copy. Items unnumbered by Gallup are given a related number with decimal addition.

BOOKS AND PAMPHLETS EDITED

OR WITH CONTRIBUTIONS

B0 HARVARD CLASS DAY   Cambridge, Massachusetts   1910

In photocopy extract. Contains "The Ode" by Thomas Stearns Eliot.

B1 CATHOLIC ANTHOLOGY   1914–1915   London   Elkin Matthews   1915

Contains "The Love Song of J. Alfred Prufrock," "Portrait of a Lady," "The Boston Evening Transcript," "Hysteria," and "Miss Helen Slingsby," by T. S. Eliot.

(1) In original paper boards. Signed on flyleaf: "Aldous Huxley May 1916".

(2) In original paper boards. With bookplate of John Johnson.

B2 ANDREW MARVELL   1621–1678   Tercentenary Tributes   London   Oxford University Press   1922

Contains "Andrew Marvell," by T.S. Eliot.

In original cloth.

B3 LE SERPENT   par Paul Valéry   with a translation into English by Mark Wardle and an introduction by T. S. Eliot   London   R. Cobden-Sanderson   1924

Edition of 525 copies

In original cloth. Number 89.

B4 SAVONAROLA   A DRAMATIC POEM   by Charlotte Eliot   with an introduction by T. S. Eliot   London   R. Cobden-Sanderson   1926

(1) In original cloth and dustwrapper.

(2) In original cloth. Pages unopened.

B5 SENECA HIS TENNE TRAGEDIES translated into English edited by Thomas Newton Anno 1581 with an introduction by T. S. Eliot London Constable and Co. New York Alfred A. Knopf 1927

In original paper boards, cloth spine, and dustwrapper.

B6 THE MOONSTONE by Wilkie Collins with an introduction by T. S. Eliot London Oxford University Press 1928

In original cloth and dustwrapper.

B7a OF DRAMATICK POESIE by John Dryden preceded by A DIALOGUE ON POETIC DRAMA by T. S. Eliot London Frederick Etchells & Hugh MacDonald 1928

Signed copies (55 numbered 1 to 55)

(1) In original cloth; vellum spine. Unnumbered. Signed: "T. S. Eliot". Inscribed on title page: "For Vivienne Haigh Eliot from her husband T. S. Eliot 28. v. 28".

(2) In original cloth; vellum spine. Number 13. Signed "T. S. Eliot". With bookplate of Charles Peter Alford.

(3) In original cloth; vellum spine. Number 14. Signed "T. S. Eliot". Pages unopened.

(4) In original cloth; vellum spine. Number 46. Signed "T. S. Eliot". Pages unopened.

(5) In original cloth; vellum spine. Number 55. Signed "T. S. Eliot". With bookplate of Alick Christopher Robinson.

B7b OF DRAMATICK POESIE by John Dryden preceded by A DIALOGUE ON POETIC DRAMA by T. S. Eliot London Frederick Etchells & Hugh MacDonald 1928

Ordinary copies (525 numbered 56 to 580)

(1–3) In original marbled paper boards, cloth spine, and dustwrapper. Numbers 496, 507, 567.

(4) In original marbled paper boards, cloth spine. Number 487.

B8 THIS AMERICAN WORLD by Edgar Ansell Mowrer with a preface by T. S. Eliot London Faber & Gwyer 1928

In original cloth. Inscribed on flyleaf: "To dear Eddie [Marsh, added in another hand] from W. W. New Year 1929. I agree with all this book says W W".

B10a EZRA POUND SELECTED POEMS edited with an intro-duction by T. S. Eliot London Faber & Gwyer 1928

First edition, ordinary copies

In original cloth and dustwrapper.

B10c EZRA POUND SELECTED POEMS edited with an intro-duction by T. S. Eliot London Faber & Faber 1949

New Edition

In original cloth and dustwrapper. Autograph on flyleaf: "Presented to Mary Trevelyan by T. S. Eliot".

B11 TRADITION AND EXPERIMENT IN PRESENT-DAY LITER-ATURE London Oxford University Press 1929

Contains "Experiment in Criticism," by T. S. Eliot.

(1) Proof copy. In original paper wrappers.

(2) In original cloth and dustwrapper. Pages unopened. Inscribed with signatures of T. S. Eliot and all other contributors, except Edith Sit-well: "for Mr. Seymour J. Stein".

(3) In original cloth and dustwrapper. With bookplate of Alfred A. Knopf.

B12 HUMANISM AND AMERICA ESSAYS ON THE OUTLOOK OF MODERN CIVILIZATION edited by Norman Foerster New York Farrar and Rinehart 1930

Contains "Religion without Humanism," by T. S. Eliot.

In original cloth.

B13 THE WHEEL OF FIRE ESSAYS IN THE INTERPRETA-TION OF SHAKESPEARE'S SOMBRE TRAGEDIES by G. Wilson Knight with an introduction by T. S. Eliot London Oxford Uni-versity Press 1930

(1) In original cloth. Inscribed on flyleaf: "To Professor John L. Myers in Gratefulness for his interest, from W. F. J[ackson]. K[night]. and G. W[ilson]. K[night]."

(2) In original cloth. With bookplate of John Johnson.

B14a INTIMATE JOURNALS by Charles Baudelaire translated by Ch. Isherwood introduction by T. S. Eliot London The Black-amore Press New York Random House 1930

Ordinary copies

(1) In original blue cloth. Number 323. With inscription on flyleaf: "For you, very dear Eve, these pages in which a freer man, terribly able of suffering, said the truth to himself. Your friend and your cause of suffering Marcel London Nov. 1945".

(2) In original blue cloth. Number 536. With bookplate of Alfred A. Knopf.

B14b INTIMATE JOURNALS by Charles Baudelaire translated by Ch. Isherwood introduction by T. S. Eliot London The Black-amore Press New York Random House 1930

Signed copies, limited to 50

(1) In original tan cloth. Number 16. Signed: "T. S. Eliot". With book-plate of John Johnson.

(2) In original tan cloth, cellophane dustwrapper, and slipcase of paper boards. Number 40. Signed: "T. S. Eliot".

B15a LONDON: A POEM and THE VANITY OF HUMAN WISHES by Samuel Johnson, LL.D. with an introductory essay by T. S. Eliot London Frederick Etchells & Hugh MacDonald 1930

Signed copies, limited to 150

(1) In original buff paper boards with blue label. Number 27. Signed: "T. S. Eliot". Pages unopened.

(2) In original buff paper boards with blue label. Number 74. Signed: "T. S. Eliot".

B15b LONDON: A POEM and THE VANITY OF HUMAN WISHES

by Samuel Johnson, LL.D.   with an introductory essay by T. S. Eliot
London   Frederick Etchells & Hugh MacDonald   1930

Ordinary copies, limited to 300

(1) In original blue paper boards with buff label. Number 419.

(2) Rebound in blue cloth. Number 210.

B16 THE EIGHTEEN-EIGHTIES   essays by Fellows of the Royal
Society of Literature   edited by Walter de la Mare   Cambridge, England   1930

Contains "The Place of Pater," by T. S. Eliot.

In original cloth and dustwrapper. With bookplate of Alfred A. Knopf.

B17a PASCAL'S PENSÉES   translated by W. F. Trotter   with an
introduction by T. S. Eliot   London & Toronto   J. M. Dent & Sons
New York   E. P. Dutton & Company   1931

In original cloth. With bookplate of John Johnson.

B18 TRANSIT OF VENUS   POEMS   by Harry Crosby   preface by
T. S. Eliot   Paris   The Black Sun Press   1931

(1) In original paper covers and dustwrapper. Number 12.

(2) In original paper covers and dustwrapper. Unnumbered copy. In
the red cloth folder issued for the four-volume *Collected Poems of
Harry Crosby.*

B19 A GARLAND FOR JOHN DONNE   1631–1931   edited by Theodore Spencer   Cambridge, Massachusetts   Harvard University Press
1931

Contains "Donne in our Time," by T. S. Eliot.

In original cloth and dustwrapper.

B20 BUBU OF MONTPARNASSE   by Charles-Louis Philippe   translated by Laurence Vail   preface by T. S. Eliot   Paris   Crosby Continental Editions   1932

In original paper wrappers. With bookplate of John Johnson.

B20.1 BUBU OF MONTPARNASSE by Charles-Louis Philippe with an introduction by T. S. Eliot New York Shakespeare House 1951

In original cloth and dustwrapper.

B21 THE CANTOS OF EZRA POUND some testimonies by Ernest Hemingway Ford Madox Ford T. S. Eliot Hugh Walpole Archibald MacLeish James Joyce and others New York Farrar & Rinehart 1933

In original paper cover-title. Inscribed on page 13 beside Hemingway's contribution: "To Lee [Samuels], all true Ernest Hemingway." Samuels was the author of *A Hemingway Check-List* (New York: Charles Scribner's Sons, 1951).

B22 THE COLLECTED POEMS OF HAROLD MONRO edited by Alida Monro with a biographical sketch by F. S. Flint and a critical note by T. S. Eliot London Cobden-Sanderson 1933

In original cloth and dustwrapper.

B23 A COMPANION TO SHAKESPEARE STUDIES edited by Harley Granville-Barker and G. B. Harrison Cambridge, England Cambridge University Press 1934

Contains "Shakespearean Criticism. From Dryden to Coleridge," by T. S. Eliot.

In original cloth.

B26a SELECTED POEMS by Marianne Moore with an introduction by T. S. Eliot New York The Macmillan Company 1935

First edition

In original cloth and dustwrapper.

B26b SELECTED POEMS by Marianne Moore with an introduction by T. S. Eliot London Faber & Faber 1935

First English edition

In original cloth and dustwrapper.

B27 POEMS OF TENNYSON   with an introduction by T. S. Eliot
London Edinburgh Paris Melbourne Toronto New York Thomas
Nelson and Sons   1936

In original cloth.

B28 ESSAYS AND STUDIES   by members of the English Association
collected by Herbert Read   Oxford   The Clarendon Press   1936

Contains "A Note on the Verse of John Milton," by T. S. Eliot.

In original cloth and dustwrapper.

B31a NIGHTWOOD   by Djuna Barnes   with an introduction by
T. S. Eliot   Harcourt, Brace and Company   1937

First edition

In original cloth.

B32 REVELATION   by Gustaf Aulén   Karl Barth   Sergius Bulga-
koff M. C. D'Arcy   T. S. Eliot   Walter M. Horton   William Temple
edited by John Baillie and Hugh Martin   London   Faber & Faber
1937

First edition

In original cloth. Inscribed on flyleaf: "M. B. Banister from Dad   Chris-
mas 1937   Coventry".

B32.1 REVELATION   by Gustaf Aulén   Karl Barth   Sergius Bulga-
koff M. C. D'Arcy   T. S. Eliot   Walter M. Horton   William Temple
edited by John Baillie and Hugh Martin   New York   The Macmillan
Company   1937

American issue

In original cloth and dustwrapper. With autograph note, in unidentified hand, on Eliot's contribution.

B33 SEVENTEENTH CENTURY STUDIES   presented to Sir Herbert Grierson   Oxford   The Clarendon Press   1938

Contains "A Note on Two Odes of Cowley," by T. S. Eliot.

In original cloth.

B34 NOCTES BINANIANÆ Certain Voluntary and Satyrical Verses and Compliments as were lately Exchang'd between some of the Choisest Wits of the Age London 1939

Contains, anonymously, the following poems by T. S. Eliot: "How to Pick a Possum," "The O'Possum Strikes Back," "The Whale and the Elephant: A Fable," "Ode to a Roman Coot," "Three Sonnets," "Vers pour La Foulque: feuillet d'album." Translation into English of "Verses for the Coot," "Album Leaflet," and "Abschied zur Bina."

First edition of 25 copies

In original paper covers. Number 9.

B35 THE QUEEN'S BOOK OF THE RED CROSS with a message from Her Majesty The Queen and contributions by fifty British authors and artists London Hodder and Stoughton 1939

Contains "The Marching Song of the Pollicle Dogs," and "Billy M'Caw: The Remarkable Parrot," by T. S. Eliot.

In original cloth and dustwrapper.

B36 THE TESTAMENT OF IMMORTALITY an anthology selected and arranged by N. G[angulee]. with a preface by T. S. Eliot London Faber & Faber 1940

In original cloth and dustwrapper.

B37 IRVING BABBITT MAN AND TEACHER edited by Frederick Manchester and Odell Shepard New York G. P. Putnam's Sons 1941

Contains a memoir by T. S. Eliot.

In original cloth.

B38 THE CHURCH LOOKS AHEAD broadcast talks by J. M. Oldham Maurice B. Reckitt Philip Mairet Dorothy L. Sayers M. C. D'Arcy, S.J. V. A. Demant T. S. Eliot with a preface by E. L. Marcell London Faber & Faber 1941

In original cloth and dustwrapper.

B39a A CHOICE OF KIPLING'S VERSE   made by T. S. Eliot   with an essay on Rudyard Kipling   London   Faber & Faber   1941

First edition

In original cloth and dustwrapper. With bookplate of John Johnson.

Second Impression 1942

In original cloth and dustwrapper. Inscribed on flyleaf: "for Mary Trevelyan from T. S. Eliot".

B39b A CHOICE OF KIPLING'S VERSE   made by T. S. Eliot with an essay on Rudyard Kipling   New York   Charles Scribner's Sons 1943

First American edition

In original cloth.

B40 MALVERN 1941   THE LIFE OF THE CHURCH AND ORDER OF SOCIETY   London   New York   Toronto   Longmans, Green and Company   1941

Contains "The Christian Conception of Education," by T. S. Eliot.

In original cloth.

B40.1 BRITAIN AT WAR   edited by Monroe Wheeler   text by T. S. Eliot   Herbert Read   E. J. Carter and Carlos Dyer   New York   The Museum of Modern Art   1941

In original paper boards. "Defense of the Islands," page 8, is reprinted from the broadside E2d.

B41 THE LITTLE BOOK OF MODERN VERSE   chosen by Anne Ridler   with a preface by T. S. Eliot   London   Faber & Faber   1942

(1) In original cloth and dustwrapper.

(2) In original cloth.With bookplate of John Johnson.

B42 INTRODUCING JAMES JOYCE   A SELECTION OF JOYCE'S PROSE by T. S. Eliot, with an introductory note   London   Faber & Faber   1942

In original cloth and dustwrapper.

B43 LONDON CALLING edited by Storm Jameson New York
London Harper & Brothers 1942

Contains "A Note on War Poetry," by T. S. Eliot.

In original cloth and dustwrapper.

B44 QUEEN MARY'S BOOK FOR INDIA with a foreword by the
Right Hon. S. L. Amery, M.P. London Toronto Bombay Sidney
George G. Harrap & Company 1943

Contains "To the Indians Who Died in Africa," by T. S. Eliot.

In original cloth.

B46 SHAKESPEARE & THE POPULAR DRAMATIC TRADITION
by S. L. Bethell with an introduction by T. S. Eliot London P. S.
King and Staples 1944

In original cloth.

B48 PROSPECT FOR CHRISTENDOM ESSAYS IN CATHOLIC
SOCIAL RECONSTRUCTION edited by Maurice B. Reckitt London Faber & Faber 1945

Contains "Cultural Forces in the Human Order," by T. S. Eliot.

In original cloth.

B49 THE DARK SIDE OF THE MOON [anonymous] with a
preface by T. S. Eliot London Faber & Faber 1946

In original cloth and dustwrapper.

B50 PAUL VALÉRY VIVANT Marseille Cahiers du Sud 1946

Contains "Leçon de Valéry," in English by T. S. Eliot and in French
translation by Henri Fluchère.

With original paper wrappers, bound in cloth.

B50.1 CATHOLICITY A STUDY IN THE CONFLICT OF CHRIS-
TIAN TRADITIONS IN THE WEST a report presented to His Grace
the Archbishop of Canterbury by E. S. Abbott H. J. Carpenter V. A.
Demant Gregory Dix T. S. Eliot [and others] Westminster
Dacre Press 1947

In original paper covers.

B51 TRIBUTE TO WALTER DE LA MARE ON HIS SEVENTY-FIFTH BIRTHDAY   London   Faber & Faber   1948

Contains the poem "To Walter de la Mare," by T. S. Eliot.

In original cloth and dustwrapper. With bookplate of L. C. Elger.

B53 EN ENGELSK BOG TILEGNET KAI FRIIS MØLLER   [with introduction in English by T. S. Eliot]   København   Gyldendalske Boghandel   1948

In original paper covers and dustwrapper.

B55 JAMES JOYCE   SA VIE SON OEUVRE   SON RAYONNE-MENT   Paris   La Hune   1949

Contains a note in English by T. S. Eliot.

Edition of 30 copies

In original paper covers. Number 11. Signed: "Bernard Gheerbrant". Same as D 104. Reprint in E2f.

B56 A PORTRAIT OF MICHAEL ROBERTS   edited by T. W. Eason and R. Hamilton   Chelsea   College of S. Mark & S. John   1949

In original paper covers.

B57 LES PRIX NOBEL EN 1948   Stockholm   P. A. Norstedt & Soner 1949

Contains T. S. Eliot's reply to the toast at the Nobel Banquet.

In original paper covers.

B58 ENGLISH POETRY AND ITS CONTRIBUTION TO THE KNOWLEDGE OF A CREATIVE PRINCIPLE   by Leone Vivante with a preface by T. S. Eliot   London   Faber & Faber   1950

In original cloth and dustwrapper.

B59 THE ADVENTURES OF HUCKLEBERRY FINN   by Samuel L. Clemens (Mark Twain)   with an introduction by T. S. Eliot   London The Cresset Press   1950

In original cloth and dustwrapper. Inscribed on flyleaf: "to Miss Mary Trevelyan with a Missourian's compliments. T. S. Eliot". Added by Mary Trevelyan: "Christmas 1950".

B60 EZRA POUND: A COLLECTION OF ESSAYS edited by Peter Russell to be presented to Ezra Pound on his sixty-fifth birthday London New York Peter Nevill 1950

Contains "Ezra Pound" and "Postscript, 1950" by T. S. Eliot.

In original cloth and dustwrapper.

B61 D. H. LAWRENCE AND HUMAN EXISTENCE by Father William Tiverton foreword by T. S. Eliot London Rockliff 1951

In original cloth and dustwrapper.

B61.1 D. H. LAWRENCE AND HUMAN EXISTENCE by Father William Tiverton foreword by T. S. Eliot New York Philosophical Library 1951

In original cloth.

B62 THOUGHTS FOR MEDITATION A WAY TO RECOVERY FROM WITHIN an anthology selected and arranged by N. Gangulee with a preface by T. S. Eliot London Faber & Faber 1951

In original cloth.

B63 FESTIVAL OF BRITAIN 1951 LONDON SEASON OF THE ARTS OFFICIAL SOUVENIR PROGRAMME London Lund Humphries and Company 1951

Contains "The Spoken Word," by T. S. Eliot.

In original paper covers.

B65 LEISURE THE BASIS OF CULTURE by Josef Pieper translated by Alexander Dru with an introduction by T. S. Eliot London Faber & Faber 1952

In original cloth.

B66 THE NEED FOR ROOTS PRELUDE TO A DECLARATION

OF DUTIES TOWARDS MANKIND by Simone Weil with a preface by T. S. Eliot London Routledge and Kegan Paul 1952

First edition

In original cloth.

B67 CONTEMPORY FRENCH POETRY by Joseph Chiari with a foreword by T. S. Eliot Manchester University Press 1952

In original cloth and dustwrapper. Inscribed on flyleaf: "To you both with admiration and affection from Jo Chiari." From the library of Richard Church.

B68 SHAKESPEARE by Henri Fluchère with a foreword by T. S. Eliot London Longmans, Green and Company 1953

In original cloth.

B69 GALA DAY LONDON photographs by Izis Bidermanas texts by John Betjeman Paul Dehn Clifford Dyment T. S. Eliot [and others] London Harvill Press 1953

Contains "Let quacks, empirics, dolts debate" (8 lines), by T. S. Eliot.

In original cloth and dustwrapper.

B72 LITERARY ESSAYS OF EZRA POUND edited with an introduction by T. S. Eliot London Faber & Faber 1954

In original cloth and dustwrapper. Inscribed on flyleaf: "Mary Trevelyan with the Introducer's respects and the Publisher's good wishes. T. S. Eliot".

B73 SYMPHONY OF COOKING compiled under the direction of Mrs. J. Eldred Newton St. Louis, Missouri Women's Association of the St. Louis Symphony Society 1954

Contains the recipe "Mrs. Runcie's Pudding," by T. S. Eliot.

In original decorated paper boards.

B74 GEDENKSCHRIFT ZUR VERLEIHUNG DES HANSISCHEN GOETHE-PREISES 1954 Hamburg 1955

"Goethe as the Sage," Eliot's address upon receiving the Hanseatic Goethe prize, pages 49–71, comes after the German translation by Ursula Clemens (pp. 11–38). Same as D181a.

(1) In original paper covers. Inscribed: "To Miss M. Trevelyan from T. S. Eliot 12.ix.55". With autograph correction by T. S. Eliot in the English text.

(2) In original paper covers. Inscribed: "to John Middleton Murry in affection T. S. Eliot 13.ix.55". With autograph correction as in (1).

(3) In original paper covers. Inscribed: "Philip Mairet from T. S. E. 6.ix.55". With autograph correction and some revision by T. S. Eliot in the English text.

B75 EZRA POUND AT SEVENTY   Norfolk, Connecticut   New Directions   1956

Contains a note by T. S. Eliot.

In original paper covers.

B76 SYMBOLISME FROM POE TO MALLARMÉ   THE GROWTH OF A MYTH   by Joseph Chiari   foreword by T. S. Eliot   London Rockliff   1956

In original cloth and dustwrapper.

B77b MY BROTHER'S KEEPER   JAMES JOYCE'S EARLY YEARS by Stanislaus Joyce   edited with an introduction and notes by Richard Ellmann   preface by T. S. Eliot   New York   The Viking Press   1958

First edition, issued in 1957

In original paper boards with cloth spine. Signed on flyleaf: "Graham Greene", with notes in his autograph on endpaper at back.

B77b.1 MY BROTHER'S KEEPER   by Stanislaus Joyce   edited with an introduction by Richard Ellmann   with a preface by T. S. Eliot London   Faber & Faber   1958

In original cloth and dustwrapper.

B79 THE ART OF POETRY   by Paul Valéry   translated by Denise

Folliot with an introduction by T. S. Eliot New York Pantheon Books 1958

In original cloth and dustwrapper. Inscribed on flyleaf: "for Philip Mairet from T. S. Eliot".

B79.1 THE ART OF POETRY by Paul Valéry translated by Denise Folliot with an introduction by T. S. Eliot London Routledge and Kegan Paul 1958

English edition

In original cloth and dustwrapper.

B80 KATHERINE MANSFIELD AND OTHER LITERARY STUDIES by J. Middleton Murry with a foreword by T. S. Eliot London Constable 1959

In original cloth and dustwrapper.

B82 ONE-WAY SONG by Wyndham Lewis with a foreword by T. S. Eliot London Methuen 1960

In original cloth and dustwrapper.

B83 JOHN DAVIDSON A SELECTION OF HIS POEMS preface by T. S. Eliot edited with an introduction by Maurice Lindsay London Hutchinson 1961

In original cloth and dustwrapper.

B84 POEMS AND VERSE PLAYS by Hugo von Hofmannsthal edited by Michael Hamburger with a preface by T. S. Eliot New York Pantheon Books 1961

In original cloth.

B85 IN PARENTHESIS by David Jones with an introduction by T. S. Eliot London Faber & Faber 1961

Limited edition of 70 copies

In original cloth and dustwrapper. Number 33. Signed: "David Jones" and "T. S. Eliot".

B86 FESTIVAL OF POETRY AT THE ROYAL COURT THEATRE
London   The Poetry Book Society   1963

Contains a note by T. S. Eliot.

In original paper covers.

B87 SELECTED POEMS AND LIBRETTI   by Hugo von Hoffmanns-
thal   edited and introduced by Michael Hamburger   New York
Pantheon Books   1963

Contains "A Note on 'The Tower,' " by T. S. Eliot.

In original cloth.

B89 A TRIBUTE TO WILFRED OWEN   compiled by T. J. Walsh
Birkenhead, Cheshire   1964

Contains a note by T. S. Eliot.

In original paper cover-title. Signed on the first leaf: "with best wishes
Jeffrey Walsh". A gift to the University of Texas from T. J. Walsh,
Director of the Wilfred Owen Memorial Library at the Birkenhead
Institute.

B90 SELECTED POEMS   by Edwin Muir   with a preface by T. S.
Eliot   London   Faber & Faber   1965

Faber paper covered edition

In original paper covers.

B91 ALDOUS   HUXLEY   1894–1963   A   MEMORIAL   VOLUME
edited by Julian Huxley   London   Chatto & Windus   1965

Contains a note by T. S. Eliot.

(1) Proof copy. In original paper wrappers, stamped with publication
date "30 September 1965".

(2) In original cloth and dustwrapper.

B91.1 ALDOUS   HUXLEY   1894–1963   A   MEMORIAL   VOLUME
edited by Julian Huxley   New York   Harper & Row   1965

Contains a note by T. S. Eliot.

First edition (American)

In original cloth and dustwrapper.

B92 RICHARD ALDINGTON AN INTIMATE PORTRAIT edited by Alister Kershaw and Fréderic-Jacques Temple Carbondale and Edwardsville Southern Illinois University Press 1965

Contains a note by T. S. Eliot.

In original paper boards.

B94 THE CRITERION 1922–1939 edited by T. S. Eliot London Faber & Faber 1967

First collected edition

In original cloth.

B a

ANTHOLOGIES AND COLLECTIONS
CONTAINING POEMS AND ESSAYS
BY T. S. ELIOT

Numbered as in Gallup, with the addition of subordinate numbers, in parenthesis, for listing more than one copy. Items unnumbered by Gallup are given a related number with decimal addition.

ANTHOLOGIES AND COLLECTIONS

CONTAINING POEMS AND ESSAYS

Ba1 OTHERS   AN ANTHOLOGY OF THE NEW VERSE   edited by Alfred Kreymborg   New York   Alfred A. Knopf   1916

Contains "Portrait of a Lady," by T. S. Eliot.

(1) In original paper boards. Signed on flyleaf: "Amos R. Wells 6/3/22".

(2) In original paper boards. Signed on flyleaf: "Alfred Kreymborg".

Ba1.1 OTHERS   AN ANTHOLOGY OF THE NEW VERSE   1917 edited by Alfred Kreymborg   New York   Alfred A. Knopf   1917

Contains "Preludes" and "Rhapsody of [sic] a Windy Night," by T. S. Eliot.

In original paper boards.

Ba1.2 CRITICISM IN AMERICA   ITS FUNCTION AND STATUS essays by Irving Babbitt   Van Wyck Brooks   W. C. Brownell   Ernest Boyd   T. S. Eliot [and others]   New York   Harcourt, Brace and Company   1924

Contains "The Perfect Critic," by T. S. Eliot.

In original cloth and dustwrapper.

Ba2 AMERICAN POETRY 1925   A MISCELLANY   New York Harcourt, Brace and Company   1925

Contains "Three Dream Songs" ("Eyes that last I saw in tears," "The wind sprang up at four o'clock," and "This is the dead land"), by T. S. Eliot. Selected and published by Louis Untermeyer without Eliot's permission.

In original cloth.

Ba3 THE BEST POEMS OF 1925   edited by L. A. G. Strong   Boston   Small, Maynard & Company   1925

Contains "The Hollow Men [Part I]," by T. S. Eliot.

In original cloth and dustwrapper.

Ba4 STYLE AND FORM IN AMERICAN PROSE   by Gorham B. Munson   Garden City, New York   Doubleday, Doran & Company   1929

Contains "The Critic and the Perception of Values," by T. S. Eliot.

In original cloth.

Ba5 TWENTIETH-CENTURY POETRY   edited by John Drinkwater Henry Seidel Canby and William Rose Benét   Boston   Houghton Mifflin Company   1929

Contains "Salutation," by T. S. Eliot.

Rebound in blue cloth.

Ba6 CAP AND GOWN   SOME COLLEGE VERSE   (fourth series) selected by R. L. Paget   Boston   L. C. Page & Company   1931

Contains "Circe's Palace," by T. S. Eliot.

In original red cloth and gray dustwrapper.

Ba7 EZRA POUND   PROFILE   AN ANTHOLOGY COLLECTED IN MCMXXXI   Milan   1932

Contains "Fragments of an Agon" (From *Wanna Go Home, Baby?*) by T. S. Eliot.

Edition of 250 copies

In original paper wrappers. Number 42.

Ba7.1 WHIPS & SCORPIONS   SPECIMENS OF MODERN SA-TIRIC VERSE   1914–1931   collected by Sherard Vines   London Wishart   1932

Contains "The Hippopotamus," "Aunt Helen," and "Mr. Apollinax," by T. S. Eliot.

In original cloth and dustwrapper.

Ba10 THE FABER BOOK OF MODERN VERSE   edited by Michael
Roberts   London   Faber & Faber   1936

Contains "Difficulties of a Statesman," by T. S. Eliot.

(1) Proof copy. In original yellow paper covers.

(2) In original cloth and dustwrapper.

Ba11 THE NEW REPUBLIC ANTHOLOGY   1915:1935   edited by
Groff Conklin   New York   Dodge Publishing Company   1936

Contains "The Idealism of Julien Benda," by T. S. Eliot.

In original cloth and dustwrapper.

Ba12 LITERARY OPINION IN AMERICA   edited with an introduction by Morton Dauwen Zabel   New York   London   Harper & Brothers   1937

Contains "Tradition and the Individual Talent" and "Poetry and Propaganda," by T. S. Eliot.

In original cloth.

Ba14 THE SHOCK OF RECOGNITION   THE DEVELOPMENT
OF LITERATURE IN THE UNITED STATES   recorded by the men
who made it   edited by Edmund Wilson   Garden City, New York
Doubleday, Doran and Company   1943

Contains "Henry James I. In Memory, and II. The Hawthorne Aspect,"
by T. S. Eliot.

In original cloth.

Ba15 CRITICISM   THE FOUNDATIONS OF MODERN LITER-
ARY JUDGMENT   edited by Mark Schorer   Josephine Miles   Gordon McKenzie   New York   Harcourt, Brace and Company   1948

Contains "Hamlet and his Problems," " 'Ulysses', Order and Myth," and
"A Dialogue on Dramatic Poetry," by T. S. Eliot.

In original cloth.

Ba16 JAMES JOYCE: TWO DECADES OF CRITICISM by Eugene Jolas Frank Budgeon Irene Hendry Richard Levin Charles Shattuck James T. Farrell Hugh Kenner T. S. Eliot [and others] edited by Seon Givens New York Vanguard Press 1948

In original cloth and dustwrapper.

Ba17 CRITIQUES AND ESSAYS IN CRITICISM 1920–1948 selected by Robert Wooster Stallman New York The Ronald Press Company 1949

Contains "The Social Function of Poetry," "Tradition and the Individual Talent," and "Hamlet and his Problems," by T. S. Eliot.

In original cloth and dustwrapper.

Ba18 THE PERMANENCE OF YEATS SELECTED CRITICISM edited by James Hall and Martin Steinmann New York The Macmillan Company 1950

Contains "The Poetry of W. B. Yeats," by T. S. Eliot.

In original cloth.

Ba19 THE HARVARD ADVOCATE ANTHOLOGY edited by Donald Hall New York Twayne Publishers 1950

Contains "Gentlemen and Seamen," by T. S. Eliot.

In original cloth.

Ba20 THE LITTLE REVIEW ANTHOLOGY edited by Margaret Anderson New York Hermitage House 1953

Contains "Eeldrop and Appleplex," "The Hippopotamus," "In Memory [of Henry James]," and a letter to Jane Heap, by T. S. Eliot.

In original paper boards with cloth spine.

Ba21 FROM THE THIRD PROGRAMME A TEN-YEARS' ANTHOLOGY edited by John Morris London The Nonesuch Press 1956

Contains "Virgil and the Christian World," by T. S. Eliot.

In original cloth and slipcase of marbled paper boards.

Ba22 THE INTELLECTUALS   A CONTROVERSIAL PORTRAIT
edited with an introduction and overviews by George B. Huszar   Glencoe, Illinois   The Free Press   1960

Contains "The Man of Letters and the Future of Europe," by T. S. Eliot.

In original cloth.

Ba23 DISCUSSIONS OF THE DIVINE COMEDY   edited with an introduction by Irma Brandeis   Boston   D. C. Heath and Company
1961

Contains "A Talk on Dante," by T. S. Eliot.

In original cloth.

Ba24 O'NEILL AND HIS PLAYS   FOUR DECADES OF CRITICISM   edited by Oscar Cargill   N. Bryllion Fagin   William J. Fisher
New York   New York University Press   1961

Contains a review of *All God's Children Got Wings,* by T. S. Eliot.

In original cloth.

Ba25 THE BED POST   A MISCELLANY OF THE YORKSHIRE
POST   edited by Kenneth Young   London   MacDonald   1962

Contains an interview given by T. S. Eliot.

In original cloth.

Ba26 WRITERS AT WORK   THE PARIS REVIEW INTERVIEWS
2nd Ser.   introduced by Van Wyck Brooks   New York   The Viking
Press   1963

Contains an interview given by T. S. Eliot.

In original cloth.

Ba27 HENRY JAMES   A COLLECTION OF CRITICAL ESSAYS
edited by Leon Edel   Englewood Cliffs, New Jersey   Prentice Hall
1963

Contains "A Prediction," by T. S. Eliot.

In original cloth.

Ba28 A DIAL MISCELLANY   edited with an introduction by William Wasserstrom   Syracuse, New York   Syracuse University Press   1963

Contains "London Letter, September 1921," "The Hollow Men" [Parts I, II, and IV], and "Literature, Science, and Dogma," by T. S. Eliot.

In original cloth.

Ba29 KIPLING AND THE CRITICS   edited with an introduction by Elliot L. Gilbert   New York   New York University Press   1965

Contains "The Unfading Genius of Rudyard Kipling," by T. S. Eliot.

In original cloth.

Ba30 THE NEW ENGLISH BIBLE REVIEWED   edited by Dennis Nineham   London   Epworth Press   1965

Contains a review of *The New English Bible* by T. S. Eliot, reprinted from *The Sunday Telegraph*, 16 December 1962.

In original cloth.

Ba31 HARVARD ADVOCATE   CENTENNIAL ANTHOLOGY   edited by Jonathan D. Culler   Cambridge, Massachusetts   Schenkman Publishing Company   1966

Contains "The Problem of Education" and nine poems written as an undergraduate, by T. S. Eliot.

In original cloth and dustwrapper.

B *l*

BOOKS CONTAINING LETTERS

OR PARTS OF LETTERS

FROM T. S. ELIOT

Numbered as in Gallup, with the addition of subordinate numbers, in parenthesis, for listing more than one copy. Items unnumbered by Gallup are given a related number with decimal addition.

BOOKS CONTAINING LETTERS

OR PARTS OF LETTERS

B*l*5 DYNAMO   by Hallie Flanagan   New York   Duell, Sloan and Pearce   1943

Contains a letter from T. S. Eliot to Hallie Flanagan.

In original cloth.

B*l*6 THE CRACK-UP   by F. Scott Fitzgerald   with other uncollected pieces, note-books and unpublished letters together with letters to Fitzgerald from Gertrude Stein, Edith Wharton, T. S. Eliot [and others] edited by Edmund Wilson   New York   New Directions   1945

In original decorated paper boards, cloth spine, and dustwrapper.

B*l*7 T. S. ELIOT   A SYMPOSIUM   compiled by Richard March and Tambimuttu   London   Editions Poetry   1948

Contains the verse address "O stalwart Sussex postman . . . ," by T. S. Eliot, parts of letter from T. S. Eliot to Conrad Aiken, and reproductions of manuscript pages by T. S. Eliot.

First edition

In original cloth and dustwrapper.

B*l*7.1 T. S. ELIOT   A SYMPOSIUM   compiled by Tambimuttu and Richard March   New York   Tambimuttu and Mass   1965

Third Impression

In original cloth and dustwrapper.

B*l*8 HALI   by G. V. Desani   Foreword by T. S. Eliot and E. M. Forster London   The Saturn Press   1950

In original cloth and dustwrapper.   Eliot refers in a letter (G878) to this "foreword," written and intended only as a letter.

B*l*9a THE LETTERS OF EZRA POUND 1907–1941 edited by D. D. Paige New York Harcourt, Brace and Company 1950

Contains a letter from T. S. Eliot to Ezra Pound.

In original cloth.

B*l*9b THE LETTERS OF EZRA POND 1907–1941 edited by D. D. Paige London Faber & Faber 1951

Proof copy. In original paper covers. Inscribed on flyleaf: "M[ary] T[revelyan] from T. S. Eliot".

B*l*10 FRIEND OF FRIENDS LETTERS TO ROBERT ROSS ART CRITIC AND WRITER edited by Margery Ross London Jonathan Cape 1952

Contains a letter from T. S. Eliot to Robert Ross.

In original cloth and dustwrapper.

B*l*11 THE FLOWERS OF FRIENDSHIP LETTERS WRITTEN TO GERTRUDE STEIN edited by Donald Gallup New York Alfred A. Knopf 1953

Contains two letters from T. S. Eliot to Gertrude Stein.

In original cloth and dustwrapper.

B*l*15 FREUNDESGABE FÜR ERNST ROBERT CURTIUS Bern Franke Verlag 1956

Contains "Brief über Ernst Robert Curtius," in English, by T. S. Eliot.

In original cloth and dustwrapper.

B*l*17 JAMES JOYCE'S WORLD by Patricia Hutchins London Methuen and Co. 1957

Contains excerpts from articles in *The Egoist,* and parts of letters from T. S. Eliot to James Joyce.

In original cloth.

B*l*19 COPEY OF HARVARD A BIOGRAPHY OF CHARLES

TOWNSEND COPELAND by J. Donald Adams Boston Houghton Mifflin Company 1960

Contains excerpts from "The Defects of Kipling," written as a student by T. S. Eliot in 1909, and parts of letters from T. S. Eliot to J. Donald Adams (G795, 803, 831).

In original cloth and dustwrapper. With bookplate of Alfred A. Knopf.

B*l*20 EZRA POUND by Charles Norman New York The MacMillan Company 1960

Contains two letters from T. S. Eliot to Ezra Pound.

(1) Unbound page proof.

(2) In original cloth and dustwrapper. Inscribed: "For the Humanities Research Center The University of Texas Charles Norman Austin, November 3, 1960."

B*l*21 AN EXHIBITION OF MANUSCRIPTS AND FIRST EDITIONS OF T. S. ELIOT The University of Texas at Austin Humanities Research Center 1961

Contains the following MSS by T. S. Eliot reproduced in facsimile: F3, 4, 6, 12; G56, 344. The following are quoted or reproduced in part: F2, 16, 24; G8, 9, 28, 36, 40, 52, 71, 76, 139, 235, 242, 501, 824.

In original paper covers.

B*l*22 THE LETTERS OF WYNDHAM LEWIS edited by W. K. Rose Norfolk, Connecticut New Directions 1963

Contains letters and excerpts of letters from T. S. Eliot to Wyndham Lewis.

In original cloth and dustwrapper.

B*l*23 THOMAS STEARNS ELIOT IN ÜBERSETZUNGEN by Hans W. Bentz Frankfurt am Main Hans W. Bentz Verlag 1963

Contains a note from T. S. Eliot to Hans W. Bentz.

In original cloth.

B*l*24 BEGINNING AGAIN AN AUTOBIOGRAPHY OF THE YEARS 1911–1918 by Leonard Woolf London The Hogarth Press 1964

Contains the inscription by T. S. Eliot in Woolf's copy of *Prufrock and Other Observations*, and three letters from T. S. Eliot to Virginia Woolf.

(1) Proof copy. In original paper covers. Stamped with publication date: "May 1964". Inscribed on cover: "R to R".

(2) In original cloth and dustwrapper.

B*l*25 THE STAGE SIXTY THEATRE CLUB PRESENTS HOMAGE TO T. S. ELIOT A Program of Poetry Drama and Music London 1965

Contains "Last Scene of 'Sweeney Agonistes': Final Version," and reproduction of manuscripts by T. S. Eliot.

In original paper covers.

B*l*26 HONNEUR À SAINT-JOHN PERSE. Paris Gallimard 1965

Contains a letter from T. S. Eliot to Jean Paulham, and a letter in French from T. S. Eliot to Saint-John Perse. Also, in French translation, Eliot's preface to *Anabasis* (A16).

Bound in cloth with original paper covers.

B*l*27 EZRA POUND PERSPECTIVES ESSAYS IN HONOR OF HIS EIGHTIETH BIRTHDAY edited with an introduction by Noel Stock Chicago H. Regnery Company 1965

Contains a letter from T. S. Eliot to Ezra Pound.

In original cloth.

B*l*28 THE HOUND & HORN THE HISTORY OF A LITERARY QUARTERLY by Leonard Greenbaum The Hague Mouton & Company 1966

Contains three letters from T. S. Eliot to Lincoln Kirstein.

In original cloth.

B*l*29 T. S. ELIOT   THE MAN AND HIS WORK   edited by Allen Tate   New York   Delacorte Press   1966

Contains letters or parts of letters from T. S. Eliot to Herbert Read, Stephen Spender, Bonamy Dobrée, Mrs. Dobrée, E. Martin Browne, and G. Wilson Knight.

In original cloth and dustwrapper.

B*l*29.1   THE TRIAL OF EZRA POUND   by Julien Cornell   New York   The John Day Company   1966

Contains a letter from T. S. Eliot to Julien Cornell (G516).

In original cloth.

B*l*30 LETTERS OF JAMES JOYCE   VOLUME II [AND III]   edited by Richard Ellmann   New York   The Viking Press   1966

Contains four letters from T. S. Eliot to James Joyce, one to Harriet Shaw Weaver, and one to Monro, Saw & Co.

In original cloth and dustwrapper.

B*l*31 THE GROUCHO LETTERS   LETTERS FROM AND TO GROUCHO MARX   New York   Simon and Shuster   1967

Contains six letters from T. S. Eliot to Groucho Marx.

In original paper boards and cloth spine.

B*l*32 FORD MADOX FORD AND THE TRANSATLANTIC RE- VIEW   by Bernard J. Poli   Syracuse, New York   Syracuse University Press   1967

Contains two letters from T. S. Eliot to Ford Madox Ford.

In original cloth.

B*l*33 THE AUTOBIOGRAPHY OF BERTRAND RUSSELL   1914– 1944   Boston   Toronto   Little, Brown and Company   1968

Contains four letters from T. S. Eliot to Bertrand Russell.

In original cloth.

B*l*34 BEING GENIUSES TOGETHER 1920–1930 by Robert Mc-Almon revised with supplementary chapters by Kay Boyle Garden City, New York Doubleday & Company 1968

Contains a letter from T. S. Eliot to Robert McAlmon, and a letter from Eliot to Ezra Pound.

In original cloth.

B*l*35 AFFECTIONATELY, T. S. ELIOT THE STORY OF A FRIENDSHIP 1947–1965 by William Turner Levy and Victor Scherle Philadelphia New York J. B. Lippincott Company 1968

Contains numerous letters or parts of letters from T. S. Eliot to William Turner Levy, selected from those listed in G.

In original cloth and dustwrapper.

B*l*36 THE MAN FROM NEW YORK JOHN QUINN AND HIS FRIENDS by B. L. Reid New York Oxford University Press 1968

Contains fourteen letters from T. S. Eliot to John Quinn.

In original cloth and dustwrapper.

C

CONTRIBUTIONS BY T. S. ELIOT

TO PERIODICALS

Numbered as in Gallup, but listed under periodical titles in alphabetical order. Under each title Eliot's contributions are listed chronologically. Titles of poems are in capitals, as in Gallup. Gallup's authority is accepted for attributing unsigned contributions. In sections C, D, and E some photocopies are listed since the librarian is, in this form, bringing into one location much of Eliot's ephemeral work. Unless bindings are indicated the item is a photocopy extract.

CONTRIBUTIONS TO PERIODICALS

Adam   London

C515 Reflections on the Unity of European Culture [I]. XIV. 158 (May 1946) 1–3.

C517 Reflections on the Unity of European Culture (II). XIV. 159/160 (June/July 1946) 1–3.

C518 Reflections on the Unity of European Culture (III). XIV. 161 (August 1946) 20–2.

C544 The Aims of Poetic Drama. XVII. 200 (November 1949) 10–16.

C576 A Message from T. S. Eliot O. M. XXI. 234 (1953) 9. A Letter to Miron Grindea, dated 25 January 1953. In original paper covers.

C576.1 The Criterion. XXI. 234 (1953) 20–1. In original paper covers.

The Adelphi   London

C511 The Social Function of Poetry. XXI. 4 (July/September 1945) 152–61. In original paper covers.

C523b Culture. XXIII. 3 (April/June 1947) 119–21. In original paper covers.

C533 Middleton Murry's 'The Free Society'. XXIV. 4 (July/September 1948) 245–7. In original paper covers.

American Literature   Durham, North Carolina

C522 Prufrock and Raskolnikov Again: A Letter from T. S. Eliot. By John C. Pope. XVIII. 4 (January 1947) [319]–321. Bound with the volume.

American Prefaces   Iowa City, Iowa

C395.1 Literature and the Modern World. V. 9 (June 1940) 132–5. In original paper covers. This article had appeared originally in November 1935, in the same journal.

American Review   New York

C354 Tradition and Orthodoxy.   II. 5 (March 1934) 513–28. In original paper covers.

The Animals' Magazine   London

C573 CAT MORGAN'S APOLOGY.   N. S. VII. 9 (September 1952) 4. In original paper covers. Reprinted as a broadside (E2g).

Arts & *Letters*   London

C73 Marivaux. II. 2 (Spring 1919) 80–5. In original paper covers.

C81 [TWO POEMS].   II. 3 (Summer 1919) 103–5. In original paper covers.

C89 Some Notes on the Blank Verse of Christopher Marlowe.   II. 4 (Autumn 1919) 194–9. In original paper covers.

C102 'The Duchess of Malfi' at the Lyric: and Poetic Drama.   III. 1 (Winter 1919/1920) 36–9. In original paper covers.

C107 Euripides and Gilbert Murray: A Performance at the Holborn Empire.   III. 2 (Spring 1920) 36–43. In original paper covers.

The Athenaeum   London

C73a The New Elizabethans and the Old.   4640 (4 April 1919) 134–6.

C73b The Post-Georgians.   4641 (11 April 1919) 171–2.

C74 American Literature.   4643 (25 April 1919) 236–7.

C76 A Romantic Patrician.   4644 (2 May 1919) 265–7.

C77 Kipling Redivivus.   4645 (9 May 1919) 297–8.

C78 Kipling Redivivus.   [A Letter] To the Editor.   4646 (16 May 1919) 344.

C79 A Sceptical Patrician.   4647 (23 May 1919) 361–2.

C80 Beyle and Balzac.   4648 (30 May 1919) 392–3.

C82 Criticism in England.   4650 (13 June 1919) 456–7.

C83 The Education of Taste.   4652 (27 June 1919) 520–1.

C85 A Foreign Mind. 4653 (4 July 1919) 552–3.

C86 The Romantic Generation, If It Existed. 4655 (18 July 1919) 616–17.

C87 Whether Rostand had Something about Him. 4656 (25 July 1919) 665–6.

C88 Was there a Scottish Literature? 4657 (1 August 1919) 680–1.

C91 Swinburne and the Elizabethans. 4664 (19 September 1919) 909–10.

C92 Hamlet and His Problems. 4665 (26 September 1919) 940–1.

C92a Murmuring of Innumerable Bees. 4666 (3 October 1919) 972.

C93 Humanist, Artist, and Scientist. 4667 (10 October 1919) 1014–15.

C94 War-paint and Feathers. 4668 (17 October 1919) 1036.

C95 The Method of Mr. Pound. 4669 (24 October 1919) 1065–6.

C96 Our Inaccessible Heritage [A Letter] To the Editor. 4669 (24 October 1919) 1076.

C98 Mr. Pound and his Poetry. [A Letter] To the Editor. 4671 (7 November 1919) 1163.

C100 The Comedy of Humours. 4672 (14 November 1919) 1180–1.

C101 The Preacher as Artist. 4674 (28 November 1919) 1252–3.

C103 The Local Flavour. 4676 (12 December 1919) 1332–3.

C104 Swinburne. 4681 (16 January 1920) 72–3. Bound with the volume.

C105 The Naked Man. 4685 (13 February 1920) 208–9. Bound with the volume.

C106 The Phoenix Society. [A Letter] To the Editor. 4687 (27 February 1920) 285. Bound with the volume.

C109 Dante as a 'Spiritual Leader.' 4692 (2 April 1920) 441–2. Bound with the volume.

C110 The Poetic Drama. 4698 (14 May 1920) 635–6. Bound with the volume.

C112 The Old Comedy. 4702 (11 June 1920) 760–1. Bound with the volume.

C113 Artists and Men of Genius. [A Letter] To the Editor. 4704 (25 June 1920) 842. Bound with the volume.

C114 The Perfect Critic. [I]. 4706 (9 July 1920) 40–1. Bound with the volume.

C115 The Perfect Critic. II. 4708 (23 July 1920) 102–4. Bound with the volume.

C116 The Perfect Critic. [A Letter] To the Editor. 4710 (6 August 1920) 190. Bound with the volume.

The Atlantic Monthly Boston, Massachusetts

C560 Poetry and Drama. 187.2 (February 1951) 30–7. Bound with the volume.

C586 The Three Voices of Poetry. 193.4 (April 1954) 38–44. Bound with the volume.

Blast London

C19 POEMS. 2 (July 1915) 48–51. In original paper covers.

The Bookman New York

C296 Experiment in Criticism. LXX. 3 (November 1929) 225–33. In original paper covers.

C301 Poetry and Propaganda. LXX. 6 (February 1930) 595–602. In original paper covers.

Les Cahiers de la Pléiade Paris

C552 [A Letter to Jean Paulhan]. X (Summer/Autumn 1950) 27–9. In original paper covers.

The Cambridge Review Cambridge, England

C259 The Idealism of Julien Benda. XLIX. 1218 (6 June 1928) 485–8.

The Catacomb London

C553 A Letter from T. S. Eliot, O.M. N.S. 1. 1 (Summer 1950) 367–8. In original paper covers.

Cecil Houses (Incorporated) 23rd Report   London

C567 Those Who Need Privacy and Those Whose Need Is Company. (1950–1) 15–17. In original paper covers.

The Chapbook   London

C108 A Brief Treatise on the Criticism of Poetry.   II. 9 (March 1920) 1–10. In original paper covers.

C122 Prose and Verse.   22 (April 1921) 3–10. In original paper covers.

C158a DORIS'S DREAM SONGS.   39 ([November] 1924) 36–7. In original paper boards.

University of Chicago Round Table   Chicago

C556 POETRY BY T. S. ELIOT.   An NBC Radio Discussion   659 (12 November 1950) 1–16. In original paper covers.

The Christian News-Letter   London

C453 Education in a Christian Society.   No. 20 (13 March 1940) Supplement [A Letter to the Editor], [1–4].

C459a [Entire issue] No. 42 (14 August 1940).

C459b [Entire issue, not including Supplement] No. 43 (21 August 1940).

C459c [Entire issue] No. 44 (28 August 1940).

C479 [Entire issue]. No. 141 (8 July 1942).

C498 Responsibility and Power.   No. 196 (1 December 1943), Supplement [A Letter to the Editor], [1–4].

C507 Full Employment and the Responsibility of Christians.   No. 230 (21 March 1945), Supplement 7–[12].

The Christian Register   Boston, Massachusetts

C347 The Modern Dilemma.   CXII. 41 (19 October 1933) [675]–676.

Christendom   London

C344 Catholicism and International Order: Opening Address to the Anglo-Catholic Summer School of Sociology. III. 11 (September 1933) [171]–184.

C455 The English Tradition: Some Thoughts as a Preface to Study. X. 38 (June 1940) [101]–108.

C461 The English Tradition: Address to the School of Sociology. X. 40 (December 1940) [226]–237.

Church Times   London

C352 The Blackshirts. [A Letter to the Editor]. CXI. 3706 (2 February 1934) 116.

C423 The Oxford Conference. [A Letter to the Editor]. CXVIII. 3889 (6 August 1937) 130.

C424 The Oxford Conference[II]. [A Letter to the Editor]. CXVIII. 3891 (20 August 1937) 184.

C603 Fr. Cheetham Retires from Gloucester Road. CXXXIX 4856 (9 March 1956) 12. Unbound, as issued.

Columbia University Forum   New York

C626 T. S. Eliot Talks about His Poetry. II. 1 (Fall 1958) 11–14. In original paper covers.

Commerce   Paris

C158 POÈME. III (Winter 1924/1925) [9–11]. In original paper covers. "A penny for the Old Guy," dated "Nov. 1924," later to be incorporated in *The Hollow Men.*

C249 PERCH' IO NON SPERO. XV (Spring 1928) [5]–11. In original paper covers.

C294 SOM DE L'ESCALINA. XXI (Autumn 1929) [99]–103. In original paper covers.

C327 DIFFICULTIES OF A STATESMAN. XXIX (Winter [1931] /1932) [79]–87. In original paper covers.

Coterie   Oxford, England

C75 A COOKING EGG. 1 (May Day 1919) 44–5. In original paper covers. Signed on half title: "Jno Tave Pabst Jr."

The Criterion   London (including *The New Criterion* and *The Monthly Criterion*)

C135 THE WASTE LAND.   I. 1 (October 1922) 50–64. (1) In original paper covers. Pages untrimmed. Autograph above title of poem: "Inscribed for William Levy by T. S. Eliot 23.12.63." (2) Bound with the volume, in decorated paper boards, cloth spine with red leather label. With bookplate of John Johnson and a few penciled notes on *The Waste Land* in an unidentified hand.

C138 Dramatis Personæ.   I. 3 (April 1923) 303–6. Bound with the volume.

C141 The Function of a Literary Review.   I. 4 (July 1923) 421 (1) In original paper covers. (2) Bound with the volume.

C144 The Function of Criticism.   II. 5 (October 1923) 31–42. Bound with the volume.

C145 The Classics in France—and in England.   II. 5 (October 1923) 104–5. Bound with the volume, in black cloth; white paper label on spine.

C152 Four Elizabethan Dramatists.   I. A Preface. II. 6 (February 1924) 115–23. Bound with the volume.

C154 A Commentary.   II. 7 (April 1924) 231–5. Bound with the volume.

C155 A Commentary. II. 8 (July 1924) 371–5. Bound with the volume.

C156 [*A review of*] The Growth of Civilisation, and The Origin of Magic and Religion. By W. J. Perry. II. 8 (July 1924) 489–91. Bound with the volume.

C157 A Commentary.   III. 9 (October 1924) [1]–5. Bound with the volume.

C159 A Commentary.   III. 10 (January 1925) 161–3. Bound with the volume.

C160 THREE POEMS.   III. 10 (January 1925) 170–1. Bound with the volume.

C161 On the Eve, A Dialogue.   III. 10 (January 1925) 278–81. Bound with the volume.

C163 A Commentary. III. 11 (April 1925) 341–4. Bound with the volume.

C164 The Ballet. III. 11 (April 1925) 441–3. Bound with the volume.

C170 The Idea of a Literary Review. IV. 1 (January 1926) 1–6. In original paper covers.

C172 A Commentary. IV. 2 (April 1926) 221–3. In original paper covers.

C173 Mr. Robertson and Mr. Shaw. IV. 2 (April 1926) 389–90. In original paper covers.

C174 [A review of] All God's Chillun got Wings, Desire under the Elms, and Welded. By Eugene O'Neill. IV. 2 (April 1926) 395–6. In original paper covers.

C175 A Commentary. IV. 3 (June 1926) 417–20. In bound reprint (London, 1967).

C183 A Commentary. IV. 4 (October 1926) 627–9. In original paper covers.

C184 FRAGMENT OF A PROLOGUE. IV. 4 (October 1926) 713–18. In original paper covers.

C185 Mr. Read and M. Fernandez. IV. 4 (October 1926) 751–7. In original paper covers.

C192 A Commentary. V. 1 (January 1927) 1–6. In original paper covers.

C192a [A translation of] Poetry and Religion. V. 1 (January 1927), 7. In original paper covers.

C193 FRAGMENT OF AN AGON. From Wanna Go Home, Baby? V. 1 (January 1927) 74–80. In original paper covers.

C194 Grammar and Usage. V. 1 (January 1927) 121–4. In original paper covers.

C195 Homage to Wilkie Collins. V. 1 (January 1927) 139–43. In original paper covers.

C203 A Commentary. V. 2 (May 1927) 187–90. In original paper covers.

C204 Popular Theologians: Mr. Wells, Mr. Belloc and Mr. Murry. V. 2 (May 1927) 253–9. In original paper covers.

C208 A Commentary.   V. 3 (June 1927) 283–6. In original paper covers.

C209 Recent Detective Fiction.   V. 3 (June 1927) 359–62. In original paper covers.

C213 A Commentary.   VI. 1 (July 1927) 1-3. In original paper covers.

C214 Political Theorists.   VI. 1 (July 1927) 69–73. In original paper covers.

C218 A Commentary.   VI. 2 (August 1927) 97–100. In original paper covers.

C219 Why Mr. Russell is a Christian.   VI. 2 (August 1927) 177–9. In original paper covers.

C223 A Commentary.   VI. 3 (September 1927) 193–6. In original paper covers.

C224 [*A translation of*] Concerning 'Intuition', by Charles Mauron. VI. 3 (September 1927) 229–35. In original paper covers.

C228 A Commentary.   VI. 4 (October 1927) 289–91. In original paper covers.

C229 [*A translation of*] A Note on Intelligence and Intuition, by Ramon Fernandez.   VI. 4 (October 1927) 332–9. In original paper covers.

C230 Mr. Middleton Murry's Synthesis.   VI. 4 (October 1927) 340–7. In original paper covers.

C234 A Commentary.   VI. 5 (November 1927) 385–8. In original paper covers.

C235 A Commentary.   VI. 6 (December 1927) 481–3. In original paper covers.

C241 A Commentary.   VII. 1 (January 1928) 1–4. In original paper covers.

C242 [*A translation of*] Prologue to An Essay on Criticism, by Charles Maurras. [1].   VII. 1 (January 1928) 5–15. In original paper covers.

C244 A Commentary,   VII. 2 (February 1928) 97–9. In original paper covers.

C245 [*A translation*] FROM 'ANABASE,' by St.-J. Perse.   VII. 2 (February 1928) 137–8. In original paper covers.

C250 A Commentary.   VII. 3 (March 1928) 193–4. In original paper covers.

C251 The *Action Française*, M. Maurras and Mr. Ward.   VII. 3 (March 1928) 195–203. In original paper covers.

C252 [*A translation of*] Prologue to an Essay on Criticism, by Charles Maurras, [2].   VII. 3 (March 1928) 204–18. In original paper covers.

C255 A Commentary.   VII. 4 (June 1928) 1–6. In original paper covers.

C256 A Reply to Mr. Ward.   VII. 4 (June 1928) 84–8. In original paper covers.

C257 Mr. Lucas's Webster.   VII. 4 (June 1928) 155–8. In original paper covers.

C264 A Commentary.   VIII. 30 (September 1928) 1–6. In original paper covers.

C265 Civilisation: 1928 Model.   VIII. 30 (September 1928) 161–4. In original paper covers.

C270 A Commentary.   VIII. 31 (December 1928) 185–90. In original paper covers.

C271 [*A translation of*] Fustel de Coulanges, by Pierre Gaxotte.   VIII. 31 (December 1928) [258]–269. In original paper covers.

C272 The Literature of Fascism.   VIII. 31 (December 1928) 280–90. In original paper covers.

C273 Freud's Illusions.   VIII. 31 (December 1928) 350–3. In original paper covers.

C282 A Commentary.   VIII. 32 (April 1929) 377–81. In original paper covers. Signed "Louis Zukofsky" on front cover.

C283 Sherlock Holmes and His Times.   VIII. 32 (April 1929) 552–6. In original paper covers.

C289 A Commentary.   VIII. 33 (July 1929) 575–9. In bound reprint.

C290 Mr. Barnes and Mr. Rowse.   VIII. 33 (July 1929) 682–91. In bound reprint.

C295 A Commentary.   IX. 34 (October 1929) 1–6. In bound reprint.

C297 A Commentary.   IX. 35 (January 1930) 181–4. In original paper covers.

C298 [*A translation of*] A Humanist Theory of Value, by Ramon Fernandez. IX. 35 (January 1930) 228–45. In original paper covers.

C299 [*A review of*] God: Being an Introduction to the Science of Metabiology. By J. Middleton Murry. IX. 35 (January 1930) 333–6. In original paper covers.

C300 [*A review of*] Baudelaire and the Symbolists. Five Essays. By Peter Quennell. IX. 35 (January 1930) 357–9. In original paper covers.

C305 A Commentary. IX. 36 (April 1930) 381–5. In original paper covers.

C309 Commentary. IX. 37 (July 1930) 587–90. In bound reprint.

C311 A Commentary. IX. 38 (October 1930) 1–4. In original paper covers.

C312 [*A translation of*] On Reading Einstein, by Charles Mauron. X. 38 (October 1930) 23–31. In original paper covers.

C315 A Commentary. X. 39 (January 1931) 307–14. In original paper covers.

C316 A Commentary. X. 40 (April 1931) 481–90. In original paper covers. Signed "Louis Zukofsky" on front cover, and with autograph corrections by Zukofsky of his article "The Cantos of Ezra Pound," pp. 424–40.

C321 A Commentary. X. 41 (July 1931) 709–16. In original paper covers.

C322 [*A review of*] Son of Woman: The Story of D. H. Lawrence. By John Middleton Murry. X. 41 (July 1931) 768–74. In original paper covers.

C325 A Commentary. XI. 42 (October 1931) 65–72. In original paper covers.

C328 A Commentary. XI. 43 (January 1932) 268–75. In bound reprint.

C333 A Commentary. XI. 44 (April 1932) 467–73. In bound reprint.

C336 A Commentary. XI. 45 (July 1932) 676–83. In bound reprint.

C337 A Commentary. XII. 46 (October 1932) 73–9. In original paper covers. Signed "Louis MacNeice" after his poem, p. 55.

C339 FIVE-FINGER EXERCISES. XII. 47 (January 1933) 220–2. In original paper covers.

C340 A Commentary. XII. 47 (January 1933) 244–9. In original paper covers.

C342 A Commentary. XII. 48 (April 1933) 468–73. In bound reprint.

C343 A Commentary. XII. 49 (July 1933) 642–7. In original paper covers.

C346 A Commentary. XIII. 50 (October 1933) 115–20. In original paper covers.

C347 [*A review of*] The Name and Nature of Poetry. By A. E. Housman. XIII. 50 (October 1933) 151–4. In original paper covers.

C350 A Commentary. XIII. 51 (January 1934) 270–8. In original paper covers. Signed "Louis MacNeice" on front cover.

C357 A Commentary. XIII. 52 (April 1934) 451–4. In bound reprint.

C363 A Commentary. XIII. 53 (July 1934) 624–30. In original paper covers.

C364 [*A review of*] The Oxford Handbook of Religious Knowledge. XIII. 53 (July 1934) 709. In original paper covers.

C365 [*A review of*] The Mystical Doctrine of St. John of the Cross. XIII. 53 (July 1934) 709–10. In original paper covers.

C366 [*A review of*] A Christian Sociology for To-day. (An abridged edition of 'Faith and Society'). By Maurice B. Reckitt. XIII. 53 (July 1934) 710. In original paper covers.

C369 A Commentary. XIV. 54 (October 1934) 86–90. In original paper covers. Signed "Louis MacNeice" after his review, p. 163.

C372 A Commentary. XIV. 55 (January 1935) 260–4. In bound reprint.

C386 A Commentary. XIV. 56 (April 1935) 431–6. In original paper covers. Stamped on front cover: "Specimen."

C389 A Commentary. XIV. 57 (July 1935) 610–13. In original paper covers.

C391 A Commentary. XV. 58 (October 1935) 65–9. In bound reprint.

C402 A Commentary. XV. 59 (January 1936) 265–9. In original paper covers.

C403 [*A review of*] Totem: The Exploitation of Youth. By Harold Stovin. XV. 59 (January 1936) 363. In original paper covers.

C404 [*A review of*] Selected Shelburne Essays. By Paul Elmer More. XV. 59 (January 1936) 363. In original paper covers.

C406 A Commentary. XV. 60 (April 1936) 458–63. In original paper covers.

C409 A Commentary. XV. 61 (July 1936) 663–8. In original paper covers.

C410 The Year's Poetry. [A Letter to the Editor]. XV. 61 (July 1936) 691. In original paper covers.

C411 Mr. Murry's Shakespeare. XV. 61 (July 1936) 708–10. In original paper covers.

C413 A Commentary. XVI. 62 (October 1936) 63–9. In original paper covers.

C415 A Commentary. XVI. 63 (January 1937) 289–93. In original paper covers.

C419 A Commentary. XVI. 64 (April 1937) 469–74. In original paper covers.

C420 Nightwood. XVI. 64 (April 1937) 560–4. In original paper covers.

C421 A Commentary. XVI. 65 (July 1937) 666–70. In original paper covers.

C426 A Commentary. XVII. 66 (October 1937) 81–6. In original paper covers.

C429 A Commentary. XVII. 67 (January 1938) 254–9. In original paper covers.

C433 A Commentary. XVII. 68 (April 1938) 478–85. In bound reprint.

C435 A Commentary. XVII. 69 (July 1938) 686–92. In original paper covers.

C438 A Commentary. XVIII. 70 (October 1938) 58–62. In original paper covers.

C441 Last words. XVIII. 71 (January 1939) 269–75. In original paper covers.

The Critic Chicago

C640 On Teaching the Appreciation of Poetry. XVIII. 5 (April-May 1960) 13–14; 78–80. In original paper covers.

The Dial New York

C117 The Possibility of a Poetic Drama. LXIX. 5 (November 1920) [441]–447. In original paper covers.

C118 The Second-Order Mind. LXIX. 6 (December 1920) [586]–589. Bound with the volume.

C123 London Letter. LXX. 4 (April 1921) [448]–453. In original paper covers.

C124 London Letter. LXX. 6 (June 1921) [686]–691. In original paper covers.

C126 London Letter. LXXI. 2 (August 1921) [213]–217. In original paper covers.

C127 London Letter. LXXI. 4 (October 1921) [452]–455. Bound with the volume.

C130 London Letter. LXXII. 5 (May 1922) [510]–513. Bound with the volume.

C133 London Letter. LXXIII. 1 (July 1922) [94]–96. In original paper covers.

C134 London Letter. LXXIII. 3 (September 1922) [329]–331. In original paper covers.

C135.1 THE WASTE LAND. LXXIII. 5 (November 1922) [473]–485. In original paper covers.

C136 London Letter. LXXIII. 6 (December 1922) [659]–662. In original paper covers.

C147 Ulysses, Order, and Myth. LXXV. 5 (November 1923) [480]–483. In original paper covers.

C150 Marianne Moore. LXXV. 6 (December 1923) [594]–597. In original paper covers.

C162 THE HOLLOW MEN, I–III. LXXVIII. 3 (March 1925) [193]–194. In original paper covers.

C200 Literature, Science, and Dogma. LXXXII. 3 (March 1927) [239]–243. Bound with the volume.

C205 'Poet and Saint . . .' LXXXII. 5 (May 1927) [424]–431. In original paper covers.

C225 The Silurist. LXXXIII. 3 (September 1927) [259]–263. Bound with the volume.

C243 Isolated Superiority. LXXXIV. 1 (January 1928) [4]–7. Bound with the volume.

C246 An Emotional Unity. LXXXIV. 2 (February 1928) [109]–112. Bound with the volume.

C253 The Poems English Latin and Greek of Richard Crashaw. LXXXIV. 3 (March 1928) [246]–250. In original paper covers.

C260 The Oxford Jonson. LXXXV. 1 (July 1928) [65]–68. In original paper covers.

C266 The Golden Ass of Apuleius. LXXXV. 3 (September 1928) [254]–257. In original paper covers.

Dock Leaves   Pembroke Dock, Wales

C594 A Note on 'In Parenthesis' and 'The Anathemata.' VI. 16 (Spring 1955) 21–3. In original paper covers.

Drama   The Quarterly Theatre Review   London

C595 Gordon Craig's Socratic Dialogues. N.S. 36 (Spring 1955) 16–21. In original paper covers.

University of Edinburgh Journal   Edinburgh

C425 Religious Drama: Mediaeval and Modern. IX. 1 (Autumn 1937) 8–17.

The Egoist   London

C42 The Letters of J. B. Yeats. IV. 6 (July 1917) 89–90. In bound reprint (New York, 1967).

C46 The Noh and the Image. IV. 7 (August 1917) 102–3. In bound reprint.

C47 Reflections on Contemporary Poetry, I. IV. 8 (September 1917) 118–19. In bound reprint.

C49 Reflections on Contemporary Poetry [II]. IV. 9 (October 1917) 133–4. In bound reprint.

C51 Reflections on Contemporary Poetry [III]. IV. 10 (November 1917) 151. In bound reprint.

C52 Correspondence. IV. 11 (December 1917) 165. In bound reprint.

C53 Turgenev. IV. 11 (December 1917) 167. In bound reprint.

C54 In Memory of Henry James. V. 1 (January 1918) [1]–2. In bound reprint.

C56 Literature and the American Courts. V. 3 (March 1918) 39. In bound reprint.

C57 Verse Pleasant and Unpleasant. V. 3 (March 1918) 43–4. In bound reprint.

C58 [A Letter] To the Editor. V. 3 (March 1918) 47. In bound reprint.

C59 Disjecta Membra. V. 4 (April 1918) 55. In bound reprint.

C60 Professional, or . . . V. 4 (April 1918) 61. In bound reprint.

C63 Observations. V. 5 (May 1918) 69–70. In bound reprint.

C63a Short Notices. V. 5 (May 1918) 75. In bound reprint.

C64 Contemporanea. V. 6 (June/July 1918) 84–5. In bound reprint.

C64a Shorter Notices. V. 6 (June/July 1918) 87. In bound reprint.

C66 Short Notices. V. 7 (August 1918) 99. In bound reprint.

C68 "Tarr." V. 8 (September 1918) 105–6. In bound reprint.

C71 Studies in Contemporary Criticism, I. V. 9 (October 1918) [113]–114. In bound reprint.

C72 Studies in Contemporary Criticism, II. V. 10 (November/December 1918) 131–3. In bound reprint.

C84 Reflections on Contemporary Poetry [IV]. VI. 3 (July 1919) 39–40. In bound reprint.

C90 Tradition and the Individual Talent [I]. VI. 4 (September/[October] 1919) 54–5. In bound reprint.

C97 Tradition and the Individual Talent, II. VI. 5 ([November]/

December 1919) 72–3. In bound reprint.

Encounter   London

C656 Miss Harriet Weaver. XVIII. 1 (January 1962) 101. Bound with the volume.

The Enemy   London

C196 A Note on Poetry and Belief. 1 (January [i.e. February] 1927) 15–17. In original paper covers.

The English Review   London

C320 [*A review of*] The Prospects of Humanism. By Lawrence Hyde. LIII. 1 (June 1931) 118, 120. Bound with the volume.

C323 [*A review of*] Essays of a Catholic Layman in England. By Hilaire Belloc. LIII. 2 (July 1931) 245–6. Bound with the volume.

C326 [*A review of*] Fashion in Literature: A Study of Changing Taste. By E. E. Kellett. LIII. 5 (October 1931) 634–6. Bound with the volume.

Essays in Criticism   Oxford, England

C559 Postscript 1950 [to 'The Three Provincialities']. I. 1 (January 1951) 41. Bound with the volume.

Forum   New York

C261 The Humanism of Irving Babbitt. 80. 1 (July 1928) [37]–44. Bound with the volume.

C278 Contemporary Literature. Is Modern Realism Frankness or Filth? [A Letter to the Editor.] 81 (February 1929, Supplement) xlvi–xlvii. Bound with the volume.

Friends of Chichester Cathedral   *Annual Report*

C566 The Value and Use of Cathedrals in England Today. (1950–51) 17–27. In original paper covers.

The Grantite Review   London

C662 T. S. Eliot . . . An Interview. XXIV. 3 (Election 1962) 16–20. In original paper covers.

Groton School Quarterly   Groton, Connecticut

C488 The Classics and the Man of Letters. XVI. 2 (March 1943) [4]–13.

Harper's Monthly Magazine   New York

C478 In Praise of Kipling's Verse. 185. 2 (July 1942) [149]–157. Bound with the volume.

The Harvard Advocate   Cambridge, Massachusetts

C5 SONG ['When we came home across the hill']. LXXXIII. 6 (24 May 1907) 93.

C5.1 SONG ['If space and time, as sages say']. LXXXIII. 7 (3 June 1907) 96.

C6 BEFORE MORNING. LXXXVI. 4 (13 November 1908) 53.

C7 CIRCE'S PALACE. LXXXVI. 5 (25 November 1908) 66.

C8 SONG ['The moonflower opens to the moth']. LXXXVI. 9 (26 January 1909) 130.

C9 ON A PORTRAIT. LXXXVI. (26 January 1909) 135.

C10 [*A review of*] The Wine of the Puritans. [By] Van Wyck Brooks. LXXXVII. 5 (7 May 1909) [80].

C11 The Point of View   [An Editorial]. LXXXVII. 6 (20 May 1909) 82.

C12 Gentlemen and Seamen.   LXXXVII. 7 (25 May 1909) 115–16.

C13 [*A review of*] Egoists. By James Huneker, LXXXVIII. 1 (5 October 1909) 16.

C14 NOCTURNE.   LXXXVIII. 3 (12 November 1909) 39.

C15 HUMORESQUE. (AFTER J. LAFORGUE). LXXXVIII. 7 (12 January 1910) [103].

C16 SPLEEN. LXXXVIII. 8 (26 January 1910) 114.

C17 [CLASS] ODE. LXXXIX. 8 (24 June 1910) [100].

C368 The Problem of Education. CXXI. 1 (Freshman Number 1934) 11–12.

C439 EIGHT POEMS. CXXV. 3 (December 1938) 9–16.

C440 Eliot on Bradley's Metaphysic. CXXV. 3 (December 1938) 24–6.

Horizon London

C466 A Message to the Fish. III. 15 (March 1941) 173–5. In original paper covers.

C468 Virginia Woolf. III. 17 (May 1941) 313–16. Bound with volume.

C528a Twenty-one Answers. XIV. 96 (December 1947) 365–9. Bound with the volume.

The Hudson Review New York

C539 From Poe to Valéry. II. 3 (Autumn 1949) [327]–342. In original paper covers.

C548 T. S. Eliot to Ezra Pound. III. 1 (Spring 1950) 55–6. In original paper covers.

C612 Homage to W. Lewis. X. 2 (Summer 1957) 167–70. In original paper covers.

International Journal of Ethics Chicago

C22 [*A review of*] Theism and Humanism. By the Rt. Hon. A. J. Balfour. XXVI. 2 (January 1916) 284–9. Bound with the volume.

C23 [*A review of*] The Philosophy of Nietzsche. By A. Wolf. XXVI. 3 (April 1916) 426–7. Bound with the volume.

C29 [*A review of*] Conscience and Christ: Six Lectures on Christian Ethics. By Hastings Rashdall. XXVII. 1 (October 1916) 111–12. Bound with the volume.

C31 [*A review of*] Religion and Science: A Philosophical Essay. By John Theodore Merz. XXVII. 1 (October 1916) 125–6. Bound with the volume.

C32 [*A review of*] The Ultimate Belief. By A. Clutton Brock. XXVII. 1 (October 1916) 127. Bound with the volume.

C33 [*A review of*] Philosophy and War. By Emile Boutroux. XXVII. 1 (October 1916) 128. Bound with the volume.

C38 [*A review of*] Elements of Folk Psychology. Outlines of a Psychological History of the Development of Mankind. By Wilhelm Wundt. XXVII. 2 (January 1917) 252–4. Bound with the volume.

C43 [*A review of*] Mens Creatrix. By William Temple. XXVII. 4 (July 1917) 542–3. Bound with the volume.

C44 [*A review of*] Religion and Philosophy. By R. G. Collingwood. XXVII. 4 (July 1917) 543. Bound with the volume.

C50 [*A review of*] A Manual of Modern Scholastic Philosophy. By Cardinal Mercier and Other Professors of the Higher Institute of Philosophy, Louvain. . . . Vol. I. XXVIII. 1 (October 1914) 137–8. Bound with the volume.

C55 Recent British Periodical Literature in Ethics. XXVIII. 2 (January 1918) 270–7. Bound with the volume.

C61 [*A review of*] La Guerra Eterna e Il Dramma del Esistenza. By Antonio Aliotta. XXVIII. 3 (April 1918) 444–5. Bound with the volume.

C62 [*A review of*] Brahmadarsanam, or Intuition of the Absolute. Being an Introduction to the Study of Hindu Philosophy. By Sre Ananda Acharya. XXVIII. 3 (April 1918) 445–6. Bound with the volume.

C65 [*A review of*] The World as Imagination (Series I). By Edward Douglas Fawcett. XXVIII. 4 (July 1918) 572. Bound with the volume.

Italian News   London

C554 Talk on Dante.   2 (July 1950) 13–18. In original paper covers.

John O'London's Weekly   London

C538a T. S. Eliot Answers Questions, by Ranjee Shahani.   LVIII. 1369 (19 August 1949) [497]–498. Unbound, wire-stitched, as issued.

The Journal of the National Book League   London

C571.1 Some Thoughts on Braille.   272 (September 1952) 75–6. In original paper covers.

The Kenyon Review   Gambier, Ohio

C677.1 Conversation with T. S. Eliot, by Leslie Paul. XXXVII. (Winter 1965) 11–21. Bound with the volume.

The Kipling Journal   London

C632 The Unfading Genius of Rudyard Kipling.   XXVI. 129 (March 1959) 9–12. In original paper covers. Inscribed on front cover: "For William [Turner Levy] to whom this issue should have been dedicated. Morton [N. Cohen]." Morton N. Cohen was a contributor to this issue of *The Kipling Journal*.

Life   New York

C542 [*Lines from*] THE COCKTAIL PARTY. XXVII. 13 (26 September 1949) 16, 18, 20, 23. In bound volume.

C582 [*Lines from*] THE CONFIDENTIAL CLERK. XXXVI. 5 (1 February 1954) 62, 64. In bound volume.

The Listener   London

C286 The Tudor Translators.   I. 22 (12 June 1929) [853]–854.

C287 The Elizabethan Grub Street.   I. 23 (19 June 1929) [853]–854.

C288 The Genesis of Philosophic Prose: Bacon and Hooker.   I. 24 (26 June 1929) 907–8.

C291 The Prose of the Preacher: The Sermons of Donne.   II. 25 (3 July 1929) 22–3.

C292 Elizabethan Travellers' Tales.   II. 26 (10 July 1929) 59–60.

C293 The Tudor Biographers.   II. 27 (17 July 1929) 94–5.

C302 Thinking in Verse: A Survey of Early Seventeenth-Century Poetry.   III. 61 (12 March 1930) 441–3.

C303 Rhyme and Reason: The Poetry of John Donne.   III. 62 (19 March 1930) 502–3.

C304 The Devotional Poets of the Seventeenth Century: Donne, Herbert, Crashaw.   III. 63 (26 March 1930) 552–3.

C306 Mystic and Politician as Poet: Vaughan, Traherne, Marvell, Milton.   III. 64 (2 April 1930) 590–1.

C307 The Minor Metaphysicals: From Cowley to Dryden. III. 65 (9 April 1930) 641–2.

C308 John Dryden. III. 66 (16 April 1930) 688–9.

C317 John Dryden. I. The Poet who Gave the English Speech. V. 118 (15 April 1931) 621–2.

C318 John Dryden. II. Dryden the Dramatist. V. 119 (22 April 1931) 681–2.

C319 John Dryden. III. Dryden the Critic, Defender of Sanity. V. 120 (29 April 1931) 724–5.

C331 Religion and Science: A Phantom Dilemma. VII. 167 (23 March 1932) 428–9.

C332 The Search for Moral Sanction. VII. 168 (30 March 1932) [445]–446, 480.

C334 Building up the Christian World. VII. 169 (6 April 1932) 501–2.

C414 The Need for Poetic Drama. XVI. 411 (25 November 1936) 994–5.

C417 The Church's Message to the World. XVII. 423 (17 February 1937) [293]–294, 326. For original typescript, see F20.

C460 The Writer as Artist: Discussion between T. S. Eliot and Desmond Hawkins. XXIV. 620 (28 November 1940) 773–4. Extracted and bound with original typescript in carbon copy (F21).

C467 Towards a Christian Britain. XXV. 639 (10 April 1941) 524–5. In original paper covers.

C475 'The Duchess of Malfy'. XXVI. 675 (18 December 1941) 825–6. Extracted and bound with original typescript in carbon copy (F22).

C476 'The Voice of His Time': T. S. Eliot on Tennyson's 'In Memoriam'. XXVII. 683 (12 February 1942) 211–12. (1) In original paper covers. (2) Extracted and bound with original typescript in carbon copy (F23).

C487 'A Dream within a Dream': T. S. Eliot on Edgar Allan Poe. XXIX. 737 (25 February 1943) 243–4. (1) In original paper covers. (2) Extracted, and bound with original typescript (F24).

C492 John Dryden's Tragedies. XXIX. 745 (22 April 1943) 486–7. Extracted and bound with part of the script for radio broadcast in mimeograph copy (F25).

C494 The Approach to James Joyce. XXX. 770 (14 October 1943) 446–7. Extracted and bound with original typescript (F26).

C521 The Significance of Charles Williams. XXXVI. 936 (19 December 1946) 894–5. (1) In original paper covers. (2) Extracted and bound with original typescript (F27).

C523 'Leçon de Valéry'. XXXVII. 939 (9 January 1947) 72.

C565 Vergil and the Christian World. XLVI. 1176 (14 September 1951) 411–12, 423–4.

The Little Review   Chicago

C40 Eeldrop and Appleplex. I.   IV. 1 (May 1917) 7–11. In original paper covers.

C45 [FOUR POEMS].   IV. 3 (July 1917) 8–11. In original paper covers.

C48 Eeldrop and Appleplex. II.   IV. 5 (September 1917) 16–19. In original paper covers.

C67 The Hawthorne Aspect.   V. 4 (August 1918) 47–53. In original paper covers.

C69 FOUR POEMS.   V. 5 (September 1918) 10–14. In original paper covers.

C284 A Letter [To the Editor].   XII. 2 (May 1929) 90. In original paper covers. Signed "Louis Zukofsky" on front cover.

The London Magazine   London

C581 A Message [on the appearance of a new literary periodical].   I. 1 (February 1954) 15–16. In original paper covers.

The Manchester Guardian   Manchester

C597 Mr. Eliot on the Scientific Approach to Poetry. 14 April 1955, p. 12.

C607 Kipling and the O. M. [A Letter] To the Editor. 11 July 1956, p. 6.

From Mary to You   Mary Institute   St. Louis, Missouri

C637 Address. Centennial Issue 1959, pp. 133–6. In original paper covers.

Measure   Chicago

C557 The Aims of Education.   1. Can "Education" be Defined? II. 1 (December 1950) [3]–16. In original paper covers.

C561 The Aims of Education.   2. The Interrelation of Aims. II. 2 (Spring 1951) [191]–203. In original paper covers.

C562 The Aims of Education.   3. The Conflict between Aims. II. 3 (Summer 1951) [285]–297. In original paper covers.

C564 The Aims of Education.   4. The Issue of Religion. II. 4 (Fall 1951) [362]–375. In original paper covers.

Mercure de France   Paris

C632.1 Rudyard Kipling.   335 (January/April 1959) 5–15. Bound in the volume.

C664.1 Miss Sylvia Beach.   349. (August/September 1963) [9]–10. In original paper covers.

Milton Bulletin   Milton, Massachusetts

C537 Leadership and Letters.   XII. 1 (February 1949) [3]–16.

The Monist   Chicago

C34 The Development of Leibniz's Monadism.   XXVI. 4 (October 1916) [534]–556. In original paper covers. Inscribed on front cover: "Prof. J. P. Nunn from C. D[elisle]. B[urns].", a contributor to this issue.

C35 Leibniz's Monads and Bradley's Finite Centers.   XXVI. 4 (October 1916) [566]–576. In original paper covers.

The Nation   London

C58b Style and Thought.   XXII. 25 (23 March 1918) 768, 770.

The Nation   New York

C499 T. S. Eliot on Kipling's Anti-Semitism. [A Letter to the Editor]. CLVIII. 3 (15 January 1944) 83. Bound with the volume.

The Nation and Athenaeum   London

C139 John Donne.   XXXIII. 10 (9 June 1923) 331–2. Bound with the volume.

C140 Ben Jonson.   [A Letter to the Editor]. XXXIII. 13 (30 June 1923) 426. Bound with the volume.

C143 Andrew Marvell.   XXXIII. 26 (29 September 1923) 809. Bound with the volume.

C146 The Beating of a Drum.   XXXIV. 1 (6 October 1923) 11–12. Bound with the volume.

C190   Mr. J. M. Robertson and Shakespeare. [A Letter to the Editor]. XL. 11 (18 December 1926) 418. Bound with the volume.

C191 Whitman and Tennyson. XL. 11 (18 December 1926) 426. Bound with the volume.

C198 Charleston, Hey! Hey!   XL. 17 (29 January 1927) 595. Bound with the volume.

C199 The Problems of the Shakespeare Sonnets.   XL. 19 (12 February 1927) 664, 666. Bound with the volume.

C207 Israfel.   XLI. 7 (21 May 1927) 219. Bound with the volume.

C210 Tennyson and Whitman.   [A Letter to the Editor]. XLI. 9 (4 June 1927) 302. Bound with the volume.

C227 The Mysticism of Blake.   XLI. 24 (17 September 1927) 779. Bound with the volume.

C240 Mr. Chesterton (and Stevenson).   XLII. 3 (31 December 1927) 516. Bound with the volume.

C254 'The Monthly Criterion' [A Letter to the Editor].   XLIII. 3 (21 April 1928) 74. Bound with the volume.

C263 An Extempore Exhumation.   XLIII. 14 (7 July 1928) 470, 472. Bound with the volume.

C267 The New Censorship.   [A Letter to the Editor]. XLIII. 24 (15 September 1928) 755. Bound with the volume.

C276 Introduction to Goethe.   XLIV. 15 (12 January 1929) 527. Bound with the volume.

The New Adelphi   London

C258 Parliament and the New Prayer Book. [A Letter] To the Editor. I. 4 (June 1928) 345–6. Bound with the volume.

C285 Second Thoughts on Humanism. II. 4 (June/August 1929) [304]–310. Bound with the volume.

New Democracy   New York

C401 TWO POEMS ["Rannoch, by Glencoe" and "Cape Ann"]. V. 8 (15 December 1935) 137.

The New England Quarterly   Brunswick, Maine

C345 [*A review of*] Letters of Mrs. Gaskell and Charles Eliot Norton, 1855–1865, edited with an introduction by Jane Whitehill. VI. 3 (September 1933) 627–8.

The New English Weekly   London

C355 Mr. Eliot's Virginian Lectures. [A Letter to the Editor]. IV. 22 (15 March 1934) 528.

C356 The Theology of Economics.   [A Letter to the Editor].   IV. 24 (29 March 1934) 575–6.

C359 Mr. T. S. Eliot's Quandaries. [A Letter to the Editor].   IV. 26 (12 April 1934) 622–3.

C360 Modern Heresies. [A Letter to the Editor]. V. 3 (3 May 1934) 71–2.

C362 'The Use of Poetry' [A Letter to the Editor].   V. 9 (14 June 1934) 215.

C371 Orage: Memories.   VI. 5 (15 November 1934) 100.

C382 Douglas in the Church Assembly.   [A Letter to the Editor]. VI. 18 (14 February 1935) 382–3.

C384 The Church Assembly and Social Credit.   [A Letter to the Editor]. VI. 20 (28 February 1935) 422.

C385 The Church and Society.   [A Letter to the Editor]. VI. 23 (21 March 1935) 482.

C387 Views and Reviews [I].   VII. 8 (6 June 1935) 151–2.

C388 Views and Reviews [II].   VII. 10 (20 June 1935) 190–1.

C390 Views and Reviews [III]. VII. 18 (12 September 1935) 351–2.

C392 Errata. [A Letter to the Editor]. VII. 22 (10 October 1935) 440.

C393 RANNOCH, BY GLENCOE. VIII. 1 (17 October 1935) 10.

C394 Pacifism. [A Letter to the Editor]. VIII. 3 (31 October 1935) 58.

C396 Views and Reviews [IV]. VIII. 4 (7 November 1935) 71–2.

C397 The Supernatural. [A Letter to the Editor]. VIII. 5 (14 November 1935) 99.

C398 WORDS FOR AN OLD MAN. VIII. 7 (28 November 1935) 131.

C405 The Church as Action: Note on a Recent Correspondence. VIII. 23 (19 March 1936) 451.

C407 The Church as Action. [A Letter to the Editor]. VIII. 26 (9 April 1936) 523.

C408 The Church as Action. [A Letter to the Editor]. IX. 2 (23 April 1936) 38.

C418 Mr. Reckitt, Mr. Tomlin, and The Crisis. X. 20 (25 February 1937) 391–3.

C430 Who Controls Population-Distribution? [A Letter to the Editor]. XII. 23 (17 March 1938) 459.

C443 A Commentary. That Poetry is made with Words. XV. 2 (27 April 1939) 27–8.

C444 A Commentary. On Reading Official Reports. XV. 4 (11 May 1939) 61–2.

C445 'That Poetry is made with Words.' [A Letter to the Editor]. XV. 4 (11 May 1939) 66.

C447 Truth and Propaganda. [A Letter to the Editor]. XV. 22 (14 September 1939) 291.

C448 A Commentary [I]. XV. 25 (5 October 1939) 331–2.

C449 A sub-Pagan Society? XVI. 9 (14 December 1939) 125–6.

C450 Christian Society. [A Letter to the Editor]. XVI. 15 (1 February 1940) 226–7.

C451 Views and Reviews. Journalists of Yesterday and Today. XVI. 16 (8 February 1940) 237–8.

C452 Views and Reviews. On Going West. XVI. 17 (15 February 1940) 251.

C454 EAST COKER. XVI. 22 (21 March 1940) [325]–328. Unbound, wire-stitched as issued.

C462 A Commentary [II]. XVIII. 7 (5 December 1940) 75–6.

C463 Views and Reviews. Waiting at the Church. XVIII. 9 (19 December 1940) 99.

C465 THE DRY SALVAGES. XVIII. 19 (27 February 1941) [217–20]. Unbound, wire-stitched as issued. Signed "Michael Hamburger" on first page.

C470 Views and Reviews. Basic Revelation. XIX. 10 (26 June 1941) 101–2.

C472 Greek Literature in Education. [A Letter to the Editor]. XX. 6 (27 November 1941) 52.

C474 Greek Literature in Education. [A Letter to the Editor]. XX. 8 (11 December 1941) 72.

C481 LITTLE GIDDING. XXI. 26 (15 October 1942) 213–17. Unbound, wire-stitched as issued.

C483 Notes towards a Definition of Culture. I. XXII. 14 (21 January 1943) 117–18.

C484 Notes towards a Definition of Culture. II. XXII. 15 (28 January 1943) 129–30.

C485 Notes towards a Definition of Culture. III. XXII. 16 (4 February 1943) 136–7.

C486 Notes towards a Definition of Culture. IV. XXII. 17 (11 February 1943) 145–6.

C489 Education for Culture. [A Letter to the Editor]. XXII. 20 (4 March 1943) 176.

C505 The 'Four Quartets.' [A Letter to the Editor]. XXVI. 15 (25 January 1945) 112.

C506 'The Germanization of England.' [A Letter to the Editor]. XXVI. 21 (8 March 1945) 167–8.

C508 'The Germanisation of Britain.' [A Letter to the Editor]. XXVI. 24 (29 March 1945) 192.

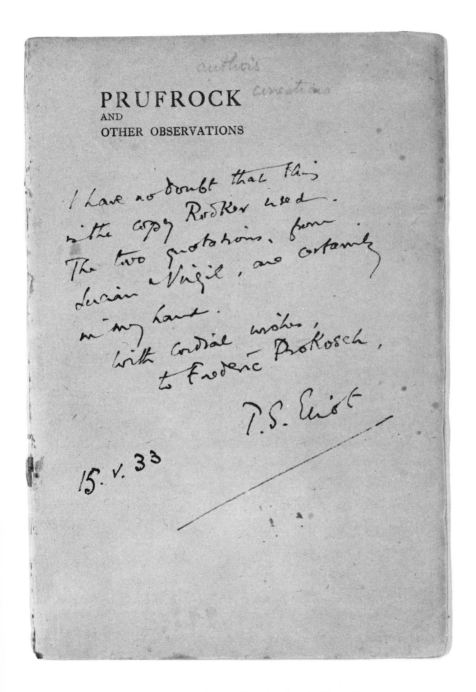

PRUFROCK *author's corrections*
AND
OTHER OBSERVATIONS

I have no doubt that this
is the copy Rodker used.
The two quotations, from
Lucian & Virgil, are certainly
in my hand.
With cordial wishes,
to Frederic Prokosch,

T. S. Eliot

15. v. 33

Inscribed half title from the first edition of *Prufrock and Other Observations*, 1917.
This and other illustrations bearing Eliot's autograph are reproduced
by permission of Valerie Eliot. A1(2)

C516 John Maynard Keynes.   XXIX. 5 (16 May 1946) 47–8.

C520 'Individualists in Verse.'   [A Letter to the Editor]. XXX. 5 (14 November 1946) 52.

C530 'Our Culture.'   XXXII. 21 (4 March 1948) 203–4.

C536 Michael Roberts.   XXXIV. 14 (13 January 1949) 164.

The New Statesman   London

C24 An American Critic.   VII. 168 (24 June 1916) 284.

C24a [*A review of*] The French Renascence.   By Charles Sarolea. VII. 169 (1 July 1916) 309–10.

C26 Mr. Leacock Serious.   VII. 173 (29 July 1916) 404–5.

C27 [*A review of*] Social Adaptation.   By L. M. Bristol. VII. 173 (29 July 1916) 405.

C30 [*A review of*] Group Theories of Religion and the Religion of the Individual.   By Clement C. J. Webb. VII. 173 (29 July 1916) 405–6. Reprinted in the *International Journal of Ethics*, XXXII (October 1916), 115–17. Bound with the volume.

C35a Charles Péguy.   VIII. 183 (7 October 1916) 19–20.

C36 Giordano Bruno.   VIII. 185 (21 October 1916) 68.

C37a [*A review of*] With Americans of Past and Present Days.   By J. J. Jusserand. VIII. 188 (11 November 1916) 141.

C39 Reflections on *Vers Libre*.   VIII. 204 (3 March 1917) 518–19.

C39a Diderot.   VIII. 206 (17 March 1917) 572–3.

C41 The Borderline of Prose.   IX. 215 (19 May 1917) 157–9.

C232 Tristan da Cunha.   [A Letter To the Editor]. XXX. 756 (22 October 1927) 44. Bound with the volume.

C247 Frenchified.   [A Letter] To the Editor. XXX. 771 (4 February 1928) 528–9. Bound with the volume.

C248 The Criterion.   [A Letter] To the Editor. XXX. 774 (25 February 1928) 662. Bound with the volume.

C281 Sleeveless Errand.   [A Letter] To the Editor. XXXII. 830 (23 March 1929) 757. Bound with the volume.

C677 A Letter from Eliot. By Nimai Chatterji. LXIX. 1773 (5 March 1965) 361. Bound with the volume.

New Verse   London

C400 Audiences, Producers, Plays, Poets.   18 (December 1935) 3–4. Unbound, wire-stitched, as issued. For original typescript see F19.

The New York Herald-Tribune   New York

C546 T. S. Eliot on the Aims of Poetic Drama.   (15 January 1950) Section V, pp. 1, 2.

The New York Times Magazine

C547 The Human Mind Analyzed by T. S. Eliot [Lines from The Cocktail Party].   (29 January 1950) 14. Bound with the volume.

C580 T. S. Eliot Talks about Himself and the Drive to Create.   By John Lehmann. (29 November 1953) 5, 44. Bound with the volume.

C584 T. S. Eliot on Life and its Paradoxes [Lines from The Confidential Clerk].   (21 February 1954) 16. Bound with the volume.

Nine   London

C543   A Message from T. S. Eliot, O. M.   I. 1 (October 1949) 6–7. In original paper covers.

Norseman   London

C495 The Social Function of Poetry.   I. 6 (November 1943) 449–57.

C502 The Responsibility of the Man of Letters in the Cultural Restoration of Europe.   II. 4 (July/August 1944) 243–8.

La Nouvelle Revue Francaise   Paris

C131 Lettre d'Angleterre [I]. IX. 104 (1 May 1922) 617–24.

C137 Lettre d'Angleterre [II]: Le Style dans la Prose Anglaise Contemporaine.   X. 111 (1 December 1922) 751–6.

C149 Lettre d'Angleterre [III].   XI. 122 (1 November 1923) 619–25.

& discarded, & how much worry & bother even the stupid naming of the Review caused us. Anyhow, I thought of the Criterion out of my own head simply because I liked the word, & I gave no thought to the meaning. Lady Rothermere liked it too, & Tom, was tired too tired & other very greatly once an apparently harmless title had been found,— which pleased Lady Rothermere, agreed, & was glad to get the matter settled.

I don't suppose he thought of it the way you have put it, because he has so many other things to think of. Now, after your letter, I feel the title must once more be changed, although the

A.L.s. from Vivien Eliot to Richard Aldington, [1922]. Here Mrs. Eliot takes responsibility for the name of the *Criterion*, which Aldington had criticized.

II. A GAME OF CHESS

THE Chair she sat in, like a burnished throne,
    Glowed on the marble, where the glass
Held up by standards wrought with fruited vines
From which a golden Cupidon peeped out
(Another hid his eyes behind his wing)
Doubled the flames of seven-branched candelatra
Reflecting light upon the table as
The glitter of her jewels rose to meet it,
From satin cases poured in rich profusion;
In vials of ivory and coloured glass
Unstoppered, lurked her strange synthetic perfumes,
Unguent, powdered, or liquid—troubled, confused
And drowned the sense in odours; stirred by the air
That freshened from the window, these ascended
In fattening the prolonged candle-flames,
Flung their smoke into the laquearia,
Stirring the pattern on the coffered ceiling.
Huge sea-wood fed with copper
Burned green and orange, framed by the coloured stone,
In which sad light a ~~coloured~~ dolphin swam.
                    Carven

9

One of three autograph corrections by Eliot, marked in the first English edition
(Hogarth Press) of *The Waste Land*, 1923. A6c(1)

C165 Rencontre.   XII. 139 (1 April 1925) [657]–658. In original paper covers.

C206 Le Roman Anglais Contemporain.   XIV. 164 (1 May 1927) [669]–675.

Others   New York

C20 PORTRAIT OF A LADY.   I. 3 (September 1915) 35–40.

Parish Magazine   St. Stephens, Gloucester Road, South Kensington, London, S.W. 7

C610 An Appeal to Our Readers.   (March/April 1957), pp. [10–11]. In original paper covers.

C633 The Panegyric [for Father Cheetham].   May, 1959, pp. [3–5]. In original paper covers.

Partisan Review   New York

C454 EAST COKER.   VII. 3 (May/June 1940) 181–7. In original paper covers.

C465 THE DRY SALVAGES.   VIII. 3 (May/June 1941) 174–80. In original paper covers.

C477 A Letter to The Editors.   IX. 2 (March/April 1942) 115–16. In original paper covers.

C482 The Music of Poetry.   IX. 6 (November/December 1942) 450–65. Bound with the volume.

Poetry   Chicago

C18 THE LOVE SONG OF J. ALFRED PRUFROCK.   VI. 3 (June 1915) 130–5. Bound with the volume.

C21 THREE POEMS.   VII. 1 (October 1915) 21–2. Bound with the volume.

C28 OBSERVATIONS.   VIII. 6 (September 1916) 292–5. In original paper covers.

C37 Classics in English.   IX. 2 (November 1916) 101–4. In original paper covers.

C519 Ezra Pound.   LXVIII. 6 (September 1946) 326–38. In original paper covers.

C551 A Letter from T. S. Eliot.   LXXVI. 2 (May 1950) 88. In original paper covers.

The Pound Newsletter   Berkeley, California

C593 [On Ezra Pound's translation of Sophocles' *Trachiniae*].   5 (January 1955) 3. Bound with Numbers 1–10.

C601 [A note for Ezra Pound's seventieth birthday]. 8 (October 1955) 7. Bound with Numbers 1–10.

Princeton Alumni Weekly   Princeton, New Jersey

C416 Paul Elmer More.   XXXVII. 17 (5 February 1937) [373]–374.

Purpose   London

C431 On a Recent Piece of Criticism.   X. 2 (April/June 1938) 90–4.

C446 The Idea of a Christian Society.   XI. 3 (July/September 1939) 162–74. In original paper covers.

C457   The Poetry of W. B. Yeats.   XII. 3/4 (July/December 1940) 115–27. In original paper covers.

C458 Hopousia.   XII. 3/4 (July/December 1940) 154–8. In original paper covers.

Review 45   London

C510 Cultural Diversity and European Unity.   II. 2 (Summer 1945) 61–9. In original paper covers.

The Saturday Review of Literature   New York

C238 SALUTATION.   IV. 20 (10 December 1927) 429. Bound with the volume.

C578 A Bang and a Whimper.   By Henry Hewes. XXXVI. 37 (12 September 1953) 44–5. Bound with the volume.

Scrutiny   Cambridge, England

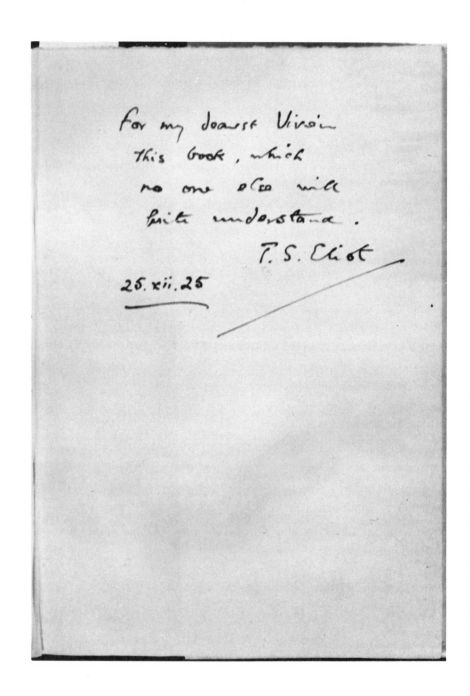

For my dearest Vivien
this book, which
no one else will
quite understand.

T. S. Eliot

25. xii. 25

Autograph inscription on fly leaf of *Poems 1909–1925*, first edition, ordinary copies,
1925. A8a(2)

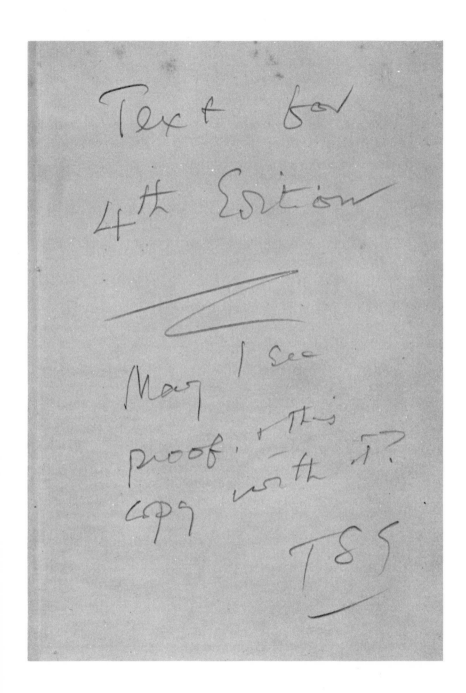

Autograph note on fly leaf of the third edition of *Murder in the Cathedral*, 1937.
A29d(1)

C528.1 [A Letter] To the Editor. XV. 1 (December 1947) 56. In bound reprint (Cambridge, England, 1963).

The Sewanee Review   Sewanee, Tennessee

C531 Milton.   LVI. 2 (April/June 1948) [185]–209. Bound with the volume.

C577.1 Vergil and the Christian World.   LXI. 1 (January/March 1953) 1–14. Bound with the volume.

C605 The Frontiers of Criticism.   LXIV. 4 (Autumn 1956) 525–43. Bound with the volume.

C679 American Literature and the American League.   LXXIV. 1 (January/March 1966), 1–20. Bound with the volume.

Report to the Court of Governors   *University of Sheffield*

C625 [Address at the] Opening of the New University Library.   Fifty-Fourth Annual Report, 1958–1959. Appendix 2, pp. 23–6. In original paper covers.

Smith Academy Record   St. Louis, Missouri

C1 A FABLE FOR FEASTERS.   VIII. 2 (February 1905) [1]–3.

C2 A Tale of a Whale.   VIII. 4 (April 1905) [1]–3.

C3 A LYRIC.   VIII. 4 (April 1905) 3.

C4 The Man who was King.   VIII. 6 (June 1905) [1]–3.

The Spectator   London

C329 George Herbert.   5411 (12 March 1932) 360–1. Bound with the volume. For original typescript, see E28.

C353 Le Morte Darthur.   CLII. 5513 (23 February 1934) 278. Bound with the volume.

C361 'The Rock'. [A Letter] To the Editor. 5528 (8 June 1934) 887. Bound with the volume.

C370 What does the Church stand for? 5547 (19 October 1934) 560–1. Bound with the volume.

C456 Man and Society. 5841 (7 June 1940) 782. Bound with the volume.

Spectrum   Santa Barbara, California

C609 Homage to Wyndham Lewis 1884–1957. I. 2 (Spring/Summer 1957) [45]. In original paper covers.

The Sunday Times   London

C528 On Milton. [A Letter] To the Editor. 16 November 1947, p. 6.

Theology   London

C215 Archbishop Bramhall. XV. 85 (July 1927) 11–17.

C493 Planning and Religion. XLVI. 275 (May 1943) 102–6.

C541 A New Translation of the Bible. [A Letter] To the Editor. LII. 351 (September 1949) 336–8.

Tiger's Eye   New York

C535 TO WALTER DE LA MARE. 6 (December 1948) 16. In original paper covers.

Time and Tide   London

C373 Notes on the Way [I]. XVI. 1 (5 January 1935) 6–[7]. In original paper covers.

C375 Notes on the Way [II]. XVI. 2 (12 January 1935) 33–4.

C376 Notes on the Way [III]. XVI. 3 (19 January 1935) 88–90.

C377 T. S. Eliot's Notes on the Way. [A Letter to the Editor]. XVI. 3 (19 January 1935) 95.

C378 Notes on the Way [IV]. XVI. 4 (26 January 1935) 118, 120–1.

C379 Mr. Milne and War. [A Letter to the Editor]. XVI. 4 (26 January 1935) 124.

C380 T. S. Eliot's Notes on the Way. [A Letter to the Editor]. XVI. 5 (2 February 1935) 154–5. In original paper covers.

Twenty copies of Words for Music were printed for the author: six on Oxhead, numbered 1-6; six on Leipzig, numbered I-VI; six on Rives, numbered a-f; and two on Imperial vellum, numbered A and B.

This is ~~number~~ *one of four preliminary trial copies in Garamond (which was then discarded in favor of Sans-Serif).*

F.P.

Item II :

"Words for Music", printed
and bound by me in New Haven
in 1934.

Five copies, as follows:

One copy on Oxhead, one of six.
One copy on Leipzig, one of six.
One copy on Rives, one of six.
One copy on Imperial vellum, one of two.

One of four preliminary trial copies
printed in Garamond, which was then
discarded in favor of Sans-Serif,
with the proof (plus pencil corrections)
of this version inserted.

Signed letter from Eliot included.

This is the only complete set of
the various editions of this brochure in
existence. They are beautifully bound and
in perfect condition.

In a fine leather-backed slip-case.

One of four preliminary trial copies of *Words for Music*, 1934, and
Prokosch's autograph note on the edition. A28.1(1), A28.1(2)

C381 Mr. Milne and War. [A Letter to the Editor]. XVI. 6 (9 February 1935) 191.

C383 T. S. Eliot's Notes on the Way [A Letter to the Editor]. XVI. 8 (23 February 1935) 272.

C563 Norman Nicholson's Notes on the Way. [A Letter to the Editor]. XXXII. 31 (4 August 1951) 746.

C568 World Tribute to Bernard Shaw. [A Letter] To the Editor. XXXII. 50 (15 December 1951) 1231–2.

C570 The Origin of Species. [A Letter] To the Editor. XXXIII. 5 (2 February 1952) 108.

C575 Charles Maurras. [A Letter to the Editor]. XXXIV. 3 (17 January 1953) 82.

C598 The Literature of Politics. XXXVI. 17 (23 April 1955) 523–4. In original paper covers.

The Times London

C399 Stilton Cheese. [A Letter] To the Editor. 29 November 1935, p. 15. Bound with the volume.

C412 Dr. Charles Harris. [A Letter] To the Editor. 13 August 1936, p. 12. Bound with the volume.

C422 The Church and the World. Problem of Common Social Action. 17 July 1937, p. 18. Bound with the volume.

C437 Professor H. H. Joachim. [A Letter] To the Editor. 4 August 1938, p. 12. Bound with the volume.

C469 Sir Hugh Walpole. [A Letter] To the Editor. 6 June 1941, p. 7. Bound with the volume.

C473 Russian Ballet. [A Letter] To the Editor. 10 December 1941, p. 5. Bound with the volume.

C490–491 South Indian Church. [Letters] To the Editor. 19 March 1943, p. 5, and 25 March 1943, p. 5. Bound with the volume.

C496 Books across the Sea. [A Letter] To the Editor. 9 November 1943, p. 5. Bound with the volume.

C500 Aristocracy. [A Letter] To the Editor. 17 April 1944, p. 5. Bound with the volume.

C501 Books for the Freed World. [A Letter] To the Editor. 8 May 1944, p. 5. Bound with the volume.

C509 Mr. Charles Williams. 17 May 1945, p. 7. Bound with the volume.

C513 Mass Deportations. [A Letter] To the Editor. 30 October 1945, p. 5. Bound with the volume.

C523a Professor Karl Mannheim. [A Letter] To the Editor. 25 January 1947, p. 7. Bound with the volume.

C524 'Lord Bishops' [A Letter] To the Editor. 11 April 1947, p. 5. Bound with the volume.

C525 UNESCO and the Philosopher. [A Letter] To the Editor. 20 September 1947, p. 5. Bound with the volume.

C526 UNESCO and Its Aims. The Definition of Culture. [A Letter] To the Editor. 17 October 1947, p. 7. Bound with the volume.

C532 Naturalized Subjects. [A Letter] To the Editor. 7 May 1948, p. 5. Bound with the volume.

C549 Thanksgiving Fund. Relations with the University. [A Letter] To the Editor. 11 April 1950, p. 7. Bound with the volume.

C550 Students from Overseas. Scope of the Lord Mayor's Fund. [A Letter] To the Editor. 17 April 1950, p. 5. Bound with the volume.

C555 On Cultural Institutes. [A Letter] To the Editor. 11 July 1950, p. 5. Bound with the volume.

C558 The Television Habit. [A Letter] To the Editor. 20 December 1950, p. 7. Bound with the volume.

C579a Mr. Eliot's Three Voices. Understanding the Poet. 20 November 1953, p. 11. In microfilm.

C588 Cold War Casualty [A Letter] To the Editor. 7 June 1954, p. 7. In microfilm.

C592 Books of the Year Chosen by Eminent Contemporaries. 26 December 1954, p. 6. In microfilm.

C600 Mr. Donald Brace. [A Letter] To the Editor. 27 September 1955, p. 11. In microfilm.

C606 Fun Fair Tower in Battersea Park. 9 July 1956, p. 9. In microfilm.

C607a "Pygmalion" [A Letter] To the Editor. 11 December 1956, p. 11. In microfilm.

attempts to set up power based NOT on right reason, not on being right, not on attempting justice. Attempts to establish secret and irresponsible power, unchecked by any ethos, and sheltered from observation.

In our time, the curse is monetary illiteracy, just as inability to read plain print was the curse of earlier centuries.

Every morning a fresh tidal wave of obscurantism and slop poured over the world's mind by the news sheets. Cui prodest. The U.S. precedes England at least in insisting on a half-yearly publication of ownership of periodicals and daily press.

No man knows the meaning of ANYTHING in ~~Times, Telegraph of~~ any ~~other~~ paper until he knows what interests control it. Curiosity in this domain is limited to an élite. It is almost unenglish to mention any such topic.

The stink of non-conformist sects has been in their losing the sense of all obscenity save that related to sex.

A stupidity which effaces the scale and grade of evil can give nothing to civilization.

You can perhaps define fanaticism as loss of the sense of gradations. Protestant sects are largely without a scale of values.

Naturally all bureaucracies are against truth and light, even though museums have a limited use. The setting of the museum above the temple is a perversion. Setting preservation of dead art above the living creation is a perversion. The avoidance of past work because a living present exploiter of past discovery fears com-

Eliot's revision for Faber and Faber of a possibly libellous passage in the first state, first edition of Ezra Pound's *Guide to Kulchur*, 1938. F38(2)

C622–623 B.B.C. Programmes. [Letters] To the Editor. 25 March 1958, p. 9, and 1 April 1958, p. 11. In microfilm.

C626a Bishop Bell. [A Letter] To the Editor. 14 October 1958, p. 13. In microfilm.

C626b Very Rev. F. P. Harton. [A Letter] To the Editor. 7 November 1958, p. 15. In microfilm.

C627 Independent Television. [A Letter] To the Editor. 11 November 1958, p. 11. In microfilm.

C630 Mr. Edwin Muir. Triumph of the Human Spirit. [A Letter] To the Editor. 7 January 1959, p. 14. In microfilm.

C634 Mr. Ashley Dukes. [A Letter] To the Editor. 7 May 1959, p. 18. In microfilm.

C636 Countess Nora Wydenbruck. [A Letter] To the Editor. 2 September 1959, p. 14. In microfilm.

C648 Sir Geoffrey Faber. A Poet among Publishers. [A Letter] To the Editor. 1 May 1961, p. 12. In microfilm.

C653a Chatterley Prosecution a Blunder. Book given Vogue, Says Mr. Eliot. 3 July 1961, p. 6. In microfilm.

C657 New English Bible. [A Letter] To the Editor. 24 March 1962, p. 9. In microfilm.

C658 The Rules of English. . . . [A Letter] To the Editor. 13 June 1962, p. 11. In microfilm.

C659 Mrs. Violet Schiff. All-embracing Interest in the Arts. [A Letter] To the Editor. 9 July 1962, p. 18. In microfilm.

C660 For Divine Reading. [A Letter] To the Editor. 21 August 1962, p. 9. In microfilm.

C661 and 663 Shakespeare's Tomb. [Letters] To the Editor. 4 September 1962, p. 11, and 14 September 1962, p. 11. In microfilm.

C664 Miss Sylvia Beach. [A Letter] To the Editor. 13 October 1962, p. 10. In microfilm.

C671 Landlord's Identity. [A Letter] To the Editor. 24 July 1963, p. 13. In microfilm.

C672 Mr. Louis MacNeice. [A Letter] To the Editor. 5 September 1963, p. 14. In microfilm.

The Times Educational Supplement London

C503 Britain and America.   Promotion of Mutual Understanding. 1540 (4 November 1944) 532. Bound with the volume.

C514 Meaning of Culture.   [A Letter to the Editor]. 1593 (10 November 1945) 535. Bound with the volume.

The Times Literary Supplement London

C99 Ben Jonson.   930 (13 November 1919) [637]–638. In bound reprint.

C109a Criticism of Poetry.   953 (22 April 1920) 256. In bound reprint.

C111 Philip Massinger.   958 (27 May 1920) [325]–326. In bound reprint.

C121 Andrew Marvell.   1002 (31 March 1921) [201]–202. Bound with the volume.

C125 John Dryden.   1012 (9 June 1921) [361]–362. Bound with the volume.

C128 The Metaphysical Poets.   1031 (20 October 1921) [669]–670. Bound with the volume.

C166 English Satire.   1247 (10 December 1925) 854. Bound with the volume.

C167 An Italian Critic on Donne and Crashaw. 1248 (17 December 1925) 878. Bound with the volume.

C168 Shakespeare and Montaigne.   1249 (24 December 1925) 895. Bound with the volume.

C169 Wanley and Chapman.   1250 (31 December 1925) 907. Bound with the volume.

C171 A Popular Shakespeare.   1255 (4 February 1926) 76. Bound with the volume.

C176 English Verse Satire.   1273 (24 June 1926) 429. Bound with the volume.

C177 The Author of 'The Burning Babe'. 1278 (29 July 1926) 508. Bound with the volume.

C178 Plague Pamphlets.   1279 (5 August 1926) 522. Bound with the volume.

C179 Creative Criticism. 1280 (12 August 1926) 535. Bound with the volume.

C180 Chaucer's 'Troilus'. 1281 (19 August 1926) 547. Bound with the volume.

C181 American Prose. 1283 (2 September 1926) 577. Bound with the volume.

C182 Lancelot Andrews. 1286 (23 September 1926) [621]–622. Bound with the volume.

C186 Hooker, Hobbes, and Others. 1293 (11 November 1926) 789. Bound with the volume.

C187 Massinger. 1294 (18 November 1926) 814. Bound with the volume.

C188 More and Tudor Drama. 1296 (2 December 1926) 880. Bound with the volume.

C188a Sir John Davies. 1297 (9 December 1926) 906. Bound with the volume.

C189 Medieval Philosophy. 1298 (16 December 1926) 929. Bound with the volume.

C197 The Phoenix Nest. 1303 (20 January 1927) 41. Bound with the volume.

C201 A Study of Marlowe. 1309 (3 March 1927) 140. Bound with the volume.

C202 Spinoza. 1316 (21 April 1927) 275. Bound with the volume.

C211 Nicolo Machiavelli (1469–1527). 1324 (16 June 1927) [413]–414. Bound with the volume.

C212 Thomas Middleton. 1326 (30 June 1927) [445]–446. Bound with the volume.

C217 Plays of Ben Jonson. 1329 (21 July 1927) 500. Bound with the volume.

C220 Wilkie Collins and Dickens. 1331 (4 August 1927) [525]–526. Bound with the volume.

C221 The Twelfth Century. 1332 (11 August 1927) 542. Bound with the volume.

C222 [*A review of*] The Playgoers' Handbook to the English Renaissance Drama. By Agnes Mure Mackenzie. 1334 (25 August 1927) 577. Bound with the volume.

C231 Parnassus Biceps. 1342 (20 October 1927) 734. Bound with the volume.

C233 A Scholar's Essays. 1343 (27 October 1927) 757. Bound with the volume.

C237 Stage Studies. 1349 (8 December 1927) 927. Bound with the volume.

C239 Bradley's 'Ethical Studies'. 1352 (29 December 1927) [981]–982. Bound with the volume.

C262 Sir John Denham. 1379 (5 July 1928) 501. Bound with the volume.

C268 Questions of Prose. [A Letter to the Editor]. 1391 (27 September 1928) 687. Bound with the volume.

C269 Three Reformers. 1397 (8 November 1928) 818. Bound with the volume.

C274 Elizabeth and Essex. 1401 (6 December 1928) 959. Bound with the volume.

C275 American Critics. 1406 (10 January 1929) 24. Bound with the volume.

C277 Turbervile's Ovid. 1407 (17 January 1929) 40. Bound with the volume.

C279 Mr. P. E. More's Essays. 1412 (21 February 1929) 136. Bound with the volume.

C280 The Latin Tradition. 1415 (14 March 1929) 200. Bound with the volume.

C314 Cyril Tourneur. 1502 (13 November 1930) [925]–926. Bound with the volume.

C324 Thomas Heywood. 1539 (30 July 1931) [589]–590. Bound with the volume.

C335 John Ford. 1579 (5 May 1932) [317]–318. Bound with the volume.

C367 John Marston. 1695 (26 July 1934) [517]–518. Bound with the volume.

C374 Dowson's Poems. [A Letter] To the Editor. 1719 (10 January 1935) 21. Bound with the volume.

C427 An Anglican Platonist: The Conversion of Elmer More. 1865 (30 October 1937) 792. Bound with the volume.

C604 Christian Social Thought. [A Letter] To the Editor. 2825 (20 April 1956) 237. Bound with the volume.

C614–615 and 617 Classic Inhumanism. [Letters] To the Editor. 2893 (9 August 1957) 483; 2895 (23 August 1957) 507; 2898 (13 September 1957) 547. Bound with the volume.

C620 The Disembodied Voice. [A Letter] To the Editor. 2916 (17 January 1958) 31. Bound with the volume.

C643 Mr. Eliot's Progress. [A Letter] To the Editor. 3045 (8 July 1960) 433. Bound with the volume.

C647 Bruce Lyttelton Richmond. 3072 (13 January 1961) 17. Bound with the volume.

C649–52 New English Bible. [Letters] To the Editor. 3087 (28 April 1961) 263; 3089 (12 May 1961) 293; 3091 (26 May 1961) 325; 3094 (16 June 1961) 373. Bound with the volume.

C665 Poetry and Criticism. [A Letter] To the Editor. 3165 (26 October 1962) 825. Bound with the volume.

C666 Poetry and Criticism. [A Letter] To the Editor. 3166 (2 November 1962) 841. Bound with the volume.

Today   London

C70 A Note on Ezra Pound. IV. 19 (September 1918) 3–9. Bound with the volume.

Townsman   London

C436 Five Points on Dramatic Writing. I. 3 (July 1938) 10. In original paper covers.

The Transatlantic Review   London

C151 [A Letter to the Editor, F. M. Ford]. I. 1 (January 1924) 95–6. In original paper covers.

Transition   Paris

C236 [A Letter to] The Editor, 'The New York Evening Post,' 26 July 1927 [with a further Letter, 22 August 1927]. 9 (December 1927) 185–6, 190. In original paper covers.

C432 Inquiry into the Spirit and Language of Night. [A Questionnaire answered by T. S. Eliot]. 27 (April/May 1938) 236. In original paper covers.

Trinity Review   Hartford, Connecticut

C587 A Tribute to Wallace Stevens.   VIII. 3 (May 1954) 9. In original paper covers.

Twentieth Century Verse   London

C428 *The Lion and The Fox* [of Wyndham Lewis].   6/7 (November/December 1937) [6–9]. In original paper covers.

The Tyro   London

C119 Notes on Current Letters.   1 (1921) [4]. In original paper covers.

C120   SONG TO THE OPHERIAN.   1 (1921) 6. In original paper covers.

C129 The Three Provincialities.   2 (1922) 11–13. In original paper covers.

Vanity Fair   New York

C142 Contemporary English Prose.   XX. 11 (July 1923) 15.

C148 A Preface to Modern Literature.   XXI. 3 (November 1923) 44, 118. Bound with the volume.

C153 A Prediction in Regard to Three English Authors, Writers who, though Masters of Thought, are likewise Masters of Art. XXI. 6 (February 1924) 29, 98. Bound with the volume.

Virginia Quarterly Review   Charlottesville, Virginia

C351 Personality and Demonic Possession.   X. 1 (January 1934) [94]–103. In original paper covers.

C358 WORDS FOR MUSIC: NEW HAMPSHIRE; VIRGINIA. X. 2
(April 1934) [200]. In original paper covers.

Welsh Review   London

C504 What is Minor Poetry?   III. 4 (December 1944) [256]–267.

World Review   London

C545 Reflections on 'The Cocktail Party.'   N.S. 9 (November 1949) 19–22. In original paper covers.

Yale Daily News   New Haven, Connecticut

C341 English Poets as Letter Writers.   LVI. 111 (24 February 1933) 3.

D

TRANSLATIONS INTO FOREIGN LANGUAGES

OF BOOKS, POEMS, AND ESSAYS

BY T. S. ELIOT

Arranged alphabetically by language; and, within language groups, chronologically under Books, Anthologies, and Periodicals. Numbering follows Gallup. Items unlisted by him are given a related number with decimal addition. Translated titles of poems are in capitals. Place of publication for periodicals is given in the first reference.

TRANSLATIONS INTO FOREIGN LANGUAGES

OF BOOKS, POEMS, AND ESSAYS

TRANSLATIONS INTO CZECH: PERIODICALS

D37 KÁZÁNÍ OHNĚ. *Kvart*, Prague, II (Summer 1930) 90–4. Part III of *The Waste Land* translated by Arnošt Vaněček.

D38 HYSTERIE. *Kvart*, II (Summer 1930) 140. "Hysteria" translated by Arnošt Vaněček.

D39 TETA HELEN. *Kvart*, II (Summer 1930) 140. "Aunt Helen" translated by Arnošt Vaněček.

D40 Tradice a individuální talent. *Listy pro Umění a Kritiku*, Prague, (1934) 272–7. "Tradition and the Individual Talent," translated by René Wellek.

TRANSLATIONS INTO DANISH: BOOKS

D49 ØDE MARKEN OG ANDRE DIGTE (København: Westermann, 1948). *The Waste Land*, "Morning at the Window," and *Journey of the Magi*, translated by Kai Friis Møller. *Gerontion*, "The Hippopotamus," "Sweeney among the Nightingales," and *Ash-Wednesday*, translated by Tom Kristensen. Edition of 235 copies. Number XVI, signed by author and translators. Loose quarto sheets unopened, in original folder and slipcase of paper boards.

D51 FAMILIENS GENFORENING ET SKUESPIL (København: H. Hagerup, 1949). *The Family Reunion* translated by Kai Friis Møller. Edition of 100 copies. Number 68, signed by author and translator. In original paper covers, dustwrapper, and slipcase of paper boards. Pages unopened.

D52 COCKTAIL PARTY. EN KOMEDIE (København: Hasselsbalchs, 1951). Translated by Kai Friis Møller. In original paper covers. Pages unopened.

D53 FIRE KVARTETTER ([Copenhagen]: Gyldendal, 1955).

Four Quartets translated by Kai Friis Møller. In original paper covers and dustwrapper. Pages unopened.

D54 GAMLE POSSUM'S BOG OM PRAKTISKE KATTE ([Copenhagen]: Strubes, 1958). *Old Possum's Book of Practical Cats* translated by Kai Friis Møller. (1) In original decorated paper boards, cloth spine, and dustwrapper. (2) In original paper covers and dustwrapper.

D56 Korene fra Skuespillet Klippen THE ROCK ([Copenhagen]: Privattryk, 1962). Choruses from *The Rock* translated by N. J. Rald and H. F. Rasmussen. In original paper covers and decorated wrappers.

TRANSLATION INTO DANISH: ANTHOLOGY

D58.1 ENGELSKE DIGTE FRA VORE DAGE (København: Ramus Naver, 1949). Contains "Morning at the Window" and *Journey of the Magi*, translated by Kai Friis Møller. Second edition. In original paper covers.

TRANSLATION INTO DUTCH: BOOK

D64 DE FAMILIEREUNIE. EEN TONEELSPEL ([Amsterdam: Boekencentrum N. V. 's-Gravenhage, 1957). *The Family Reunion* translated by H. W. J. M. Keuls. In original paper covers and decorated wrappers.

TRANSLATION INTO DUTCH: ANTHOLOGY

D66 GEDICHTEN TONEEL EN ESSAYS. Met een inleiding over auteur en werk door Michel van der Plas. Hasselt: Heideland, 1962. Contains "The Love Song of J. Alfred Prufrock," "The Hippopotamus," *Journey of the Magi*, "How unpleasant to meet Mr. Eliot," and *The Cocktail Party*, translated by Martinue Nijhoff; "Aunt Helen," "Cousin Nancy," "Mr. Apollinax," *Marina*, "Coriolan," "Cape Ann," *The Dry Salvages I*, "Tradition and the Individual Talent," "Poetry and Drama," translated by Bert Voeten; *The Waste Land* translated by Theo van Baaren; *Ash-Wednesday, East Coker, Murder in the Cathedral*, and "Baudelaire," translated by Michel van der Plas; *A Song for Simeon* translated by Gabriel Smit; "The Function of Criticism," "Lancelot Andrews," *Dante*, "Pensées of Pascal," "The Social Function of Poetry," and *The Three Voices of Poetry,* translated by Hans Edinga. In original cloth with leather spine. Sent to the University of Texas library by T. S. Eliot (G869, To the Acquisitions Assistant, 19 September 1962).

TRANSLATIONS INTO DUTCH: PERIODICALS

D69 Over de Eenheid der Europeesche Cultuur. *Internationale Echo,* London, II. 8 (April 1947) [247]–256. "Reflections on the Unity of European Culture," abridged and translated.

D71 EN TOT MIJN ZIEL ZEI IK. *Vrij Nederland* (13 November 1948). Excerpt from *East Coker* (37 lines). Translated by St. John Blanchard Nixon?

D72 OCHTEND AAN HET RAM. *Kroniek van Kunst en Kultuur,* Amsterdam, X. 1 (January 1949) 47. "Morning at the Window" translated by D. A. M. Binnendijk.

D73 DRIE GEDICHTEN. *Gids,* Utrecht, CXIII.7 (July 1950) 1–7. "The Hippopotamus," "The Love Song of J. Alfred Prufrock," and "Lines for Cuscuscaraway and Mirza Murad Ali Beg," translated by M. Nijhoff.

TRANSLATIONS INTO FINNISH: BOOKS

D81 COCKTAILKUTSUT. KOMEDIA (Helsingissa: Kustannusosakeyhtiö Otava, 1951). *The Cocktail Party* translated by E[ino]. S. Repo and Ville Repo. In original paper boards and dustwrapper.

D82 YKSITYISSIHTEERI. KOMEDIA (Helsingissa: Kustannusosakeyhtiö Otava, 1955). *The Confidential Clerk* translated by Eino S. Repo and Ville Repo. In original cloth and dustwrapper.

TRANSLATION INTO FINNISH: ANTHOLOGY

D83 Tuhat Laulujen Vuotta Valikoima Länsimaista Lyriikkaa. (Helsinki: Werner Söderström, 1957). Contains *A Song for Simeon, Animula,* "The Burial of the Dead," and *The Hollow Men,* translated by Aale Tynni. In original cloth and dustwrapper.

D85 MEURTRE DANS LA CATHÉDRALE (Neuchâtel: Baconnière, 1943). *Murder in the Cathedral* translated by Henri Fluchère. In original paper covers and dustwrapper.

D87 POÈMES 1910–1930 (Paris: du Seuil, 1947). Translations by Pierre Leyris of the following poems on pages opposite the English texts: "The Love Song of J. Alfred Prufrock," "Preludes," "La Figlia che Piange," "Morning at the Window," "The Boston Evening Transcript," "Aunt Helen," "Mr. Apollinax," *Gerontion*, "The Hippopotamus," "Sweeney among the Nightingales," *The Waste Land, Ash-Wednesday, Journey of the Magi, A Song for Simeon, Animula,* and *Marina.* Also included are "Lune de Miel" and "Dans le Restaurant." (a) Edition of 510 copies. Number 203. In original paper covers and dustwrapper. Pages unopened. (b) Ordinary edition. Bound in cloth with the original paper covers. With bookplate of John Johnson.

D89 Rudyard Kipling: Poèmes. Choisis et préfacés par T. S. Eliot. (Paris: Robert Laffont, 1949). *A Choice of Kipling's Verse* translated by Jules Castier. In original paper covers.

D90 Essais choisis (Paris: du Seuil, 1950). Contains the following essays translated by Henri Fluchère: "Tradition and the Individual Talent," "The Function of Criticism," "Rhetoric and Poetic Drama," "Dialogue on Dramatic Poetry," "Seneca and his Elizabethan Translations," "Four Elizabethan Dramatists," "Christopher Marlowe," "Shakespeare and the Stoicism of Seneca," "Hamlet," "Ben Jonson," "Thomas Middleton," "Thomas Heywood," "Cyril Tourneur," "John Ford," "Philip Massinger," "John Marston," "The Metaphysical Poets," "Andrew Marvell," "William Blake," "Swinburne as Poet," "Baudelaire," *What is a Classic?, Milton*; also "Edgar Poe et la France." Edition of 105 copies. Number 31. In original paper covers. Pages unopened.

D91 QUATRE QUATUORS (Paris: du Seuil, 1950). *Four Quartets* translated by Pierre Leyris. Bound in red cloth with original paper covers sewn in at the back. With bookplate of John Johnson.

D92 LA COCKTAIL-PARTY, SUIVI DE LA RÉUNION DE FAMILLE, ET PRÉCEDÉ DE LE BUTS DU DRAME POÉTIQUE (Paris: du Seuil, 1952). *The Cocktail Party, The Family Reunion,* and *The Aims of Poetic Drama,* translated by Henri Fluchère. In original paper covers.

D93 L'Arbre de la nuit (Nightwood) [by Djuna Barnes]. Introduction de T. S. Eliot (Paris: du Seuil, 1957). *Nightwood* with the introduction by T. S. Eliot, translated by Pierre Leyris. In original paper covers.

D95 De la poésie et de quelques poètes (Paris: du Seuil, 1964). *On Poetry and Poets* translated by Henri Fluchère. In original cloth.

D101.1 Théâtre. Second cahier. Le Théâtre Anglais d'hier et d'aujourd'hui (Paris: du Pavois, 1945). With selections from *Murder in the Cathedral* translated by Henri Fluchère. Edition of 250 copies. Number 145. In original paper covers and dustwrapper.

D102.1 Aspects de la littérature anglaise 1918–1945. Presentés par Kathleen Raine et Max-Pol Fouchet (Paris: Fontaine, 1946). Contains the following poems: *A Song for Simeon* translated by Sophie Deroisin; *Burnt Norton* translated by Pierre Saffroy, "avec la collaboration de l'auteur." In original paper covers and dustwrapper.

D103.1 Anthologie de la poésie anglaise contemporaine. Poèmes choisis et présenté par G.-A. Astre (Paris: L'Arche, 1949). Contains *Gerontion* and *Ash-Wednesday*, translated by Pierre Leyris. Edition of 2900 copies numbered 26–2925; numbers 1443, 1466, and 2780, in original paper covers and dustwrapper. Pages unopened.

D104 James Joyce sa vie son oeuvre son rayonnement (Paris: La Hune, 1949). Contains a letter by T. S. Eliot translated on the page opposite the English text. Same as B55.

D105.1 Panorama des idées contemporaines. Sous la direction de Gaetan Picon (Paris: Gallimard, 1957). Contains selections from "Tradition and the Individual Talent" and *The Music of Poetry*, translated by Henri Fluchère. In original cloth.

TRANSLATIONS INTO FRENCH: PERIODICALS

D108 LA CHANSON D'AMOUR DE J. ALFRED PRUFROCK. *Navire d'Argent*, Paris, 1 (1 June 1925) [23]–29. "Prufrock" translated by Sylvia Beach and Adrienne Monnier.

D109 LA TERRE MISE À NU. *Esprit*, Paris, 1 (May 1926) [174]– 194. *The Waste Land* translated by Jean de Menasce, "revue et approuvée par l'auteur, d'aprés la dernière édition de *Poems* (1909–1925)".

D110 Note sur Mallarmé et Poe. *Nouvelle Revue Française*, Paris, XIV, 158 (1 November 1926) [524]–526. Translated by Ramon Fernandez.

D111 Deux attitudes mystiques: Dante et Donne. *Chroniques*, Paris,

3 (1927) 149–73. "A translation, by Jean de Menasce, of one of the unpublished Clark Lectures" (Gallup). In original paper covers. Signed on title page, "T. S. Eliot 1927".

D115 Courte introduction à la méthode de Paul Valéry. *Échanges*, Paris, I (December 1929) [90]–94. "A Brief Introduction to the Method of Paul Valéry" translated by Georgette Camille.

D117 Les Caractères féminins chez Thomas Middleton. *Les Cahiers du Sud*, Marseille, Special number (June–July 1933) [204]–206. Part of the essay "Thomas Middleton" translated by G[eorgette]. C[amille].

D120 VOYAGES DES MAGES. *Mesures*, Paris, II. 3 (15 July 1936) [53]–57. *Journey of the Magi*, translated by Georges Cattaui.

D121 LES HOMMES CREUX. *Mesures*, II. 3 (15 July 1936) [58]–67. *The Hollow Men*, translated by George Cattaui.

D122 Poésie impersonnelle. *Messages*, Paris, I. 2 (1939) 51–[54]. Part of "Tradition and the Individual Talent" translated by Geoffrey Stutfield and Jean Lescure.

D123 MEURTRE DANS LA CATHÉDRALE (FRAGMENTS). *Les Cahiers du Sud*, XXVII (May 1940) [319]–328. Parts of *Murder in the Cathedral* translated by Henri Fluchère.

D125 La Musique de la poésie. *Fontaine*, Algiers, 27/28 (June–July 1943) [17]–32. *The Music of Poetry* translated by Rachel Bespalof.

D126 LES TROIS SAUVAGES. *Fontaine*, 27/28 (June–July 1943) [164]–165. *The Dry Salvages*, Part I, translated by Yvan Goll.

D127 LA FIGLIA CHE PIANGE. *Fontaine*, 27/28 (June–July 1943) 166. Translated by Jean Wahl.

D128 GERONTION. *Fontaine*, 27/28 (June–July 1943) 166–7. Selections (ll. 1–7, 34–48) translated by Jean Wahl.

D129 MERCREDI DES CENDRES. *Fontaine*, 27/28 (June–July 1943) 167–8. Translated by Jean Wahl.

D130 Des organes publics et privés de la coopération intellectuelle. *Fontaine*, 31 (1943)[1]–7.

D132 CANTIQUE DE SIMÉON. *Fontaine*, 37/40 (1944), [384]–385. *A Song for Simeon* translated by Sophie Deroisin.

D133 BURNT NORTON. *Fontaine*, 37/40 (1944) 386–96. Translated by Pierre Saffroy.

D134 EAST COKER. *Lettres*, Geneva, 2 (31 May 1944) 24–[33]. Translated by Roger Montandon.

D135 LITTLE GIDDING IV. *Formes et Couleurs*, Paris, VII 2 (March 1945) [73]. Translated by Jean Vogel.

D136 POÉMES. *Arts et Livres*, Marseille, 3 (April 1945) 3–5. "Burial of the Dead" and "Death by Water" from *The Waste Land*, translated by Jean Bourrilly.

D137 L'Homme de lettres et l'avenir de l'Europe. *La Table Ronde*, Paris, 2 (April 1945) [89–104]. "The Man of Letters and the Future of Europe" translated by Dominique Aury. In original paper covers.

D140 RAPSODIE POUR LA VENT DES TÉNÈBRES. *Saturne*, Paris, (1946) 37–40 (Carte du Ciel, Cahiers de Poésie, 2). "Rhapsody on a Windy Night" translated by Christian Dédéyan. Edition of 1400 copies. Number 113. In original paper covers and dustwrapper. Pages unopened.

D141 TROIS POÈMES. *Fontaine*, 48/49 (January/February 1946) [169]–188. "Preludes," "Sweeney among the Nightingales," and "The Fire Sermon," in English with a translation on opposite pages by Pierre Leyris. In original paper covers and decorated wrappers.

D143 DEUX POÈMES D'ARIEL. *Clair de Terre*, Paris, (1947) 137–41. (Carte du Ciel, Cahiers de Poésie, 3). *Animula* and *Marina* translated by Pierre Leyris. In original paper covers.

D144 LA TERRE VAINE. *La Licorne*, Paris, I (Spring 1947) [113]–137. *The Waste Land* translated by Pierre Leyris.

D146 Réflexions sur l'unité de la culture européenne. *Écho*, London, II. 8 (April 1947) [247–255]. "Reflections on the Unity of European Culture," abridged and translated.

D147 Les poètes metaphysiques. *Les Cahiers du Sud*, XXXV. 292 (1948) [487]–498. "The Metaphysical Poets" translated by Henri Fulchère.

D148 [Hommage à Charles Maurras]. *Aspects de la France et du Monde*, Paris, II.8 (25 April 1948) 6.

D149 Milton. *La Table Ronde*, 6 (June 1948) [926]–955. Translated by Henri Fulchère.

D152 Baudelaire. *La Revue Hommes et Mondes*, Paris, 29 (December 1948) [541]–552.

D153 Edgar Poe et la France. *La Table Ronde*, 12 (December 1948) 1973–92. An early version, translated by Henri Fluchère, of *From Poe to Valéry*. In original paper covers.

D154 LITTLE GIDDING. *Dieu Vivant*, Paris, 13 (1949) 69–81. Translated by Pierre Leyris.

D155 LA RÉUNION DE FAMILLE. *L'Âge Nouveau*, Paris, 49–50 (May 1950) 9–21. *The Family Reunion*, Act III, Scene 2, translated by Henri Fluchère.

D156 Un feuillet unique. *Les Cahiers de la Pléiade*, Paris, X (Summer–Autumn 1950) 27–9. A letter to Jean Paulhan, the editor, on St.-John Perse with a translation by Dominique Aury. In original paper covers and wrappers.

TRANSLATIONS INTO GERMAN: BOOKS

D164 MORD IM DOM (Berlin: Suhrkamp, 1946). *Murder in the Cathedral* translated by Rudolf Alexander Schröder. In original paper covers.

D168 Die Idee Einer Christlichen Gesellschaft (Wien: Amandus, 1949). *The Idea of a Christian Society* translated by Herbert Furreg. In original cloth and dustwrapper.

D175 OLD POSSUMS KATZENBUCH (Berlin und Frankfurt am Main: Suhrkamp, 1952). *Old Possum's Book of Practical Cats*, with translation by Erich Kastner, Annemarie Seidel, Rudolf Alexander Schröder, Nora Wydenbruck, Friedrich Podszus, Peter Suhrkamp, Carl Zuckmayer, and Werner Peterich. In original paper boards and dustwrapper.

D180 Marianne Moore. Gedichte Eine Auswahl. Eingeleitet von T. S. Eliot (Wiesbaden: Limes, 1954). Introduction by T. S. Eliot, translated by M. V. Schlüter. In original paper boards and dustwrapper.

D181 DER PRIVATSEKRETÄR. KOMÖDIE (Berlin und Frankfurt am Main, 1954). *The Confidential Clerk* translated by Nora Wydenbruck and Peter Suhrkamp. In original paper boards and dustwrapper.

D181a Gedenkschrift zur Verleihung des Hansischen Goethe-Preises, 1954. Hamburg, 1955. Contains "Goethe as the Sage," translated by Ursula Clemens. Same as B74.

D183 Saint-John Perse. Dichtungen mit Texten von Válery Larbaud, Hugo von Hofmannsthal, T. S. Eliot, Paul Claudel, und Alain Bosquet (Berlin: Hermann Luchterhand, 1957). Contains T. S. Eliot's Introduction translated. In original cloth and dustwrapper.

D184 Dichter und Dichtung: Essays (Frankfurt am Main: Suhrkamp, 1958). Essays selected and translated from various English volumes. Nine essays from *Poetry and Poets*: "Goethe as the Sage," "Johnson as Critic and Poet," "Byron," "Rudyard Kipling," "Virgil and the Christian World," "Yeats," "The Three Voices of Poetry," "The Social Function of Poetry," "The Frontiers of Criticism." Two essays from *The Use of Poetry and the Use of Criticism*: "Wordsworth and Coleridge," "Shelley and Keats." Three essays from *Selected Essays 1917–1932*: "Christopher Marlowe," "John Dryden," and "Arnold and Pater." Also "Modern Literature and The Classics" and "Religion and Literature." In original cloth and dustwrapper.

D189.1 Wie ich arbeite [Note in theatre program for *Der Privatsekretär* produced in Linz, Austria, during British Week 1960, pp. 3–6; 11–14]. Translation of remarks by T. S. Eliot in the London *Daily Express* interview (Gallup C618). Unbound, as issued.

D190 GEDICHTE (Frankfurt am Main: Suhrkamp, 1964). "The Love Song of J. Alfred Prufrock" translated by Klaus Günther Just; "Preludes," *The Hollow Men*, "Rhapsody on a Windy Night," and "Coriolan," translated by Hans Magnus Enzensberger; *Gerontion, Journey of the Magi, A Song for Simeon, Animula, Marina*, and choruses from *The Rock*, translated by Eva Hesse; *The Waste Land* translated by Ernst Robert Curtius; *Ash-Wednesday* translated by Rudolf Alexander Schröder; *Sweeney Agonistes* translated by Erich Fried. In original paper boards and dustwrapper.

TRANSLATION INTO GERMAN: ANTHOLOGY

D195 ENGLISCH HORN. Anthologie angelsächsischer Lyrik von den Anfängen bis zur Gegenwart (Berlin: Phaidon, 1953). Contains *The Journey of the Magi* translated by Georg von der Vring. In original cloth and dustwrapper.

TRANSLATIONS INTO GERMAN: PERIODICALS

D202 DAS WÜSTE LAND. *Neue Schweizer Rundschau*, Zürich,

XX.4 (April 1927) 362–77. *The Waste Land* translated by Ernst Robert Curtius.

D204 PERCH' IO NON SPERO.....*Neue Schweizer Rundschau*, XXIII. 12 (December 1930) 917–18. Part I of *Ash-Wednesday* translated by Max Rychner.

D206 Tradition und individuelle Begabung. *Europäische Revue*, Vienna, XII. 11 (November 1936) 874–82. "Tradition and the Individual Talent" translated by Hans Hennecke.

D207 Demokratie und Dichtung. *Innere Reich*, Munich, VI. 6 (September 1938) 638–41. Part of "A Commentary," *Criterion*, XVII. 66 (October 1937) 81–4, translated by Fritz Wolcken.

D208 Pascal. *Die Neue Rundschau*, Berlin, 1 (January 1939) [25]–39. Bound with the volume.

D211 SOMMERMITTNACHT. *Die Neue Rundschau*, 1 (October 1945) 108–9. *East Coker* I, translated by Richard Friedenthal. Bound with the volume.

D214 THE DRY SALVAGES. *Atlantis*, Zürich, XVIII. 7 (July 1946) 319–24. *The Dry Salvages* translated by Nora Wydenbruck.

D216 Der Katholizismus und die Ordnung der Welt. *Der Turm*, Vienna, II. 5–6 (1947) 178–81. A translation of "Catholicism and the International Order."

D217 Ein Telegramm von T. S. Eliot. *Der Turm*, II. 5–6 (1947) 227. On the production of *Murder in the Cathedral* in Vienna.

D219 LA FIGLIA CHE PIANGE. *Göttinger Universitäts-Zeitung*, II. 23 (7 November 1947) 3. Translated freely by Dietrich Bischoff.

D220 Was ist ein Klassiker? *Antike und Abendland*, Hamburg, III (1948) 9–25. *What is a Classic?* translated by W. E. Süskind. Also in a reprint by Wissenshaftliche Buchgesellschaft, Darmstadt, 1963. In original paper cover-title, "Wege zu Vergil."

D221 Was ist ein Klassiker? *Merkur*, Baden-Baden, 7 (1948) [1]–21. *What is a Classic?* translated by Heinrich Stammler.

D222 BURNT NORTON. *Deutsche Beiträge*, Munich, II. 6 (1948) 500–504. Translated by Ursula Clemen.

D224 ASCHERMITTWOCH. *Göttinger Universitäts-Zeitung*, III. 5 (13 February 1948) 3. *Ash-Wednesday*, Part I, translated freely by Dietrich Bischoff.

D225 EAST COKER. *Neue Schweizer Rundschau*, Zürich, n.s. XV. 12 (April 1948) 743–8. Translated by Nora Wydenbruck.

D226 GEDICHTE. *Die Neue Rundschau*, Amsterdam, 13 (Winter [1948]–1949) [75]–84. Contains chorus from *The Rock, Ash-Wednesday I*, song from *Sweeney Agonistes, A Song for Simeon, The Hollow Men*, translated by Kurt Heinrich Hansen. Bound with the volume.

D229 Kulturelle Verschiedenheit und Europäische Einheit. *Thema*, Munich, 3 (1949) 11–13. Part of *Notes towards the Definition of Culture* translated by Fritz Volquard Arnold.

D231 Über Kultur und Politik. *Die Neue Rundschau*, 14 (Spring 1949) [173]–185. Parts of *Notes towards the Definition of Culture* translated by Gerhard Hensel. Bound with the volume.

D238 Shakespeares Verskunst. *Der Monat*, Berlin, II. 20 (May 1950) [198]–207.

D240 Zur Anabasis von Saint-John Perse. *Das Lot*, Berlin, IV (October 1950) [57]–59. Introduction by T. S. Eliot, translated by Leonharda Gescher. In original paper covers.

D241 Von Poe zu Valéry. *Merkur*, IV (December 1950) 1252–67.

TRANSLATIONS INTO GREEK: BOOKS

D252 [THE WASTE LAND AND OTHER POEMS. Athens: Ikaros, 1949]. Contains *The Waste Land, The Hollow Men, Marina*, "Difficulties of a Statesman," and choruses from *Murder in the Cathedral*, translated by George Sefaris. Edition of 400. Number 128. In original paper covers.

D255 [MURDER IN THE CATHEDRAL. Athens, 1949]. Translated by A. Zacharopoulos. In original cloth and dustwrapper.

TRANSLATIONS INTO GREEK: PERIODICALS

D265 [POEMS: GERONTION. THE WASTE LAND. ASH-WEDNESDAY. DANS LE RESTAURANT. LUNE DE MIEL.] *O Kyklos*, Athens, II. 5 (July 1933) 185–213. Translations by T. K. Papatzonis, N. Randos, A. Melachrinos and K. Emmanouel.

D272 THE DRY SALVAGES. *Tetradio Proto* (First Quarter 1945) 12–19. Translated by Alexander Xydis.

D362.1 LA TERRA DESOLATA. FRAMMENTO DI UN AGONE. MARCIA TRIONFALE (Firenze: Sansoni, 1958). *The Waste Land,* "Fragment of an Agon," and "Triumphal March," translated by Mario Praz on pages opposite the English texts. Contains also a letter in facsimile from T. S. Eliot to Mario Praz dated 13 December 1933. In original paper covers.

D366 Tre poesie di T. S. Eliot (Milano: Pesce d'Oro, 1958). *A Song for Simeon,* "La Figlia che Piange," and *Animula* translated by Eugenio Montale. Edition of 1000. Number 397. In original paper covers. Reprinted from *Quaderno di traduzioni* (Milano: Edizione della Meridiana, 1948).

D367 Teatro di T. S. Eliot (Milano: Bompiani, 1958). *Murder in the Cathedral, The Family Reunion, The Confidential Clerk,* translated by Salvatore Rosati and Alberto Castelli. In original cloth and dustwrapper.

TRANSLATIONS INTO ITALIAN: ANTHOLOGIES

D385 Poeti americani 1662–1945 (Torino: Francesco de Silva, 1949). Contains "The Love Song of J. Alfred Prufrock" and *The Waste Land* translated by Mario Praz; "The wind sprang up at four o'clock" translated by G. Bassani. In original paper covers and dustwrapper. Pages unopened.

D387 Lirici americani. Edited by Alfredo Rizzardi (Caltanissetta; Roma: Salvatore Sciascia, 1955). Contains, in translation, *Animula, Marina,* and selections from *Burnt Norton, East Coker,* and *The Dry Salvages.* In original paper wrappers.

TRANSLATIONS INTO ITALIAN: PERIODICALS

D400 CANTO DI SIMEONE. *Solaria,* Florence, (December 1930) 11–12. *A Song for Simeon* translated by Eugenio Montale.

D402 LA TERRA DESOLATA. *Cicoli,* Genoa, II. 4 (July–August 1932) [27]–57. *The Waste Land* translated by Mario Praz.

D405 IL CANTO D'AMORE DI J. ALFRED PRUFROCK. *Lettera-*

tura, Florence, I. 2 (April 1937) [87]–90. "The Love Song of J. Alfred Prufrock" translated by Luigi Berti. Bound with the volume.

D406 MERCOLEDÌ DELLE CENERI. *Letteratura*, I. 2 (April 1937) [91]–96. *Ash-Wednesday* translated by Luigi Berti. Bound with the volume.

D407 DA SWEENEY AGONISTES, FRAMMENTO D'UN MELO-DRAMA ARISTOFANESCO. *Letteratura*, I. 2 (April 1937) [97]–102. "Fragment of an Agon" translated by Mario Praz. Bound with the volume.

D411 EAST COKER [I, V]. *Poesia*, Rome, I (January 1945) 161–5. Translated by Emilio Cecchi.

D412 GLI UOMINI VUOTI. *Poesia*, I (January 1945) 165–70. *The Hollow Men* translated by Emilio Cecchi.

D413 SOM DE ESCALINA. *Poesia*, I (January 1945) 170–1. Part III of *Ash-Wednesday* translated by Emilio Cecchi.

D418 L'uomo di lettere e l'avvenire dell'Europa. *Inventario*, Florence, I. 3–4 (Autumn–Spring 1946–47) [13]–18. "The Man of Letters and the Future of Europe" translated.

D419 Un poeta americano guida di poeti nuovi. *La Fiera Letteraria*, Rome, II. 1 (2 January 1947) 3–4. A translation of "Ezra Pound" (C519, in *Poetry*, September 1946).

D420 Che cos'è un classico? *Poesia*, Milan, VI (March 1947) 11–31. *What is a Classic?* translated by Jacopo Darca.

D422 Riflessioni sulla unità della cultura europea. *Eco Del Mondo*, Milan, II. 11 (July 1947) [633]–640. "Reflections on the Unity of European Culture," translated and abridged.

D441 [Message of thanks to Count Salazar on receiving news of the award of the gold medal on behalf of Florence]. *Rivista. The Journal of the British-Italian Society*, London, 139 (August–September 1959) 5. Eliot's letter in English with a translation. Unbound, as issued.

TRANSLATIONS INTO JAPANESE: BOOKS

D455 [THE COCKTAIL PARTY, THE FAMILY REUNION, MURDER IN THE CATHEDRAL, THE WASTE LAND, ESSAYS. Tokyo:

Shinchosha, 1954]. Translated by Tsuneari Fukada and Ken'ichi Yoshidā. In original cloth and dustwrapper.

D462 [After Strange Gods. Tokyo: Arechi Shuppansha, 1957]. Translated by Masaru Ōtake. In original paper boards and dustwrapper. Opposite the title page, a letter from T. S. Eliot, 8 April 1934, reproduced in facsimile.

TRANSLATION INTO NORWEGIAN: BOOK

D503 Fremmede Guder. En elementarbok i moderne kjetteri (Oslo: J. W. Cappelens, 1958). *After Strange Gods* translated by Fredrik Wulfsberg. In original paper covers. Pages unopened.

TRANSLATIONS INTO NORWEGIAN: PERIODICALS

D511 MARINA. *Spectrum*, Oslo, 4 (1947) 179–[180]. Translated by André Bjerke.

D511.1 MARINA. *Minerva*, Oslo, 3 (1948) 205–6. Translated by Emil Boyson. In original paper covers.

D518 Politisk tenkning og praktisk politikk. *Minerva* 3 (1958) 195–201. *The Literature of Politics* translated by Lars Roar Langslet. In original paper covers.

TRANSLATION INTO ORIYA: BOOK

D520 [THE WASTE LAND AND OTHER POEMS. Cuttack, India, 1956]. Translated by Jnanindra Barma. With a preface for this volume by T. S. Eliot, also translated. In original paper boards.

TRANSLATIONS INTO POLISH: PERIODICALS

D530 O Przetrwanie Naszej Cywilizacji. *Przegląd Polski*, London, I.2 (August 1946) 3–6. Introduction to *The Dark Side of the Moon* translated by Teresy Ichnowskiej.

D531 JAŁOWA ZIEMIA [and] PRÓŻNI LUDZIE. *Twórczość*, Cracow, II. 10 (October 1946) 5–22. *The Waste Land*, translated by Czesław Milosz, and *The Hollow Men*, translated by Wladysław Dulęba.

TRANSLATION INTO PORTUGUESE: PERIODICAL

D545 Um poema de T. S. Eliot. *Tavola Redonda. Folhas de Poesia,* II (December 1951) [4–5]. *Ash-Wednesday,* II, translated by Fernando Guedes.

TRANSLATION INTO SERBO-CROATIAN: ANTHOLOGY

D553a.1 Antologija Savremene Engleske Poezije 1900–1950 (Beograd, 1957). Contains "Prelude III," translated by Miodrag Pavolović; *Gerontion,* translated by Isidora Sekulić; *The Hollow Men,* translated by Svetozar Brkić; *Ash-Wednesday,* translated by Miodrag Pavlović; *Journey of the Magi,* translated by Svetozar Brkić; *Burnt Norton,* translated by Svetozar Brkić. In original paper covers and dustwrapper.

TRANSLATIONS INTO SPANISH: BOOKS

D559 La idea de una sociedad cristiana (Buenos Aires; Mexico City: Espasa-Calpe, 1942). *The Idea of a Christian Society* translated by Carlos M. Reyles. In original paper covers.

D560 Los poetas metafísicos y otros ensayos sobre teatro y religión [2 vols]. (Buenos Aires: Emecé Editores, 1944). *Selected Essays 1917–1932* translated by Sara Rubinstein. In original paper covers and dustwrapper. Pages unopened.

D565 ASESINATO EN LA CATEDRAL (Madrid: Ediciones y Publicaciones Españolas, 1949). With a preface by T. S. Eliot "para la edición española," pp. [25]–30. In original paper covers and wrappers. Pages unopened.

D569 REUNIÓN DE FAMILIA (Buenos Aires: Emecé Editores, 1953). *The Family Reunion* translated by Rosa Chacel. In original paper covers.

D571 Función de la poesía y función de la crítica (Barcelona: Seix Barral, 1955). *The Use of Poetry and the Use of Criticism* translated by Jaime Gil de Biedma. In original paper covers and dustwrapper. The dustwrapper is decorated with a portrait of Shelley.

D576 ASESINATO EN LA CATEDRAL (Mexico City: Universidad Nacional Autónoma de México, 1960). *Murder in the Cathedral* translated by Jorge Hernández Campos. In original paper covers.

D590 EL PÁRAMO. *Contemporáneos*, Mexico City, 26–27 (July–August 1930) 15–32. *The Waste Land* translated into Spanish prose by Enrique Munguía, Jr. Bound with the volume.

D591 LOS HOMBRES HUECOS. *Contemporáneos*, 33 (February 1931) 132–6. "The Hollow Men" translated by León Felipe. Bound with the volume.

D595 La música de la poesía. *Atenea*, Santiago, Chile, LXXIII, 219 (September 1943) [251]–274. "The Music of Poetry" translated by Octavio G. Barreda. Bound with the volume.

D597 EAST COKER. *Orígenes*, Havana, III. 9 (Spring 1946) 21–7. Translated by José Rodríguez Feo.

D601 Milton. *Realidad*, Buenos Aires, II. 4 (July–August 1948) [1]–27. Bound with the volume.

TRANSLATIONS INTO SWEDISH: BOOKS

D614 Dikter (Stockholm: Albert Bonniers, 1942). "The Love Song of J. Alfred Prufrock," *Gerontion*, "Whispers of Immortality," and *East Coker*, translated by Gunnar Ekelöf; "Morning at the Window," "La Figlia che Piange," and *Marina*, translated by Erik Blomberg; *The Waste Land*, translated by Karin Boye and Erik Mesterton; *Ash-Wednesday* translated by Erik Lindegren; "Triumphal March" translated by Johannes Edfelt; *Murder in the Cathedral*, Chorus I, translated by Anders Österling; and Chorus II, translated by Erik Lindegren and Karl Vennberg; *Burnt Norton* translated by Arthur Lundkvist. In original paper covers. Pages unopened.

D623 Om Poesi. Essayer (Stockholm: Bonniers, 1958). Seven essays comprising Part I of *On Poetry and Poets*, translated by Per Erik Wahlund. In original paper covers. Pages unopened.

TRANSLATION INTO SWEDISH: ANTHOLOGY

D629 Satiricon de Elaka. *Böckernas Bok* (Stockholm: Tidens, 1958). Contains "The Hippopotamus" translated by Erik Lindegren. In original paper covers. Pages unopened.

D631 Två dikter. *Ord och Bild*, Stockholm, XLVI (1937) 164. "Eyes that last I saw in tears" and "The wind sprang up at four o'clock," translated by Johannes Edfelt.

D632 EAST COKER. *Bonniers Litterära Magasin*, Stockholm, X. 6 (July–August 1941) 423–8. Translated by Gunnar Ekelöf.

D633 J. ALFRED PRUFROCKS KÄRLEKSSANG. *Bonniers Litterära Magasin*, XI, 4 (April 1942) 255–59. "The Love Song of J. Alfred Prufrock" translated by Gunnar Ekelöf.

D636 RAPSODI EN BLÅSIG NATT. *Ord och Bild*, Stockholm, LIV. 9 (1945) 407–8. "Rhapsody on a Windy Night" translated by Gunnar Ekelöf.

D637 THE DRY SALVAGES. *Bonniers Litterära Magasin*, XIV, 2 (February 1945) 103–9. Translated by Th. Warburton.

D638 Författaren och Europas Framtid. *Bonniers Litterära Magasin*, XV. 1 (January 1946) 23–8. "The Man of Letters and the Future of Europe" translated by Sonja Bergvall.

D639 En Skalds Tankar om den Europeiska Kulturen. *Bonniers Litterära Magasin*, XV. 8 (October 1946) 651–8. "Reflections on the Unity of European Culture" translated by Nils Holmberg.

D640 SWEENEY AGONISTES. *Prisma*, Stockholm, 5 (1948) 4–15. Translated by Erik Lindegren and Erik Mesterton.

D641 Sagt av Eliot. *Prisma*, 5 (1948) 18–24. Selections from T. S. Eliot's essays, chosen and translated by Erik Lindegren and Erik Mesterton.

D643 Strindbergs inflytande på T. S. Eliot betydande. *Svenska Dagbladet*, Stockholm, (20 January 1949) p. 7. Translation of the address to the Anglo-Swedish Society in London, 6 January 1949, for the Strindberg Centenary meeting.

D644 Nobelprisets Innebörd. *Bonniers Litterära Magasin*, XVIII. 2 (February 1949) 112–13. Translation of the speech accepting the Nobel Prize for Literature.

D647 ANIMULA. *Ord och Bild*, LX. 1 (1951) 12. Translated by Teddy Brunius and Göran B. Johansson.

D648 Huckleberry Finn. *Bonniers Litterära Magasin*, XX. 10 (December 1951) 751–6. Introduction to *Huckleberry Finn* translated by Sven Barthel.

D648.1 HYSTERIA. *All Varldens Berattare Tidskriften för Litterär Underhällning*, VIII. 10 (October 1952) 741. "Hysteria" translated by Teddy Brunius. In original paper covers.

TRANSLATION INTO TURKISH: ANTHOLOGY

D653 Çagdaş Amerikan Şiirlerï ([Istanbul]: Şairler Yapraği, Yayinlari, 1956). Contains *Ash-Wednesday* and "Preludes" I and II, translated by Özdemir Nutku. In original paper covers.

TRANSLATION INTO TURKISH: PERIODICAL

D655 MECUSILERIN YOLCULUGU. *Varlik*, Istanbul, (1 June 1954) p. 25. *Journey of the Magi* translated by Ahmet Bağişgil. In original paper covers.

TRANSLATION INTO UKRANIAN: BOOK

D657 [MURDER IN THE CATHEDRAL]. Munich: " 'On the Mountain,' Ukranian publishers in the Western World," 1963. Translated by Zenpon Tarnawsky; with the following poems in an Appendix: *The Wasteland*, translated by Eaghor G. Kostetzky; and *Ash-Wednesday* and *Journey of the Magi*, translated by Vadym Lesytch. Contains a letter, 22 March 1956, from T. S. Eliot to the editor, E. G. Kostetzky, reproduced in facsimile. Edition of 300 copies. In original paper covers.

E

MISCELLANY: SYLLABUSES, LEAFLETS
AND BROADSIDES, FOREIGN EDITIONS,
MUSICAL SETTINGS, AND RECORDINGS
BY T. S. ELIOT

Divided and numbered as in Gallup. Items unlisted by him are given a related number with decimal addition.

MISCELLANY: SYLLABUSES, LEAFLETS AND BROADSIDES, FOREIGN EDITIONS, MUSICAL SETTINGS, AND RECORDINGS

1. SYLLABUSES

E1a Oxford University Extension Lectures. Six Lectures on Modern French Literature. Oxford, 1916. 11 pp. Outlines of lectures, beginning with the origins of modern literature in "Romanticism," and concluding with "Questions for the Future."

E1b University of London. Extension Board. Modern English Literature. London, 1916. 7 pp. Lists of topics and readings for the principal Victorian authors.

E1c London County Council. The County Secondary School. Twenty-five Lectures on Victorian Literature. Beginning on 28th September 1917. 2 pp. List of subject or titles including one lecture on "The Social Framework" and five lectures on "The Makers of Nineteenth Century Ideas," and concluding with a lecture on "The Laureates of Nonsense—Edward Lear, Lewis Carroll, and the Makers of Light Verse."

E1d University of London. Extension Board. Modern English Literature. London, 1918. 8 pp. List of eighteen topics in Elizabethan literature, with outlines and recommended readings.

2. LEAFLETS AND BROADSIDES

E2c.1 [Blurb on dustwrapper, *Herbert Read. An Introduction to His Work* by Various Hands, edited by Henry Treece (1944)]. Eliot refers to the blurb in a letter to Treece, 11 August 1943 (G392). This and other blurbs which Eliot wrote for Faber and Faber dustwrappers are listed only when there is evidence at Texas of Eliot's authorship. Gallup explains the exclusion of these from his *Bibliography* (p. 12).

E2c.2 [Blurb on dustwrapper, *Notes towards the Definition of Culture* (1948)]. Eliot signed this blurb with autograph initials on the dust-wrapper of the copy which he gave to Mary Trevelyan [A 51 a (1)].

E2c.3 [Blurb on dustwrapper, *The Solitudes and Other Poems* by Ronald Duncan (1959)]. Eliot sent copy for approval, with his letter to Duncan, 6 October 1959 (G 837).

E2d [Lines written by T. S. Eliot to accompany an Exhibition of photographs, 1940. The broadside is not at Texas, but the text is reprinted in B40.1].

E2e Language Study Leaflet No. 107. Record Nos. C 3398–603. FOUR QUARTETS. "His Master's Voice Recording" made under the auspices of the British Council. Author's Note. Broadside with a note on the authority of a poet's reading of his own poems. First issued in September 1947. (1) Pub. No. 2540/6/48 [June 1948]. (2) Pub. No. 2540/11/53 [November 1953].

E2f James Joyce 1882–1941. I C A [Institute of Contemporary Arts Exhibition, 14 June to 12 July 1950, London]. Broadside (99.2 × 73.8 cm.) folded three times. Contains "The Approach to James Joyce," reprinted from *The Listener* (C494; F26); and a note on Joyce, dated "Nativity of the B[lessed]. V[irgin]. M[ary]. [September 8]: 1949," reprinted from *James Joyce sa Vie son Oeuvre son Rayonnement* (B55).

E2g Cat Morgan's Apology. New Haven, Connecticut: Bibliographical Press, Broadside (27 × 20.4 cm.), one of 30 copies printed.

E2l [Address] At the Memorial Service for William Collin Brooks, M. C. Late chairman of the Statist Company Ltd. At St. Bride's Church, Fleet Street, London, on May 1, 1959. Broadside "published by the Proprietors of 'The Statist' at their offices, 51 Cannon St., E. C. 4, in the City of London. . . ."

E2l.1 Author Against Critics. Broadside (24.9 × 18.4 cm.) Reprinted from *The Times Literary Supplement*, Friday 6 May 1955. Contains passages from T. S. Eliot's recent address to the Authors' Club.

E2l.2 London Library. Broadside (20.4 × 9.2 cm.). A letter reprinted from *The Times*, London, Thursday 5 November 1959.

3. FOREIGN EDITIONS

Japanese

E3d.(4) Essays on Poetry and Criticism. With introduction and notes by Kazumi Yano. Tokyo: Shohakusha, 1959. Six essays, with introduction and notes in Japanese. In original cloth and dustwrapper.

Swedish

E3e.(1) MURDER IN THE CATHEDRAL. Stockholm; London: The Continental Book Company, 1945. In original paper covers and dustwrapper.

E3e.(2) Twelve Modern Poets. An Anthology edited by Artur Lundkvist. Stockholm; London: The Continental Book Company, 1946. In original paper covers and dustwrapper.

4. MUSICAL SETTINGS

E4e [For original MS see K1].

E4o Ildebrando Pizzetti. Assassinio nella cattedrale, tragedia musicale in due atti e un intermezzo. Milan: Ricordi, 1958. Opera score for *Murder in the Cathedral* with text adapted from the Italian translation by Alberto Castelli. Bound with the original paper covers.

E4u [For original MS see K3].

5. RECORDINGS

E5a [THE HOLLOW MEN; GERONTION]. Thomas Stearns Eliot Reading his Poems. Harvard University Phonograph Records No. 3 (SS 5052–53). Also Harvard Vocarium Records P 990–91 (SS 5952–53). Recorded in Cambridge, Massachusetts, 1933, and published in March 1934.

E5f FOUR QUARTETS. Angel Record 45012 (Library Series). Recorded in London, 1947, and published originally in 1947 by the Gramaphone Co. Ltd.

E5g-h [THE WASTE LAND; ASH-WEDNESDAY; LANDSCAPES: NEW HAMPSHIRE. VIRGINIA; SWEENEY AMONG THE NIGHTINGALES]. Library of Congress Recording Laboratory. LC 1886 LP. PL3A. LC 1887 LP. PL3B. 4 sides 33 1/3 r.p.m. Recorded in Washington, D.C., 1948, and published in 1949.

E5i [THE LOVE SONG OF J. ALFRED PRUFROCK; PORTRAIT OF A LADY; PRELUDES; MR. ELIOT'S SUNDAY MORNING SERVICE; ASH-WEDNESDAY; A SONG FOR SIMEON; MARINA; TRIUMPHAL MARCH; O LIGHT INVISIBLE, from *The Rock*; DOES THE BIRD SING IN THE SOUTH, from *Murder in the Cathedral*; IN AN OLD HOUSE THERE IS ALWAYS LISTENING, from *The Family Reunion*]. T. S. Eliot Reading Poems and Choruses. Caedmon TC 1045. 2 sides 12 in. 33 1/3 r.p.m. Recorded in London 26–8 September 1955, the titles selected by T. S. Eliot.

E5j OLD POSSUM'S BOOK OF PRACTICAL CATS. Spoken Arts 758. 2 sides. 12 in. 33 1/3 r.p.m. Recorded in London under the auspices of the British Council.

E5j.1 THE WASTE LAND. Caedmon TC 2006A.

F

MANUSCRIPTS: LITERARY WORKS

AND NOTES

BY T. S. ELIOT

Numbered consecutively, but arranged in the following order: POEMS (1–12), PLAYS (13–16), PROSE WORKS (17–28), NOTES AND COMMENTS (29–44), and INSCRIPTIONS IN BOOKS NOT HIS OWN (45–51). Within each category MSS are listed according to the date of their first publication; or if unpublished, according to a date assigned to the MS. Some of the MSS are illustrated or reproduced in An Exhibition of Manuscripts and First Editions of T. S. Eliot *(The University of Texas at Austin, 1961).*

MANUSCRIPTS: LITERARY WORKS

AND NOTES

POEMS

F1 THE BOSTON EVENING TRANSCRIPT 1917

Typescript, signed, 1 p. (28 × 21.6 cm.); watermark "Strathmore Bond 25% cotton fiber USA."

Dated "13.iv.61" with one signature in light blue, followed by the correction in darker blue ink: "Inscribed in error on 13.iv.61[.] Inscribed, in full cognisance of what I am doing, for Revd. William Turner Levy Ph.D. by T. S. Eliot on 2.i.62". Eliot is making a gift of an early typescript; the only variant from the printed versions is the capitalized title without any italic characters. Levy's meeting with Eliot on 2 January 1962 is described in *Affectionately, T. S. Eliot*, pp. 126–9.

F2 THE WASTE LAND 1922

Autograph manuscript in ink, with corrections, signed, 24 pp. (25.4 × 20.3 cm.); watermark "Croxley Script."

A copy made in 1960 for an auction to benefit The London Library. The autograph title page, except for the signature added later, is like the separate title in *Poems 1909–1925*, including dedication to Ezra Pound.

The major variant is an extra line—"(The ivory men make company between us)"—coming after l. 137 (II. A Game of Chess). When it was noticed, Eliot explained in a letter (G856) that it had been in the original draft, but "for some reason or other was omitted from the published text. It came back to my mind when I was making the copy." A few other variants in punctuation and spelling; also some variant words, which are corrected. "Rising to meet you" (l. 29) is corrected from "rising to greet you". "The pleasant whining of a mandoline" (l. 261) is corrected from "The pleasant whining of a violin". Two pages illustrated in *An Exhibition . . . of T. S. Eliot*, pp. 17–18.

F3 ["EYES THAT LAST I SAW IN TEARS"]   1924

Autograph manuscript, 1 p. (25.4 × 20.3 cm.); on lined paper without watermark.

These fifteen lines, in a fair copy undated, were first published in *The Chapbook* (1924), the first of "Doris's Dream Songs"; reprinted in a "different context," as Eliot explains in a footnote, in *The Criterion*, III. 10 (January, 1925), the second of "Three poems"; and reprinted again in *Collected Poems 1909–1935*, in a third context—the first of the "Minor Poems." Script illustrated in *An Exhibition . . . of T. S. Eliot*, p. 21.

F4 THE HOLLOW MEN, I.   A PENNY FOR THE OLD GUY.   1925

Typescript, with autograph corrections and additions in pencil, signed, 1 p. (25.5 × 20.3 cm.); without watermark.

On back of the sheet, an autograph note, signed R[ayner]. J. H[eppenstall]., describes it as "A typescript of Eliot's, given by him to Ottoline Morrell, and by her to me—about 1922."

The general title "The Hollow Men, I." is added in lead pencil; "by T. S. Eliot" is added in blue pencil. The word "dry" in the text ("In our dry cellar") is an autograph revision of "dark," which is itself a revision of "damp" in the original typescript. Two lines after line 15 in the typescript—"Waters of tenderness/Sealed springs of devotion"— are cancelled in the typescript itself. The lines as corrected, without the general title, were published and dated "November 1924," in *Commerce*, III (1924–1925) [9–11]. Script illustrated in *An Exhibition . . . of T. S. Eliot*, p. 20.

F5 JOURNEY OF THE MAGI   1927

Autograph manuscript, signed, 3 pp. (25.4 × 20.3 cm.); watermark "Croxley Script," page [1] with letterhead of Faber and Faber Limited.

Inscribed by Eliot on each page: "Fair copy made 24 July 1961 by T. S. Eliot for *The Signet*", literary society at Harvard College. A variant appears in the omission of l. 34 ("This set down"), and in a few marks of punctuation.

F6 ["HOW UNPLEASANT TO MEET MR. ELIOT"] 1933

Typescript without title, and with many corrections in autograph, 1 p. (28 × 21.6 cm.); watermark "Hammermill Bond Made in USA," with letterhead T. S. ELIOT B-11 ELIOT HOUSE CAMBRIDGE.

Corrections and revisions added as a joke, but the text finally restored to that of the published version. "He deliberately put it on the letter paper headed 'Eliot House, Cambridge' . . . the poem was written sometime prior to his stay at Eliot House in [1932]/33 . . ." (Letter of Angela Miles Secretary to Mr. Eliot, G853). The lines were published in "Five-finger exercises V. Lines for Cuscuscaraway and Mirza Murad Ali Beg" (*Criterion*, XII. 47 (January 1933) 220–2. Script illustrated in *An Exhibition . . . of T. S. Eliot*, p. 22.

F7 ASH-WEDNESDAY 1930

Typescript in mimeograph, 10 pp.

Text prepared to be "read by the author" in two recording sessions, 21 and 22 August 1951, for broadcast on the B.B.C. Third Programme. Title page signed "Terence Roger Tiller," the producer, with his autograph corrections and notations throughout.

Three sections of the poem were read and recorded on 21 August. Parts of II and III were repeated the next day before recording IV, V, and VI. The typescript twice omits the preposition "of," but the word is restored in Tiller's autograph. A line in Section III ("The deceitful face of hope and of despair") was typed and first recorded "The deceitful face of hope and despair". Eliot refers to these recording sessions in a letter to Terence Tiller (G589).

F8 CAPE ANN 1935

Typescript with revision in Eliot's autograph, 1 p. (25.4 × 20.3 cm.); watermark "Colne Valley Parchment."

Autograph note by Frederic Prokosch at top: "Set in Centaur 252/10." Only two trial copies were printed in Centaur for *Two Poems* [A30 (1)]. Line 12, "To its true owner, the tough one, the sea gull", is corrected from "To its last owner, the tough one, the sea gull." The first edition (A30) was set from this script.

F9 USK 1935

Typescript with correction in autograph, 1 p. (25.4 × 20.3 cm.)

Autograph note by Frederic Prokosch at top; "Set in Perpetua 239/10." Typographical error corrected in autograph. The first edition was set from this script.

F10 *FROM* EAST COKER 1940

Typescript, 1 p. (25.5 × 20.3 cm.); without watermark.

A copy of the ten lines published as the second paragraph of Part I. A variant appears in the phrase "In the warm haze the sultry light", which in the printed version reads "In a warm haze the sultry light".

F11 THE DRY SALVAGES (*LES TROIS SAUVAGES*) 1941

Typescript in carbon with autograph revisions, 10 pp. (25.4 × 20.3 cm.); watermark "Ludgate Typewriting W. Straker Ltd."

Following are examples of the variant readings, which antedate the first edition:

1. "The problem once solved then the brown god is forgotten" (first edition omits "then").

2. "Its hints of earlier and other existence" (first edition reads "creation" for "existence").

3. "The soothing menace of wave that breaks on water," (first edition reads "menace and caress" for "soothing menace").

4. "And heard in the stillness of the silent fog" (first edition reads "And under the oppression of the silent fog").

5. "And through the fog the pretemporal ground swell" (first edition reads "And the ground swell, that is and was from the beginning").

6. "Or even development: the latter a cheerful fallacy" (first edition reads "partial" for "cheerful").

7. "To report the convolutions of the sea monster," (first edition reads "behavior" for "convolutions").

8. Two lines in the typescript are omitted from the first edition: "And here is implied Atonement/And Atonement makes action possible" (Section V, 37–8).

9. Two lines are not in the typescript, but appear in the first edition: "Who are only undefeated/ Because we have gone on trying" (Section V, 45–6).

The last eighteen lines of this script are printed in *An Exhibition . . . of T. S. Eliot*, p. 35.

F12 [THE DRY SALVAGES] 1941

Autograph manuscript, 1 p. (24.5 × 19.3 cm.); on stiff back cover of a writing tablet.

Eighteen lines written in ink with a note at the top in blue pencil "One more version of the end", signed "T. S. E.", and at the bottom "Please incorporate", addressed to Philip Mairet, editor of *The New English Weekly*. Except for two details of punctuation this is the final version, printed in *The New English Weekly*, 27 February 1941. In a letter to Philip Mairet (G344), Eliot returning corrected proof expresses particular concern "to get the last six lines right." He quotes the lines once again and explains the importance to him of the final revision "because, however I have tried it, it turns out to be something to which people will give a topical allusion—not part of the fundamental intention—and if so, then it must not be a wrong twist which will put the rest of the poem out of joint." The letter and the autograph manuscript are illustrated in *An Exhibition . . . of T. S. Eliot*, pp. 24–5.

PLAYS

F13 [THE COCKTAIL PARTY] 1950

Typescript in carbon with some autograph revisions, 137 pp. (25.4 × 20.4 cm.); watermark for Acts I, II, III "Colne Valley Parchment Made at Croxley"; for Act IV "Dickinson Bond 1804 Made at Croxley."

In a brown envelope addressed in Eliot's autograph to "Henry Sherek Esq. . . ." but not sent through the mail. A white paper label pasted over part of the address identifies the content of the envelope: "The Cocktail Party Original Script." This is a carbon copy of an original typescript in which the play is divided into four acts, instead of three. Act I begins with Julia speaking: "Do tell us that story you told the other day, about Lady Kahn and the wedding cake." In the final version this is the twelfth line and the name has been changed to "Lady Klootz." The pencilled changes in Eliot's autograph are few: "special" for "great" (p. 108), "reverence" for "look up to" (p. 114), are examples of about nine revisions.

F14 THE COCKTAIL PARTY 1950

Typescript in mimeograph with autograph corrections by Mary Trevelyan, as dictated by Eliot, signed "M. T." Title plus 149 pp. (25.4 × 20.4 cm.)

Inscribed on the title page: "Proof Copy given me by T.S.E. Corrections dictated by him. M.T." A later version of the play than F13. The changes added in Mary Trevelyan's autograph are substantial ones which appear to have been dictated by Eliot from a text very similar to that of the first edition. In a stapled binding with a heavy black paper cover and a yellow cloth spine.

F15 [THE CONFIDENTIAL CLERK] 1954

Autograph manuscript of excerpts, with queries addressed to Eliot signed "Mary [Trevelyan]", 3 pp. (33.2 × 20.6 cm.); watermarked "193 Mill," on lined sheets torn from a large notebook.

F16 THE ELDER STATESMAN 1959

Typescript in carbon with corrections in Eliot's autograph, 88 pp. (25.5 × 20.3 cm.); watermark "Croxley Script" and "Croxley Extra Strong."

Act I is dated "9 February 1958"; Act II, "20 February 1958."

PROSE WORKS

F17 ON THE EVE   A DIALOGUE 1925

Typescript, 4 pp. (26 × 20.3 cm.); watermark "Nonpareil Linen."

Published in *The Criterion*, III, 10 (January 1925) 278–81, with a few differences in punctuation and spelling, and corrections of typographical errors.

F18 CRITICAL NOTE [ON THE POETRY OF HAROLD MONRO] 1933

Typescript with autograph revisions, signed "T. S. E." in typed characters with "Eliot" completed in autograph, 4 pp. (28.1 × 21.6 cm.).

Published in *The Collected Poems of Harold Monro*, edited by Alida

Monro (London: Cobden-Sanderson, 1933). This is the original type-script sent to the editor.

F19 [AUDIENCES, PRODUCERS, PLAYS, POETS]   1935

Typescript, signed, with autograph revisions, 2 pp. (26.9 × 20.3 cm.); watermark "Colne Valley Parchment."

The title and Eliot's name beside the signature are added in block letters, probably by the editor of *New Verse*, Geoffrey Grigson. Printed in *New Verse* 18 (December 1935) 3–4.

F20 THE CHURCH'S MESSAGE TO THE WORLD   1937

Typescript with autograph corrections, 9 pp. (33.5 × 21 cm.); watermark "Portland Bond."

Bound in black cloth with green leather spine; in a red cloth folder and slipcase containing "8 Radio Typescripts" by T. S. Eliot (F20–F 27). Broadcast 16 February 1937. Printed in *The Listener* (17 February 1937) and in *The Idea of a Christian Society* (1939).

F21 THE WRITER AS ARTIST   1940

Typescript in carbon of a discussion with Desmond Hawkins, with autograph corrections, including some by Eliot, 9 pp. (eight are 33 × 20.4 cm. and one is 25.4 × 20.4 cm.).

Bound in black cloth with green leather spine; one of the "8 Radio Typescripts" (F20–F27). Broadcast 22 November 1940. Printed in *The Listener* (28 November 1940), the printed text extracted and bound in with the typescript.

F22 *THE DUCHESS OF MALFY*   BY WEBSTER   1941

Typescript in carbon, 7 pp. (33.5 × 21 cm.).

Bound in black cloth with green leather spine; one of "8 Radio Typescripts" (F20–F27). Broadcast 25 November 1941. Printed in *The Listener* (18 December 1941), the printed text extracted and bound in with the typescript. Four sentences on p. 1 of the typescript are omitted in the published text. They recommend critical essays on Webster by Swinburne, Rupert Brooke and F. L. Lucas "because their approach to Webster is in some ways different from my own."

F23 TENNYSON'S *IN MEMORIAM*, 1942

Typescript in carbon with autograph corrections, 7 pp. (33 × 20.4 cm.).

Bound in black cloth with green leather spine; one of "8 Radio Typescripts" (F20–F27). Broadcast 20 January 1942. Printed in *The Listener* (12 February 1942) with a new title, "The Voice of his Time. T. S. Eliot on Tennyson's 'In Memoriam'"; the printed text extracted and bound in with the typescript. The uncorrected typescript includes a contrast between Tennyson's experience of old age and that of Dante, Shakespeare, and Milton. "We should perhaps think of Tennyson rather in comparison with Virgil." The entire passage—suggesting the experience of an old poet's trappings of success—was cut.

F24 EDGAR POE 1943

Typescript with autograph corrections, 6 pp. (25.4 × 20.4 cm.); watermark "Silver Linen."

Bound in black cloth with green leather spine; one of "8 Radio Typescripts" (F20–F27). Broadcast 12 February 1943. Printed in *The Listener* (25 February 1943) with the new title " 'A Dream within a Dream.' T. S. Eliot on Edgar Allan Poe," the printed text extracted and bound in with the typescript. Also bound in is the typescript of three poems by Poe which Eliot read for the broadcast: "To Helen," "For Annie," and "Ulalume."

F25 JOHN DRYDEN EXTRACTS FROM *THE INDIAN EMPEROR* 1943

Typescript in mimeograph with autograph corrections and producer's notes, 6 pp. (33 × 20.4 cm.).

Bound in black cloth with green leather spine; one of "8 Radio Typescripts" (F20–F27). The broadcast (1 April 1943) included performance by actors and a talk by Eliot which is represented here only in the printed text "John Dryden's Tragedies" extracted from *The Listener* (22 April 1943).

F26 JAMES JOYCE 1943

Typescript with autograph revisions, 7 pp. (25.5 × 20.4 cm.) without watermark.

Bound in black cloth with green leather spine; one of "8 Radio Type-scripts" (F20–F27). Broadcast 26 September 1943. Printed in *The Listener* (14 October 1943), entitled "The Approach to James Joyce," the printed text extracted and bound in with the original typescript.

F27 CHARLES WILLIAMS 1946

Typescript with autograph revisions, 6 pp. (33.5 × 21 cm.).

Bound in black cloth with a green leather spine; one of "8 Radio Type-scripts" (F20–F27). Broadcast 5 October 1946. Printed in *The Listener* (19 December 1946) as "The Significance of Charles Williams," the printed text extracted and bound in with the typescript.

F28 GEORGE HERBERT 1932

Typescript with autograph revisions, 5 pp. (26.8 × 20.8 cm.) without watermark.

Eliot observes in a letter (G858) that this appears to be the typescript which he sent to *The Spectator*, for the article published 12 March 1932.

NOTES AND COMMENTS

F29 On *The Exiles* by Henry Treece   1951

Typescript, 1 p. (25.5 × 20.4 cm.).

A blurb written for the dustwrapper of Treece's book, but not used because of his objection, expressed in a letter to Peter F. du Sautoy of Faber and Faber. Du Sautoy replied 14 November 1951 (I 16), and Eliot wrote later (G 609). Eliot's blurb praises the work as one which "should establish the author as a poet of plan and construction rather than of fitful lyric inspiration."

F30 Criticism of a manuscript on ballet by Rayner Heppenstall   1936

Typescript, 2 pp. (25.2 × 20.2 cm.); watermark "Colne Valley Parch-ment Made at Croxley." Two sheets are tipped at the left margin to a sheet of heavier paper.

In two letters (G257–8) Eliot offered to publish Heppenstall's book but indicated the need for revision, especially in Chapter I. In this typescript he indicates the particular revision needed: ". . . the first chapter ought to be written last. It has the quite usual weakness of trying to say everything, and of trying to say everything at the beginning . . . your business is not to look enthusiastic, but to arouse enthusiasm in others. . . . Make Chapter I an *introduction* to what is to come afterwards, not a *manifesto*. You should be *talking to people*, not merely talking to yourself to clear up your own ideas. . . . Generalizations in general belong to the end, rather than the beginning of a composition, when they are developed at any length." Heppenstall's *Apology for Dancing* was published by Faber and Faber in 1936.

F31 On *Sebastian* (*Fragment*) by Rayner Heppenstall 1935

Typescript, 3 pp. (26 × 20.3 cm.) with autograph notes by T. S. Eliot in margins. Three sheets are tipped in at the left margin to a sheet of heavier paper.

Eliot refers to this poem and to these notes in a letter to Heppenstall (G255): "I can't agree with you that the passage from Hamlet employs sibilants in quite the same way as the phrases I underlined." The phrases underlined in the typescript are "hottest kiss" (1. 6) and "reminiscent praise" (1.88). The lines which invite comparison with *Hamlet* are "that canon 'gainst self-slaughter/Itself is the Almighty." Eliot's comments are general as well as specific: "I find the poem very obscure, and *therefore* in need of much greater *surface justification*. E.g. Mallarmé is very obscure, but his poems are worth while even when you don't understand them. . . ."

F32 On *Tristan and the Watchers* by Henry Treece

Typescript in carbon, 25 pp. (25.5 × 20.5 cm.) with autograph notes by T. S. Eliot in margins.

Eliot criticizes the allusion to "bower bird" ("My bower bird whistled her name, not mine"): "The bower bird is found only in Australia." And he criticizes the use of "minions" ("your blue eyes/Were not yet failure's minions,"): "not a good word."

F33 On *Towards a Personal Armageddon* by Henry Treece 1942

Typescript in carbon, 18 pp. (26 × 20.2 cm.) with autograph notes by T. S. Eliot in margins.

Eliot questions the dedication—"For J. F. Hendry"—after the title: "better omit. . . . poems shd. be written for their own sake, not for particular people." This sequence of poems was published in *Invitation and Warning* (London: Faber & Faber, 1942) without dedication, but when published separately in America: (Prairie City, Illinois: James A. Decker Press, n.d.) the dedication is included.

F34 On *The Never-Ending Rosary* by Henry Treece   1942

Typescript 17 pp. (26 × 20.2 cm.) with autograph notes by T. S. Eliot in margin of one poem.

Critical notes on the second poem in the sequence ("Sharper than ever, the bright beaks of words/ Charm my slim finger"). Eliot questions the "point" of certain epithets and images. The second stanza, he writes, "is altogether too difficult." The text appears unchanged in *Invitation and Warning* (London: Faber & Faber, 1942).

F35 On *Y Ddraig Goch* (*The Red Dragon*) by Henry Treece   1944

Typescript in carbon, signed, 1 p. (26.8 × 21.2 cm.) with autograph notes by T. S. Eliot in margin.

Eliot questions the use of certain words and idioms. Beside the line "His fiery breath fried all besieging knights," Eliot asks, "how can you fry without fat & a pan?" This poem was published in *Modern Welsh Poetry*, ed. Keidrych Rhys (London: Faber & Faber, 1944), unaffected by Eliot's criticism.

F36 On *To Light You to Bed* by Walter de la Mare   1948

Autograph manuscript with inscription, signed, by Walter de la Mare on the fly leaf of *The Traveller* (London: Faber & Faber, 1946): "To T. S. Eliot a token of remembrance & with all good wishes from W. J. de la Mare April 25 1948 To Light You to Bed . . . Christmas 1897." With notes in Eliot's autograph in the margins round the sonnet.

Eliot's notes are critical of archaic or romantic diction ("doth," "unto," "dream," mazed"). At one point he remarks: "shouldn't use 'dream' twice in one sonnet."

F37 On *The Palisades of Fear* by Ronald Bottrall   1948

Typescript in carbon, 53 pp. (26.7 × 20.4 cm.), with autograph notes by T. S. Eliot in the margins of seventeen poems.

Eliot's notes frequently question details in diction, syntax, or thought: "why?"; "Does not seem the right adj."; "I don't grasp the construction . . ."; ". . . The image ["Stygian quays"] doesn't work very well." In several instances Eliot's suggestions lead to a revision by Bottrall.

In "Cul-de-Sac (For Umberto Morra)," beside the lines "I rise and strike my wound/Which splinters dumb of sound/Leaving me foundered, broke across the middle," Eliot questions the words "wound," "splinters," and "foundered." Bottrall rewrites the lines on the same page: "I sit among the drowned/And sing my private wound/Derelict, foundered, broke across the middle." This is the version that appears in *The Collected Poems*, London: Sidgwick & Jackson, 1961, p. 156.

In "Palisades of Fear," beside the lines "Was it not love/Of yourself, burning like a lover/But directed inwards? Up above/Was there not a reflecting mirror?" Eliot makes queries that lead to Bottrall's autograph revision on the same page: "Was it not pride/Of yourself, burning like a lover/But perverted inwards? On each side/Was there not a reflecting mirror?"

Eliot expresses general criticism in a letter to Bottrall (G489). Though told he could keep the typescript Eliot returns it because "I believe that marginal comment is the most useful form of criticism of unpublished verse."

F38 Revisions in *Guide to Kulchur* by Ezra Pound (London: Faber & Faber, 1938)

First state of the first edition, with autograph deletions and alterations by T. S. Eliot.

"Copies of [this] book were already bound when the publishers decided that certain passages were libellous and must be deleted . . ." (Donald Gallup, *A Bibliography of Ezra Pound*, A45, p. 87). In this copy, T. S. Eliot has marked the changes to be made by the printer before regular publication. "Ezra Pound was allowed to have five unexpurgated copies for his personal use . . . and the publishers retained one copy for their files" (Gallup). The changes in Eliot's autograph, as incorporated in the published book, are described by Gallup, except for three.

(1) On p. 157, l. 25, in the phrase "Kraft zur Frende" "zur" is changed to "durch."

(2) On p. 196, ll. 13–14, in the sentence "No man knows the meaning of ANYTHING in *Times, Telegraph* or any other paper until he knows what interests control it," the words *"Times," "Telegraph,"* "or," and "other" are deleted.

(3) On p. 241, in the last line, initials that might be identifiable are changed to read A, B, C, and D; and the line is moved to the top of p. 242, as described by Gallup.

F39 On *The Era of Atomic Power* Report of a Commission Appointed by The British Council of Churches (London: S.C.M. Press, Ltd. 56 Bloomsbury Street, 1946)

With the signature of T. S. Eliot on the paper cover, and inscription by Mary Trevelyan: "Given to me by T. S. Eliot with annotations in his hand." Annotations consist principally of a cryptic grade or valuation placed beside each chapter heading in the table of contents. With a typed note inserted on letterhead of Faber and Faber: "With Mr Eliot's compliments." Also inserted is a letter to Eliot from J. H. Oldham (H27).

F40 On "A Thomist Approach to the Vedanta," by Bernard Kelly. *Blackfriars*, XXXVII. 430 (January 1956) 4–12.

Inscribed on the front paper cover: "Given to me by T. S. Eliot, with some annotations in his hand. M[ary]. T[revelyan]." The annotations consist of vertical lines on p. 10, and a question mark on p. 11.

F41 On *The President's Report* *Harvard University* 1954–1955

Autograph notes by T. S. Eliot in margins. Inscribed on front paper cover by Mary Trevelyan: "Given to me by T. S. Eliot with annotations in his hand. M[ary]. T[revelyan]."

F42 On *The Convocation of Canterbury and the Church of India* The Speeches delivered on Tuesday 5 July 1955 in the Library of Lambeth Palace (London: S. P. C. K., 1955).

Autograph notes by T. S. Eliot in margins. Inscribed on front paper cover by Mary Trevelyan: "Given to me by T. S. Eliot with annotations in his hand."

F43 On *The Convocation of Canterbury and the Church of South India* Presidential Address to the Canterbury Convocation by the Archbishop of Canterbury, Dr. G. F. Fisher. 11 October 1955.

Autograph notes by T. S. Eliot in margins (pp. 3, 5, 6, 7).

F44 On *The Convocation of York and the Church of South India* The Debates on the Report of the Joint Committee on Relations with the Church of South India in the Session of the Full Synod of the Convocation of York, Tuesday 5 July 1955. Reprinted from *The Journal of Convocation* (July 1955). (London: S.P.C.K., 1955).

Autograph notes in margins by T. S. Eliot. Inscribed on front paper cover by Mary Trevelyan: "Given to me by T. S. Eliot, with annotations in his hand. M.T."

INSCRIPTIONS IN BOOKS NOT HIS OWN

F45 In *Personae & Exultations of Ezra Pound* (London: Elkin Mathews, 1913)

Inscription and note signed on flyleaf by T. S. Eliot: "John Hayward from T. S. Eliot (Pound's copy with dates and minor corrections in his own hand)."

F46 In *Whisky* by Aeneas Macdonald (Edinburgh: The Porpoise Press, 1930)

Autograph inscription, signed on flyleaf: "for Harold Monro from T. S. E."

F47 In *Alfred Nobel* by H. Schuck & R. Sohlman (London: William Heinemann, 1929)

Autograph inscription, signed, on flyleaf: "Presented to Mary Trevelyan by T. S. Eliot", and autograph note added by Mary Trevelyan: "Nobel Prize 1948".

F48 In *Harrap's Standard French and English Dictionary* Edited by

J. E. Mansion (London, Sidney, Toronto, Bombay: George B. Harrap & Company, 1949)

Autograph inscription, signed on flyleaf of Volume I: "To Miss Mary Trevelyan Christmas 1951 from her friend T. S. Eliot. P.S. This inscription comprehends Vol II (Eng.-French)."

F49 In *Period Piece   A Cambridge Childhood,* by Gwen Raverat (London: Faber & Faber, 1952)

Inscribed twice, in ink over pencil, on flyleaf: "Mary Trevelyan from T. S. Eliot".

F50 In *The Posthumous Papers of the Pickwick Club,* by Charles Dickens (London, New York, Toronto: Oxford University Press, 1932)

Autograph inscription, signed on flyleaf: "This is Vol. 1 of The Works of Charles Dickens in course of publication by the O. U. P. and consequently in course of presentation to M. T. (Mary Trevelyan that is) by T. S. E., on the express understanding that she will read each volume from cover to cover in the order in which they are received. Christmas 1955. T. S. Eliot".

F51 In *The End of Time. A Meditation on the Philosophy of History* by Josef Pieper (London: Faber & Faber, 1954)

Autograph inscription by T. S. Eliot on flyleaf: "M[ary]. T[revelyan]. from T. S. E. (on to Evanston & try this on them)".

G

MANUSCRIPTS: LETTERS

FROM T. S. ELIOT

Arranged chronologically and described with the following information:

1) The name of the recipient, completed within brackets when it does not appear complete in the letter.

2) The address from which Eliot writes, capitals being used regularly for printed letterheads.

3) The date on a letter given in a standard form; or supplied in brackets when it is only implicit in the letter. Letters for which a year only can be supplied are placed at the end of that year.

4) The initials, when they appear, of a typist or secretary. Those which have been identified are listed below:

    AB Ann Bradby
    MB Mary Bland
    NB Natalie Balk-Foote
    PB Pamela Baker
    BOD Bridget O'Donovan
    IPF Irene P. Fassett
    VF Valerie Fletcher
    AM Ann MacFadyen
    LM Linda Melton
    CBS Constance B. Shelton
    EW Erica Wright

5) A standard abbreviated form to indicate Autograph (A.) or Typed (T.), Signed (s) or unsigned. Unless shown to be different the signature is "T. S. Eliot." Common abbreviations are also used for letters (L.), Post Card (P. C.), and Note (N.).

6) The number of pages and the dimensions of the sheet.

7) A partial indication of content or subject matter.

MANUSCRIPTS: LETTERS

G1 To [John C.] Squire 18 Crawford Mansions, Crawford St., [London,] W.1. 29 March 1917

A. L. s. 1 p. (22.8 × 17.8 cm.)

Submitting a contribution to the literary editor of *The New Statesman*; Eliot has been at work in Lloyd's Bank for only ten days.

G2 To [Richard Aldington] [1917?]

A. L. s. "Tom" 2 pp. (22.4 × 17.4 cm.)

On William Blake as a chapter in the history of heresy; also on Aldington's recent meeting with Edmund Gosse and Eliot's own forthcoming luncheon with Israel Gollancz, representatives of the established world of publishing.

G3 To Richard [Aldington] "Sunday" [1917?]

A. L. s. "Tom" 2 pp. (25.4 × 20.3 cm.)

On their plans to help Ezra Pound; and on the suggestion by Mrs. Eliot of a small critical book by one person rather than a collection of essays. Eliot published *Ezra Pound His Metric and Poetry* anonymously in 1917.

G4 To [Harold] Monroe [i. e. Monro] 18 Crawford Mansions, Crawford St., [London,] W.1 5 August 1919

A. L. s. 2 pp. (17.8 × 11.4 cm.)

Explaining his inability to contribute to a critical symposium. Harold Monro was editor of *The Chapbook*.

G5 To Richard Aldington "19 Sep" *postmark* [1920?]

A. N. (on back of an envelope)

On the possible usefulness to them of a new magazine *Theatrecraft* published, according to Eliot's note, by Harold Monro.

G6 To Russell Green   9 Clarence Gate Gardens, London, N.W.1   16 November 1920

A. P. C. s. (9 × 11.5 cm.)

On Eliot's difficulty in fulfilling promises of work, and his unwillingness to make new promises.

G7 To Richard [Aldington]   9 Clarence Gate Gardens, [London,] N.W.1   23 June 1921

A. L. s. "T. S. E." 4 pp. (22.2 × 7.3 cm.)

Announcing his temporary removal to 12 Wigmore Street so that his mother, who is visiting from America, may occupy the Eliots' flat.

G8 To [Richard] Aldington   9 Clarence Gate Gardens, [London,] N.W.1   6 July 1921

T. L. s. "T. S. E." 2 pp. (26.5 × 20.2 cm.)

Agreeing to Aldington's suggestion that Eliot send literary criticism to Holbrook Jackson, editor of *To-Day*.

G9 To R[ichard]. A[ldington].   9 Clarence Gate Gardens, [London,] N.W.1   16 August 1921

A. L. s. "T. S. E." 3 pp. (22.7 × 17.6 cm.)

Announcing the possibility of a new literary venture in which Eliot will be involved and which will have some financial backing.

G10 To R[ichard]. A[ldington].   9 Clarence Gardens, [London,] N.W.1   8 September 1921

T. L. s. "T. S. E." 1 p. (24.3 × 20.1 cm.)

Expressing gratitude for the recognition given to Eliot's work by Aldington's article on *The Sacred Wood*, published by Holbrook Jackson, editor of *To-Day* (September 1921).

G11 To Richard Aldington   9 Clarence Gate Gardens, [London,] N.W.1   16 September 1921

A. L. s. "T. S. E." 4 pp. (22.7 × 17.1 cm.)

Concerning an article just completed on the Metaphysical poets.

G12 To Richard Aldington   London, N.W.1   8 October 1921 *postmark*

A. P. C. s. "Tom" (8.9 × 11.5 cm.)

Promising to write tomorrow when less sleepy.

G13 To Richard Aldington   London, N.W.1   15 October 1921 *postmark*

A. P. C. s. "T." (8.9 × 11.5 cm.)

Complaining against a review of Middleton Murry in a recent issue of the *Times Literary Supplement*.

G14 To Richard Aldington   ALBERMARLE HOTEL, CLIFTONVILLE, MARGATE [Kent]   29 October 1921 *postmark*

A. P. C. s. "T. S. E." (8.7 × 13.8 cm.)

Condemning Desmond MacCarthy, literary editor of *The New Statesman*, particularly for his attacks on Ezra Pound and Marianne Moore.

G15 To Richard Aldington   ALBERMARLE HOTEL, CLIFTONVILLE, MARGATE [Kent]   3 November 1921 *postmark*

A. P. C. s. "T." (8.7 × 13.8 cm.)

Suggesting why Bruce Richmond, editor of *The Times Literary Supplement*, may not have printed Eliot's letter on verse reviewing.

G16 To Richard Aldington   THE ALBERMARLE HOTEL, CLIFTONVILLE, MARGATE [Kent]   6 November 1921

A. L. s. "Tom" 4 pp. (20.5 × 12.9 cm.)

Expressing admiration for the seventeenth-century poets Denham and Oldham, as well as the desire to see what Aldington has recently written of Waller. Aldington published "A Note on Waller's Poems" in *To-Day*, VIII. 48 (December 1921) 245–8.

G17 To Richard [Aldington]   9 Clarence Gate Gardens, [London,] N.W.1   17 November 1921

T. L. s. "Tom" 3 pp. (22.8 × 17.7 cm.)

On H. D.'s poetry, which Eliot thinks is overrated by Aldington.

G18 To Richard [Aldington]   9 Clarence Gate Gardens, [London,] N.W.1   [October–November 1921?]

T. L. s. "Tom" 3 pp. (22.6 × 17.6 cm.)

On his offer to help Eliot with practical support.

G19 To Richard [Aldington]   La Turbie [Alpes Maritimes]   17 December [1921?]

T. L. s. "Tom" 1 p. (25.3 × 20.1 cm.)

On Eliot's concern with the reception of his book, having seen only one review, that of Leonard Woolf. Though not named the book is perhaps *The Sacred Wood*.

G20 To Richard [Aldington]   Savoy Hotel, La Turbie, A[lpes]. M[aritimes].   11 December [1921?]

T. L. s. "Tom" 1 p. (25.4 × 20.3 cm.)

On Eliot's intention to visit Pound, whom he has not seen for four years, in Rapallo.

G21 To Richard [Aldington]   THE ALBEMARLE HOTEL, CLIFTONVILLE, MARGATE [KENT]   [1921?]

A. L. s. "T. S. E." 2 pp. (20.4 × 12.9 cm.)

On receiving Aldington's article on Cowley.

G22 To Richard [Aldington]   9 Clarence Gate Gardens, [London,] N.W.1   [1921?]

A. L. s. "Tom" 6 pp. (22.8 × 17.6 cm.)

On the doctor's order that Eliot go away for three months, a period for which the bank has given him a leave with salary.

G23 To Richard [Aldington] [1921?]

T. L. s. "Tom" 1 p. (22.7 × 17.6 cm.)

On Aldington's desire to give Eliot some practical support.

G24 To Richard [Aldington] [1921?]

A. L. s. "Tom" 1 p. (25.2 × 20.1 cm.)

Requesting bibliography on Marini and Marinism, and Gongora and Gongorism, for use in lectures which Eliot is preparing on English poetry in the seventeenth century.

G25 To Richard [Aldington] 9 Clarence Gate Gardens, [London,] N.W.1 "Wednesday" [1921?]

A. L. s. "Tom" 1 p. (24.2 × 19.9 cm.)

On Eliot's new consultations with doctors and on his moving back from Wigmore Street after his mother's departure.

G26 To [Clifford] Bax 9 Clarence Gate Gardens, [London,] N.W.1 6 February 1922

T. L. s. 1 p. (25.4 × 20.4 cm.)

Replying to a request for a contribution to *The Golden Hind*, edited by Clifford Bax from October 1922 to July 1924.

G27 To Richard [Aldington] 9 Clarence Gate Gardens, [London,] N.W.1 17 February 1922

A.L. incomplete, without signature 2 pp. (20.2 × 12.5 cm.)

Referring to the plan to write three articles on blank verse for Bruce Richmond, editor of *The Times Literary Supplement*.

G28 To T. Sturge Moore 12 Wigmore Street, London, W.1 3 April 1922

T. L. s. 1 p. (26.6 × 20.4 cm.)

Requesting a contribution for the quarterly which Eliot will edit, and suggesting some topics which he would like to see treated.

G29 To [T.] Sturge Moore   12 Wigmore Street, [London,] W.1   10 April 1922

A. L. s. 2 pp. (20.2 × 12.6 cm.)

More on the topics which Sturge Moore might treat in his article for the still unnamed quarterly.

G30 To Ch[arles]. Du Bos   12 Wigmore Street, London, W.1   7 May 1922

A. L. s. 1 p. (26.5 × 20.3 cm.)

Expressing gratitude for Du Bos's excellent translation of Eliot's chronicle in the *Nouvelle Revue Française.*

G31 To Richard Aldington   Castle Hotel, Tunbridge Wells [Kent] 12 May 1922 *postmark*

A. P. C. s. "T." (8.8 × 11.3 cm.)

Living in Kent for a change of air, Eliot comes to London every day.

G32 To Richard Aldington   Castle Hotel, Tunbridge Wells [Kent] 17 May 1922

A. L. s. "Tom" 5 pp. (20.3 × 12.7 cm.)

On Eliot's appreciation of Bruce Richmond's kindness and his great patience in waiting for a promised article on Seneca for the *Times Literary Supplement.*

G33 To [an unidentified French editor]   9 Clarence Gate Gardens, London, N.W.1   10 June 1922

A. L. s. 3 pp. (20.9 × 13 cm.)

Replying to excuse his delay in sending a promised contribution, and recommending Wyndham Lewis, "un des nos meilleurs escrivains (et certainement notre meilleur peintre)."

G34 To [T.] Sturge Moore   12 Wigmore Street, [London,] W.1   11 June 1922

A. L. s. 2 pp. (20.3 × 12.7 cm.)

Approving Sturge Moore's plan to publish a long article in two successive issues of the forthcoming quarterly.

G35 To T. Sturge Moore   9 Clarence Gate Gardens, Regents Park, [London,] N.W.1   27 June 1922

T. L. s. 1 p. (26.5 × 20.3 cm.)

Suggesting to Moore a need to limit his essay to about 5000 words.

G36 To Richard Aldington   9 Clarence Gate Gardens, [London,] N.W.1   30 June 1922

T. L. s. "Tom" 2 pp. (26.5 × 20.3 cm.)

On a visit to Ezra Pound in Verona and on Pound's effort to provide Eliot with some regular income through the Society of Bel Esprit.

G37 To Richard Aldington   9 Clarence Gate Gardens, London, N.W.1   4 July 1922

T. L. s. "Tom" 2 pp. (26.7 × 19.9 cm.)

On the plan, through Bel Esprit, to provide a regular income for Eliot.

G38 To Richard [Aldington]   9 Clarence Gate Gardens, London, N.W.1   10 July 1922

T. L. s. "Tom" 1 p. (26.5 × 20.2 cm.)

Thanking Aldington for recommending F. S. Flint as a translator and possible contributor to the still unnamed quarterly.

G39 To F. S. Flint   9 Clarence Gate Gardens, [London,] N.W.1   13 July 1922

T. L. s.2 pp. (26.6 × 20.4 cm.) with envelope.

Inviting Flint to consider making translations for the new quarterly, and suggesting for the first issue a Spanish essay by Ramon Gomez de la Serna and a German essay by Hermann Hesse.

G40 To Richard Aldington 9 Clarence Gate Gardens, [London,] N.W.1 13 July 1922

T. L. s. "Tom" 2 pp. (26.1 × 20.5 cm.)

Expressing Eliot's concern about his very personal stake in the success of the new quarterly. He wishes not to use an article by Aldington, but would like him to translate Valéry Larbaud's work on Joyce's *Ulysses*. "The 'Ulysses' of James Joyce" appeared in *The Criterion*, I.1 (October 1922) 94–103.

G41 To Richard Aldington 9 Clarence Gate Gardens, London, N.W.1 17 July 1922

T. L. s. "Tom" 1 p. (26.5 x 20.1 cm.)

Because of the personal offense expressed by Aldington, Eliot now wishes to use Aldington's article in the first issue of *The Criterion*.

G42 To F. S. Flint 9 Clarence Gate Gardens, [London,] N.W.1 18 July 1922

T. L. s. 1 p. (26.7 × 20.2 cm.) with envelope

On Eliot's pleasure that Flint will write for the new quarterly and on his respect for the art of translation.

G43 To T. Sturge Moore 9 Clarence Gate Gardens, London, N.W.1 25 July 1922 *postmark*

A. P. C. s. (8.9 × 11.5 cm.)

Expressing delight with the offer to send his manuscript.

G44 To T. Sturge Moore 9 Clarence Gate Gardens, [London,] N.W.1 28 July 1922 *postmark*

A. P. C. s. (8.9 × 11.5 cm.)

Acknowledging receipt of his manuscript.

G45 To [T.] Sturge Moore 9 Clarence Gate Gardens, [London,] N.W.1 29 July 1922

A. L. s. 1 p. (20.2 × 12.5 cm.)

On Eliot's interest and pleasure in Sturge Moore's essay "The Legend of Tristram and Isolt, I," which will appear in the first issue of *The Criterion* (October 1922).

G46 To F. S. Flint   9 Clarence Gate Gardens, [London,] N.W.1   15 August 1922

T. L. s. 1 p. (26.6 × 20.2 cm.) with envelope

Concerning the article by Ramon Gomez de la Serna, which Flint has translated and privately criticized. Eliot will use it not in the first but in the second issue.

G47 To F. S. Flint   9 Clarence Gate Gardens, [London,] N.W.1   17 August 1922

T. L. s. 1 p. (26.6 × 20.3 cm.) with envelope

Proposing to meet with Flint to discuss Ramon Gomez de la Serna.

G48 To F. S. Flint   THE CRITERION, 9 CLARENCE GATE GARDENS, [LONDON,] N.W.1   22 September 1922

A L s. 1 p. (26.4 × 20.3 cm.)

Sending galleys in Flint's translation of "Recent German Poetry" by Hermann Hesse. Eliot has instructed the printer to add to Flint's name.

G49 To F. S. Flint   THE CRITERION, 9 CLARENCE GATE GARDENS, [LONDON,] N.W.1 18 October 1922

T. L. s. 1 p. (26.4 × 20.2 cm.) with envelope

Expressing the wish to talk things over when Eliot returns from "a fortnight's holiday and rest."

G50 To F. S. Flint   THE CRITERION, 9 CLARENCE GATE GARDENS, [LONDON,] N.W.1   6 November 1922

T. L. s.   1 p. (26.4 × 20.2 cm.)

Requesting another brief translation of de la Serna, and a translation of a German essay on Balzac by Ernst Robert Curtius.

G51 To Richard [Aldington] 9 Clarence Gate Gardens, London, N.W.1 8 November 1922

T. L. s. "T. S. E." 1 p. (26.6 × 20.3 cm.)

Discussing Larbaud's article on Joyce, and Eliot's own difficulty in writing on *Ulysses* for *The Dial*, as he has promised.

G52 To Richard Aldington 9 Clarence Gate Gardens, London, N.W.1 15 November 1922

T. L. s. "T. S. E." 1 p. (26.7 × 20.2 cm.)

The Waste Land as now a thing of the past, and of Eliot's working toward a new form and style.

G53 To R[ichard] A[ldington]. 9 Clarence Gate Gardens, London, N.W.1 18 November 1922

T. L. s. "Tom" 1 p. (26.7 × 20.2 cm.)

Enclosing and commenting on the report in *The Liverpool Post* for 16 November 1922 concerning the Society of Bel Esprit.

G54 To Richard [Aldington] Savoy Hotel, La Turbie, Alpes Maritimes 26 November [1922]

T. L. s. "T." 2 pp. (25.4 × 20.2 cm.)

On Eliot's disappointment that Aldington was not in the first issue of *The Criterion*, and hoping that he will be able to offer something soon.

G55 To Richard [Aldington] 9 Clarence Gate Gardens, London, N.W.1 7 December 1922

T. L. s. "Tom" 2 pp. (25.1 × 20.4 cm.)

Concerning Eliot's letter to *The Liverpool Post* and the help sought and received from Bruce Richmond.

G56 To Richard [Aldington] THE CRITERION, 9 CLARENCE GATE GARDENS, [LONDON,] N.W.1 15 December 1922

A. L. s. "T. S. E." 2 pp. (26.4 × 20.1 cm.)

Expressing continued gratitude to Aldington for attempting to help through the organization of Bel Esprit. Illustrated in reduced facsimile in *An Exhibition of . . . T. S. Eliot* (University of Texas at Austin, 1961), p. 19.

G57 To Richard [Aldington]   9 Clarence Gate Gardens [London, N.W.1]   4 January 1923

A. L. s. "Tom" 1 p. (25.1 × 20.4 cm.)

Arranging to meet for lunch. "I only have *one hour!*"

G58 To F. S. Flint   THE CRITERION, 9 CLARENCE GATE GARDENS, [LONDON,] N.W.1   18 January 1923

T. L. s. 1 p. (26.4 × 20.2 cm.) with envelope

Expressing thanks for Flint's work in translating Ramon Gomez de la Serna which has been so highly praised by J. B. Trend, a specialist in Spanish literature.

G59 To F. S. Flint   THE CRITERION, 9 CLARENCE GATE GARDENS, [LONDON,] N.W.1   29 January 1923 [Eliot writes 1922 but the postmark is 1923]

T. L. s. 2 pp. (26.4 × 20.2 cm.) with envelope

Asking permission to send Spanish, German, or Norwegian articles for review.

G60 To Richard Aldington   THE CRITERION, 9 CLARENCE GATE GARDENS, [LONDON,] N.W.1   29 January 1923

T. L. s. "Tom" 1 p. (26.2 × 20.1 cm.)

Asking if Aldington would review French and Italian periodicals.

G61 To F. S. Flint   THE CRITERION, 9 CLARENCE GATE GARDENS, [LONDON,] N.W.1   2 February 1923

T. L. s. 1 p. (26.4 × 20.2 cm.)

Suggesting that the length of notes on foreign periodicals should be proportionate to their value.

G62 To Richard Aldington THE CRITERION, 9 CLARENCE GATE GARDENS, [LONDON,] N.W.1 2 February 1923

T. L. s. "Tom" 1 p. (26.2 × 20.1 cm.)

Expressing pleasure that Aldington will report on the French periodicals.

G63 To Richard Aldington THE CRITERION, 9 CLARENCE GATE GARDENS, [LONDON,] N.W.1 9 February 1923

T. L. s. "T." 1 p. (26.3 × 20.2 cm.)

Inviting Aldington to use a book of translations by Robert Trevelyan as a pretext for an essay on Greek verse translation.

G64 To F. S. Flint THE CRITERION, 9 CLARENCE GATE GARDENS, [LONDON,] N.W.1 20 February 1923

T. L. s. 1 p. (26.3 × 20.2 cm.) with envelope

Requesting short notes on two German periodicals.

G65 To Richard Aldington THE CRITERION, 9 CLARENCE GATE GARDENS, [LONDON,] N.W.1 20 February 1923

T. L. s. "Tom" 1 p. (26.2 × 20.1 cm.)

Requesting notes on French periodicals which may be short unless Aldington finds something of special importance.

G66 To [Charles] Du Bos "at 2, Milestone Cottages, Old Fishbourne, near Chichester, Sussex" 1 May 1923

A. L. s. 1 p. (22.8 × 17.6 cm.)

Expressing pleasure in Du Bos's forthcoming visit to London.

G67 To Charles Du Bos THE CRITERION, 9 CLARENCE GATE GARDENS, [LONDON,] N.W.1 11 May 1923

T. L. s. 1 p. (26.2 × 20.2 cm.)

Expressing disappointment at having missed their meeting in London.

G68 To Richard Aldington   THE CRITERION, 9 CLARENCE GATE GARDENS, [LONDON,] N.W.1   11 May 1923

T. L. s. "Tom" 1 p. (26.2 × 20.1 cm.)

On Mrs. Eliot's illness.

G69 To Wilhelm Lehmann   THE CRITERION, 17 THAVIES INN, LONDON, E.C.1   14 May 1923

T. L. s. 2 pp. (26.3 × 20.1 cm.) with envelope

Expressing much interest in a letter by Lehmann on contemporary German literature.

G70 To F. S. Flint   THE CRITERION, 9 CLARENCE GATE GARDENS, [LONDON,] N.W.1   27 May 1923

T. L. s.   1 p. (26.4 × 20.3 cm.)

Asking Flint to send his translation to Aldington, now secretary to *The Criterion*.

G71 To [L. A. G.] Strong   9 CLARENCE GATE GARDENS, [LONDON,] N.W.1   3 July 1923

A. L. s. 2 pp. (22.6 × 17.7 cm.)

Declining permission to publish part of *The Waste Land* in an anthology.

G72 To [Charles] Du Bos   THE CRITERION, 9 CLARENCE GATE GARDENS, [LONDON,] N.W.1   14 August 1923

A. L. s. 1 p. (26.3 × 20.2 cm.)

Expressing gratitude for an invitation to visit France.

G73 To [Wilhelm] Lehmann   9 Clarence Gate Gardens, London, N.W.1   14 August 1923

A. L. s. 2 pp. (26.4 × 20.2 cm.)

Apologizing for delay, due to Mrs. Eliot's severe illness, in acknowledging receipt of German books.

G74 To Richard [Aldington]   "Sunday" [1923?]

A. L. s. "T." 2 pp. (22.8 × 17.6 cm.)

On contributions and topics for *The Criterion*: the reputation of Katherine Mansfield. Cantos of Ezra Pound (for July 1923) and a story by Ford Madox Ford (for October 1923).

G75 To Richard Aldington   London   23 August 1922 *postmark*

A. P. C. s. "T. S. E." (8.7 × 13.8)

On his plan to arrive August 28th. Written on a picture postcard of Salisbury cloister.

G76 To Richard [Aldington]   THE CRITERION, 17 THAVIES INN, LONDON, E.C.1   8 October [1923?]

T. L. s. "Tom" 1 p. (26.3 × 20.3 cm.)

On Eliot's consciousness of the influences on his English prose.

G77 To Richard [Aldington]   "Monday" [1923?]

A. L. s. "T. S. E." 1 p. (26.6 × 20.2 cm.)

Expressing anger that Herbert Read has written openly of Eliot as editor of *The Criterion*.

G78 To Richard [Aldington]   9 C[larence] G[ate] G[ardens] London [N.W.1]   [1923?]

A. L. s. "T." 3 pp. (20.9 × 13 cm.)

On Aldington's work on Pound's poem, and on Eliot's editorial for a forthcoming issue of *The Criterion*.

G79 To [Wilhelm Lehmann?]   [1923?]

A. N. s. "T. S. E." 1 p. (13.1 × 10.3 cm.)

Expressing interest in Lehmann's opinion of *The Waste Land*, which, Eliot feels, will translate better into German than into any other language.

G80 To Richard [Aldington]   9 CLARENCE GATE GARDENS, LONDON, N.W.1   "Tuesday 8 April" [1924]

A. L. s. "Tom" 4 pp. (22.5 × 17.6 cm.)

On Eliot's expectation of a salary so that he may leave the bank in June.

G81 To F. S. Flint   THE CRITERION, 17 THAVIES INN, LONDON, E. C. 1   8 April 1924

T. L. s. 1 p. (26.4 × 20.4 cm.)

Inviting Flint to do the French review since Aldington has left his position with *The Criterion.*

G82 To Virginia Woolf   2 Milestone Cottages, Old Fishbourne, Nr. Chichester, Sussex   1 May 1924

T. L. s. "T. S. E." 1 p. (26.4 × 20.4 cm.)

On the strong desire for a contribution from Mrs. Woolf, and on his reading *Jacob's Room.*

G83 To Virginia Woolf   THE CRITERION, 17 THAVIES INN, LONDON, E.C.1   12 June [1924]

T. L. s. "T. S. E." 1 p. (26.3 × 20.3 cm.)

Asking that the proof for "Character in Fiction" be returned so that it may appear in *The Criterion,* II.8 (July 1924). Eliot speaks of the strong impression which the essay made when it was read in Cambridge, 18 May 1924.

G84 To F. S. Flint   THE CRITERION, 17 THAVIES INN, LONDON, E.C.1   10 August 1924

A. L. s. "T. S. E." 1 p. (26.4 × 20.3 cm.)

Sending a book for review to Flint on holiday, Eliot notes in passing his dislike for most Americans.

G85 To Virginia [Woolf]   38 Burleigh Mansions, [London,] W.C.2   27 August 1924

T. L. s. "Thos. Eliot" 1 p. (26.3 × 20.3 cm.)

On seeing his mother off at Liverpool; and offering to send three essays on the seventeenth century which the Hogarth Press may publish as a small book.

G86 To Richard [Aldington]   9 Clarence Gate Gardens, [London,] N.W.1   15 September 1924

T. L. s. "Tom" 1 p. (26.2 × 20.3 cm.)

Expressing thanks for Aldington's willingness to do a translation; and inviting him to bring Bruce Richmond if he can when he visits next week. Richmond was editor of *The Times Literary Supplement*.

G87 To Richard Aldington   23 Adelphi Terrace House, Robert Street, Adelphi, London, W.C.2   6 November 1924

T. L. s. "Tom" 1 p. (26.3 × 20.2 cm.)

On having received from Ezra Pound a manuscript of a new poet and being puzzled by Pound's approval.

G88 To Virginia [Woolf]   9 Clarence Gate Gardens, [London,] N.W.1   12 November 1924

A. L. s. "T. S. (if you wish) Eliot" 4 pp. (17.7 × 11 cm.)

Acknowledging receipt of *Homage to John Dryden* and expressing more satisfaction with its appearance, especially its cover, than with its content.

G89 To A. E. Coppard   THE CRITERION, 24 RUSSELL SQUARE, LONDON, W.C.1   23 December 1924

T. L. s. "I. P. Fassett [Secretary]" 1 p. (26.3 × 20.2 cm.)

Accepting "The Field of Mustard" for publication. It appeared in April 1925.

G90 To Richard [Aldington]   THE CRITERION, 24 RUSSELL SQUARE, LONDON, W.C.1   "Wednesday" [1924?]

A. L. s. "Tom" 2 pp. (26.3 × 20.3 cm.)

Thanking Aldington for an appreciative article in *Vogue*.

G91 To [Richard Cobden-Sanderson] [1923–1924?]

T. N. 2 pp. (25.6 × 20.4 cm.)

A memorandum of what each should say in a joint meeting with Lady Rothermere about the way in which she is supporting *The Criterion*.

G92 To Virginia [Woolf]   THE CRITERION, 17 THAVIES INN, LONDON, E.C.1   4 February [1925]

A. L. s. "T. S. E." 2 pp. (26.4 × 20.4 cm.)

On the Eliots' strong desire for some small cottage of their own in the country. The date 1925 is suggested by the allusion to J. M. Keynes's praise of the *Homage to John Dryden*, published in October 1924.

G93 To Virginia [Woolf]   THE CRITERION, 17 THAVIES INN, LONDON, E.C.1 "Sunday 19/iv" [April 1925]

A. L. s. "T. S. E." 1 p. (26.4 × 20.4 cm.)

Expressing a strong desire to visit, though Vivien Eliot is quite confined with her illness.

G94 To Richard [Aldington]   THE CRITERION, 17 THAVIES INN, LONDON, E.C.1   30 May 1925

A. L. s. "T. S. E." 1 p. (25.4 × 20.2 cm.)

On Aldington's review of Cocteau.

G95 To F. S. Flint   23 Adelphi Terrace House, Robert Street, [London,] W.C.2   12 June 1925

T. L. S. "T. S. E." 1 p. (25.5 × 20.3 cm.) with envelope

On poems by Flint submitted for publication.

G96 To L. A. G. Strong   23 Adelphi Terrace House, Robert Street, [London,] W.C.2   12 June 1925

T. L. s. 1 p. (25.5 × 20.4 cm.)

Reply to Strong's request for permission to reprint a poem. "The Hollow Men Part I" appeared in *The Best Poems of 1925*, edited by L. A. G. Strong.

G97 To L. A. G. Strong   23 Adelphi Terrace House, Robert Street, London, W.C.2   30 June 1925   TSE/IPF

T. L. s. 1 p. (25.5 × 20.4 cm.)

Giving permission to use Part I only of the three poems printed in *The Dial* as *The Hollow Men*.

G98 To Richard Aldington   9 Clarence Gate Gardens, [London,] N.W.1   31 July 1925

A. L. s. "T. S. E." 2 pp. (22.6 × 17.3 cm.)

Acknowledging receipt of information on the poet Giovanni Battista Marini (1569–1625).

G99 To Richard Aldington   9 Clarence Gate Gardens, [London,] N.W.1   18 August 1925 *postmark*

A. P. C. s. "Tom" (8.8 × 11.3 cm.)

Arranging to meet for lunch, or later in the day.

G100 To [Richard] Cobden [–Sanderson]   [September 1925]

A. L. s. "T. S. E." 2 pp. (25.3 × 20.5 cm.)

On a recent dental operation which Eliot underwent. An autograph note at top of sheet gives date of receipt, 9 September 1925.

G101 To Richard Aldington   THE CRITERION, 17 THAVIES INN, LONDON, E.C.1   15 September 1925

A. L. s. "T. S. E." 1 p. (25.4 × 20.2 cm.)

On Eliot's being asked to write an essay for *Vogue* on contemporary American poetry, and his concern that it will not conflict with Aldington's plans.

G102 To Virginia [Woolf]   9 Clarence Gate Gardens, [London,] N.W.1   28 October 1925

A. L. s. "T. S. E." 1 p. (22.6 × 17.5 cm.)

Asking if he may have a promised essay within two weeks.

G103 To Virginia [Woolf]   THE CRITERION, 17 THAVIES INN, LONDON, E.C.1   "Sunday" [1925]

A. L. s. "T. S. E." 1 p. (26.4 × 20.4 cm.)

Thanking her for an inscribed copy of *The Common Reader*, which Eliot values as important itself and as text for a future work of his own.

G104 To T. Sturge Moore   THE NEW CRITERION, 24 RUSSELL SQUARE, W.C.1   1 February 1926   TSE/IPF

T. L. s. 1 p. (25.7 × 20.4 cm.)

Declining to publish the third part of an essay in a third consecutive issue of *The Criterion*.

G105 To [Richard] Cobden-Sanderson   THE NEW CRITERION, 24 RUSSELL SQUARE, LONDON, W.C.1   3 February 1926

A. L. s. 1 p. (26.2 × 20.4 cm.)

Condolence on the death of Cobden-Sanderson's mother.

G106 To Richard Aldington   THE NEW CRITERION, 24 RUSSELL SQUARE, LONDON, W.C.1   12 February 1926   TSE/IPF

T. L. s. "T. S. E." 1 p. (25.6 × 20.4 cm.)

On Eliot's pleasure with his recent lecture in Cambridge.

G107 To Richard Aldington   THE NEW CRITERION, 24 RUSSELL SQUARE, LONDON, W.C.1   18 February 1926

T. L. s. "Tom" 2 pp. (25.6 × 20.4 cm.)

Inviting Aldington to review Carl Sandburg and suggesting the need to explode his inflated reputation.

G108 To Richard Aldington   THE NEW CRITERION, 24 RUSSELL SQUARE, LONDON, W.C.1   17 March 1926

T. L. s. "Tom" 2 pp. (25.6 × 20.6 cm.)

On the possibility of publishing a translation of works by [Louis Auguste Paul] Rougier.

G109 To Richard Aldington THE NEW CRITERION, 24 RUSSELL SQUARE, LONDON, W.C.1 29 March 1926 TSE/IPF

T. L. s. "Tom" 2 pp. (25.6 × 20.6 cm.)

On changing the day of the weekly *Criterion* dinner from Friday to Tuesday.

G110 To Richard Aldington THE NEW CRITERION, 24 RUSSELL SQUARE, LONDON, W.C.1 9 April 1926 TSE/IPF

T. L. s. "Tom" 1 p. (25.6 × 20.6 cm.)

Commenting on the effect of reading Edward Gibbon.

G111 To L. A. G. Strong THE NEW CRITERION, 24 RUSSELL SQUARE, LONDON, W.C.1 8 July 1926 TSE/IPF

T. L. s. 1 p. (25.6 × 20.5 cm.)

Returning poems offered to *The New Criterion.*

G112 To T. Sturge Moore THE NEW CRITERION, 24 RUSSELL SQUARE, LONDON, W.C.1 15 November 1926 TSE/IPF

T. L. s. 1 p. (25.6 × 20.5 cm.)

Asking for an unpublished poem for *Commerce.*

G113 To T. Sturge Moore THE NEW CRITERION, 24 RUSSELL SQUARE, LONDON, W.C.1 18 November 1926 TSE/IPF

T. L. s. 1 p. (25.6 × 20.4 cm.)

Acknowledging receipt of a poem for *Commerce.* Eliot thinks the French editors may want Valéry Larbaud or St. Léger Léger to translate the poem into French verse.

G114 To T. Sturge Moore THE NEW CRITERION, 24 RUSSELL SQUARE, LONDON, W.C.1 25 November 1926 TSE/IPF

T. L. s. 1 p. (25.6 × 20.4 cm.)

On Eliot's inability to use a long poem in *The New Criterion* before next June.

G115 To Richard Aldington THE NEW CRITERION, 24 RUSSELL SQUARE, LONDON, W.C.1 2 December 1926

T. L. s. "Tom" 1 p. (25.6 × 20.4 cm.)

Urging attendance at a *Criterion* dinner.

G116 To T. Sturge Moore   THE NEW CRITERION, 24 RUSSELL SQUARE,
LONDON, W.C.1   7 February 1927   TSE/IPF

T. L. s. 1 p. (25.7 × 20.5 cm.)

Refusing Moore's offer to pay a small printer's charge.

G117 To Richard [Aldington]   THE MONTHLY CRITERION, 24 RUSSELL
SQUARE, LONDON, W.C.1   12 February 1927

A. L. s. "Tom" 1 p. (26.5 × 20.8 cm.)

On *transition*, which he sees but does not read; and on Ezra Pound's
pseudonyms.

G118 To Richard [Aldington]   24 Russell Square, [London,] W.C.1
24 February 1927

T. L. s. "Tom" 2 pp. (22.7 × 17.4 cm.)

On the relations of science to philosophy and poetry, with references to
Whitehead and I. A. Richards. Eliot's review of Richards' *Science and
Poetry* appeared in *The Dial*, LXXXII. 3 (March 1927).

G119   To Virginia Woolf   THE NEW CRITERION, 24 RUSSELL SQUARE,
LONDON, W.C.1   25 February 1927

T. L. s. "Tom" 1 p. (25.7 × 20.4 cm.)

Suggesting Harold Monro's Poetry Bookshop as a deserving recipient of
financial support.

G120 To [Richard] Cobden-Sanderson   FABER AND GWYER, LTD., 24
RUSSELL SQUARE, LONDON, W.C.1   8 April 1927

A. L. s. 1 p. (25.3 × 20.3 cm.)

On the death of Eliot's father-in-law at the end of March.

G121 To David Garnett   THE NEW CRITERION, 24 RUSSELL SQUARE,
LONDON, W.C.1   2 May 1927   TSE/IPF

T. L. s. 1 p. (25.6 × 20.4 cm.)

Inviting contributions of fiction to *The Monthly Criterion.*

G122 To A. E. Coppard   THE NEW CRITERION, 24 RUSSELL SQUARE, LONDON, W.C.1   2 May 1927   TSE/IPF

T. L. s. 1 p. (25.5 × 20.3 cm.)

Expressing admiration for "The Field of Mustard," and asking for more stories of that quality.

G123 To Richard Aldington   FABER AND GWYER, LTD., 24 RUSSELL SQUARE, LONDON, W.C.1   2 May 1927   TSE/IPF

T. L. s. "Tom" 1 p. (25.1 × 20.2 cm)

On Eliot's recent preoccupation with making *The Criterion* into a monthly, and with work as executor of his father-in-law.

G124 To [Richard Aldington]   3 May 1927

T. N. s. "Tom" 1 p. (25.1 × 20.2 cm.)

Sent with the letter of 2 May, concerning plans to review Aldington's books in *The Criterion.*

G125 To T. Sturge Moore   THE MONTHLY CRITERION, 24 RUSSELL SQUARE, LONDON, W.C.1 [letterhead of *The New Criterion* corrected in autograph]   13 May 1927   TSE/IPF

T. L. s. 1 p. (25.6 × 20.5 cm.)

Thanking Moore for an interesting letter on Father Brown's book *The World of Imagery.* The letter is printed in *The Monthly Criterion,* VI. 2 (August 1927), 158–61.

G126 To Richard [Aldington]   FABER AND GWYER, LTD., 24 RUSSELL SQUARE, LONDON, W.C.1   16 May 1927

T. L. s. "Tom" 1 p. (25.2 × 20.1 cm.)

On religious beliefs, on the ideal of impersonality, and on D. H. Lawrence.

G127 To T. Sturge Moore   THE MONTHLY CRITERION, 24 RUSSELL SQUARE, LONDON, W.C.1   9 July 1927

A. L. s. 1 p. (26.5 × 20.8 cm.)

Expressing thanks for an interesting essay, "Mr. Middleton Murry's Synthesis" (*The Monthly Criterion*, VI. 4 [October 1927] 340–7).

G128 To T. Sturge Moore THE MONTHLY CRITERION, 24 RUSSELL SQUARE, LONDON, W.C.1   3 August 1927

T. L. s. 1 p. (26.5 × 20.8 cm.)

Requesting a review of *The Life of Blake*, by Mona Wilson.

G129 To Donald S. Friede THE CRITERION, 24 RUSSELL SQUARE, LONDON, W.C.1   29 August 1927   TSE/IPF

T. L. s. 1 p. (26.4 × 20.8 cm.)

Expressing hope for a less hurried visit than the recent one.

G130 To T. Sturge Moore FABER AND GWYER, LTD., 24 RUSSELL SQUARE, LONDON, W.C.1   7 September 1927   TSE/IPF

T. L. s. 1 p. (25.9 × 20.3 cm.)

Explaining the delay in reporting a decision about publishing Moore's book.

G131 To A. E. Coppard THE MONTHLY CRITERION, 24 RUSSELL SQUARE, LONDON, W.C.1   30 September 1927   TSE/IPF

T. L. s. 1 p. (26.4 × 20.8 cm.)

Reporting that he has not yet heard from Coppard's agent from whom he hoped to receive a story.

G132 To [Richard] C[obden].-S[anderson]. THE MONTHLY CRITERION, 24 RUSSELL SQUARE, LONDON, W.C.1   19 October 1927

T. L. s. 1 p. (26.4 × 20.3 cm.)

Concerning his acceptance of so much hospitality from the Cobden-Sandersons, written in the language of a seaman's log.

G133 To Richard Cobden-Sanderson THE MONTHLY CRITERION, 24 RUSSELL SQUARE, LONDON, W.C.1   24 October 1927

T. L. s. "T. S. E." 1 p. (26.6 × 20.3 cm.)

On Eliot's gratitude for the hospitality of the Cobden-Sandersons.

G134 To Richard Aldington FABER AND GWYER, LTD., 24 RUSSELL SQUARE, LONDON, W.C.1   24 October 1927   TSE/IPF

T. L. s. "Tom" 1 p. (25.2 × 20.1 cm.)

Asking if Aldington wished to be recommended to give a course of lectures on English literature at the University of Madrid.

G135 To Charles Du Bos   57 CHESTER TERRACE, LONDON, S.W.1   27 October 1927

T. L. s. 1 p. (17.4 × 10.9 cm.)

Introducing Mr. and Mrs. Padriac Colum.

G136 To [Richard] Cobden [-Sanderson]   FABER AND GWYER, LTD., 24 RUSSELL SQUARE, LONDON, W.C.1   1 November 1927

T. L. s. "T. S. E." 1 p. (25.4 × 20.3 cm.)

Replying to the invitation of the Cobden-Sandersons. Eliot writes in the voice and language of a seaman.

G137 To Richard [Aldington]   THE MONTHLY CRITERION, 24 RUSSELL SQUARE, LONDON, W.C.1   1 November 1927

T. L. s. "Tom" 1 p. (26.2 × 20.6 cm.)

Agreeing with Aldington's relatively low estimate of the introduction to *Seneca* which Eliot wrote for the series of Tudor translations edited by Charles Whibley.

G138 To A. D. Peters   THE MONTHLY CRITERION, 24 RUSSELL SQUARE, LONDON, W.C.1   7 November 1927

T. L. s. 1 p. (26.5 × 20.8 cm.)

Returning to his agent two stories by A. E. Coppard as being unsuitable for *The Monthly Criterion*.

G139 To Leonidas Warren Payne, Jr. THE MONTHLY CRITERION, 24 RUSSELL SQUARE, LONDON, W.C.1   7 November 1927   TSE/IPF

T. L. s. 1 p. (26.5 × 20.8 cm.) with envelope

Expressing thanks for a copy of *Selections from Later American Writers*, edited by Professor Payne of The University of Texas. Eliot expresses regret that a rather insignificant poem like "Cousin Nancy" was chosen as representative of his work.

G140 To T. Sturge Moore FABER AND GWYER, LTD., 24 RUSSELL SQUARE, LONDON, W.C.1   5 December 1927   IPF

T. L. s. "I. P. Fassett for and on behalf of T. S. Eliot" 1 p. (25.8 × 20.2 cm.)

Explaining that *The Criterion* is to suspend publication with the current issue.

G141 To [Richard] Cobden [-Sanderson] THE MONTHLY CRITERION, 24 RUSSELL SQUARE, LONDON, W.C.1   10 December 1927

T. L. s. "T. S. E." 1 p. (26.4 × 20.8 cm.)

Inviting him to meet to celebrate either the "demise" or the "resurrection" of *The Criterion*.

G142 To Richard Aldington FABER AND GWYER, LTD., 24 RUSSELL SQUARE, LONDON, W.C.1   13 December 1927   TSE/IPF

T. L. s. "Tom" 2 pp. (25.1 × 20.1 cm.)

Concerning Lady Rothermere's withdrawal of support from *The Criterion*. ". . . if the 'Criterion' is re-established, it will be in a much stronger position than before. All this has happened within the last two weeks. . . ."

G143 To R[ichard]. Cobden-Sanderson THE MONTHLY CRITERION, 24 RUSSELL SQUARE, LONDON W.C.1   13 December 1927

T. L. s. "T. S. E." 1 p. (26.5 × 20.3 cm.)

Inviting him to attend a meeting to discuss possible ways of continuing *The Criterion*.

G144 To T. Sturge Moore FABER AND GWYER, LTD., 24 RUSSELL SQUARE, LONDON, W.C.1   30 Demember 1927   IPF

T. L. s. 2 pp. (25.3 × 20.2 cm.)

Returning "In Defense of Beauty" on behalf of Faber and Gwyer. Hopeful now of enlisting enough support to continue *The Criterion*, Eliot asks again for Moore's review of *The Life of Blake* by Mona Wilson.

G145 To Sally [Mrs. Richard Cobden-Sanderson] THE MONTHLY CRITERION, 24 RUSSELL SQUARE, LONDON, W.C.1   2 February 1928

T. L. s. 1 p. (26.4 × 20.7 cm.)

Expressing the desire, in making the gift of a parrot, to satisfy her particular wishes.

G146 To Richard Aldington FABER AND GWYER, LTD., 24 RUSSELL SQUARE, LONDON, W.C.1   29 February 1928   TSE/IPF

T. L. s. "Tom" 1 p. (25.2 × 20.2 cm.)

Replying to an inquiry about Walter de la Mare.

G147 To Richard [Aldington] THE MONTHLY CRITERION, 24 RUSSELL SQUARE, LONDON, W.C.1   8 March 1928

T. L. s. "Tom" 2 pp. (26.4 × 20.6 cm.)

Praising Aldington's pamphlet on Rémy de Gourmont, and promising a review which he would like to write himself. Aldington had sent an inscribed copy of *Remy de Gourmont A Modern Man of Letters*, University of Washington Chapbooks, No. 13 (Seattle 1928).

G148 To [Richard] Cobden [-Sanderson] THE MONTHLY CRITERION, 24 RUSSELL SQUARE, LONDON, W.C.1   "Monday" [May 1927–March 1928?]

T. L. s. "T. S. E." 1 p. (26.5 × 20.3 cm.)

On meeting to discuss affairs of *The Criterion*.

G149 To[Richard] Cobden [-Sanderson] THE MONTHLY CRITERION, 24 RUSSELL SQUARE, LONDON, W.C.1   15 March 1928

T. L. s. "Thos." 1 p. (26.5 × 20.8 cm.)

Apologizing for not keeping an appointment.

G150 To Richard Cobden-Sanderson THE MONTHLY CRITERION, 24 RUSSELL SQUARE, LONDON, W.C.1   19 March 1928

T. L. s. "Thos." 1 p. (26.5 × 20.8 cm.)

Confirming an appointment for lunch.

G151 To T. Sturge Moore THE MONTHLY CRITERION, 24 RUSSELL SQUARE, LONDON, W.C.1   4 April 1928

T. L. s. 1 p. (23.6 × 20.2 cm.) part of the sheet cut at top and bottom.

Concerning the translation by Thomas MacGreevy of an unnamed work, which Eliot has asked to be sent directly to Sturge Moore.

G152 To Richard Aldington THE MONTHLY CRITERION, 24 RUSSELL SQUARE, LONDON, W.C.1   10 July 1928

T. L. s. "Tom" 1 p. (26.4 × 20.6 cm.)

Acknowledging receipt of a copy of *Remy de Gourmont* with Aldington's introduction, which Eliot has just read with pleasure.

G153 To Charles Du Bos THE MONTHLY CRITERION, 24 RUSSELL SQUARE, LONDON, W. C.1   10 August 1928

T. L. s. 1 p (26.4 × 20.7 cm.)

Inviting a contribution and recalling that they spoke two years ago of Du Bos doing an essay on Walter Pater.

G154 To Glenn Hughes THE MONTHLY CRITERION, 24 RUSSELL SQUARE, LONDON, W.C.1   12 September 1928

T. L. s. 1 p. (26.5 × 20.7 cm.)

Inviting him to lunch.

G155 To Glenn Hughes THE MONTHLY CRITERION, 24 RUSSELL SQUARE, LONDON, W.C.1   3 October 1928

T. L. s. 1 p. (26.5 × 20.7 cm.)

Replying to a request for a contribution.

G156 To Glenn Hughes   THE MONTHLY CRITERION, 24 RUSSELL SQUARE, LONDON, W.C.1   30 October 1928

T. L. s. 1 p. (26.5 × 20.7 cm.)

Declining to publish a volume of translations from Japanese.

G157 To Glenn Hughes   THE MONTHLY CRITERION, 24 RUSSELL SQUARE, LONDON, W.C.1   12 November 1928

T. L. s. 1 p. (26.5 × 20.8 cm.)

Expressing interest in Hughes's book on the theatre, but suggesting that the English would be less receptive to it than Americans.

G158 To Maria Cristina Chambers   THE MONTHLY CRITERION, 24 RUSSELL SQUARE, LONDON, W.C.1   23 November 1928

T. L. s. in photocopy 1 p. (22.5 × 18.7 cm.)

Expressing thanks for her encouraging appreciation of *The Criterion.* Miss Chambers wrote the story "John of God" that had been published in *The Criterion.*

G159 To Glenn Hughes   FABER AND GWYER, LTD., 24 RUSSELL SQUARE, LONDON, W.C.1   16 December 1928 *postmark*

A. P. C. s. "T. S. E." (8.8 × 13.9 cm.)

Acknowledging receipt of sad personal news.

G160 To [Godfrey?] Childe   THE MONTHLY CRITERION, 24 RUSSELL SQUARE, LONDON, W.C.1   17 December 1928

T. L. s. 1 p. (26.3 × 20.6 cm.)

Alluding to "the pagan ceremonies which turn Christmas into a hideous farce."

G161 To Sally [Mrs. Richard Cobden-Sanderson]   THE MONTHLY

CRITERION, 24 RUSSELL SQUARE, LONDON, W.C.1 "Tuesday" [1927–1928?]

A. L. s. "T. S. E." 1 p. (26.4 × 20.7 cm.)

On a mutual interest in pet animals.

G162 To Richard Church FABER AND GWYER, LTD., 24 RUSSELL SQUARE, LONDON, W.C.1 25 February 1929

T. L. s. "T. S. E." 1 p. (25.4 × 20.2 cm.)

Acknowledging receipt of the review of Darley, and approving especially the comment on Edmund Blunden.

G163 To Glenn Hughes THE MONTHLY CRITERION, 24 RUSSELL SQUARE, LONDON, W.C.1 4 April 1929

T. L. s. 1 p. (26.5 × 20.8 cm.)

Reporting that he finds no reason now to conceal his authorship of *Ezra Pound His Metric and Poetry*, published anonymously in 1917.

G164 To Harold [Monro] FABER AND GWYER, LTD., 24 RUSSELL SQUARE, LONDON, W.C.1 4 June 1929

T. L. s. "Tom" 1 p. (25.4 × 20.2 cm.)

On poems which Monro may or may not use for a forthcoming anthology.

G165 To [Charles] Du Bos FABER AND GWYER, LTD., 24 RUSSELL SQUARE, LONDON, W.C.1 29 June 1929

T. L. s. 1 p. (25.3 × 20.1 cm.)

Acknowledging receipt of three books inscribed by Du Bos, and promising a review.

G166 To Harold [Monro] FABER AND FABER, LTD., 24 RUSSELL SQUARE, LONDON, W.C.1 29 June 1929

T. L. s. "T. S. E." 1 p. (25.5 × 20.5 cm)

On permissions for an anthology.

G167 To Charles Du Bos THE CRITERION, 24 RUSSELL SQUARE, LONDON, W.C.1   5 October 1929

T. L. s. 2 pp. (26.4 × 20.3 cm.)

Expressing Faber and Faber's interest in publishing the work of Du Bos. But a book on Byron would now seem to be an impractical venture. Eliot would welcome one on Pater.

G168 To Ezra Pound THE CRITERION, 24 RUSSELL SQUARE, LONDON, W.C.1   9 December 1929

A. L. s. "T." 2 pp. (24.2 × 15.9 cm.)

Concerning Louis Zukofsky and his essay on Henry Adams.

G169 To Louis Zukofsky THE CRITERION, 24 RUSSELL SQUARE, LONDON, W.C.1   28 December 1929

T. L. s. 2 pp. (26.4 × 20.8 cm.)

Asking Zukofsky to write for the English public a more elementary essay on Henry Adams than the one which Pound sent to Eliot; and asking also to see Zukofsky's essay on Pound's *Cantos*.

G170 To Ronald Bottrall FABER AND FABER, LTD., 24 RUSSELL SQUARE, LONDON, W.C.1   22 July 1930

T. L. s. 1 p. (25.2 × 20.6 cm.)

On Eliot's inability at present to commit Faber and Faber to another volume of poems.

G171 To Donald [S.] Friede FABER AND FABER, LTD., 24 RUSSELL SQUARE, LONDON, W.C.1   26 August 1930

T. L. s. 1 p. (25.7 × 20.6 cm.)

Expressing Eliot's willingness to have an errata slip indicate the misprint which appears in an anthology.

G172 To Ernest Rhys FABER AND FABER, LTD., 24 RUSSELL SQUARE, LONDON, W.C.1   16 October 1930

T. L. s. 1 p. (25.4 × 20.6 cm.)

Accepting the invitation to write on Pascal for the Everyman Library edition. This letter is printed in Ernest Rhys, *Letters from Limbo* (London, 1936) p. 248.

G173 To Mr. and Mrs. [Richard] Cobden-Sanderson 68 CLARENCE GATE GARDENS, REGENTS PARK, LONDON, N.W.1 21 November 1930

T. L. s. 2 pp. (22.6 × 17.6 cm.)

Declining an invitation to a cocktail party, with a discourse on the cocktail.

G174 To Edward W. Titus FABER AND FABER, LTD., 24 RUSSELL SQUARE, LONDON, W.C.1 6 January 1931

T. L. s. 1 p. (25.3 × 20.3 cm.)

On an essay which Eliot is writing about the modern poet's relation to his limited public, and to his political and religious beliefs.

G175 To William Plomer FABER AND FABER, LTD., 24 RUSSELL SQUARE, LONDON, W.C.1 7 September 1931

T. L. s. 1 p. (25.1 × 20.4 cm.)

Regarding the manuscript of Plomer's poems.

G176 To Harold Monro FABER AND FABER, LTD., 24 RUSSELL SQUARE, LONDON, W.C.1 10 September 1931

T. L. s "Tom" 1 p. (25.6 × 20.5 cm.)

Asking permission to delay his contribution until October 29th.

G177 To William Plomer FABER AND FABER, LTD., 24 RUSSELL SQUARE, LONDON, W.C.1 22 October 1931

T. L. s 1 p. (25.2 × 20.1 cm.)

Expressing appreciation for the inscribed copy of *Sado*.

G178 To F. R. Leavis THE CRITERION, 24 RUSSELL SQUARE, LONDON, W.C.1 28 October 1931

T. L. s. 1 p. (25.5 × 20.9 cm.)

On his interest in the work of Leavis.

G179 To Geoffrey West [Geoffrey Harry Wells]   THE CRITERION, 24 RUSSELL SQUARE, LONDON, W.C.1   30 March 1932

T. L. s. with autograph postscript 1 p. (26.5 × 20.9 cm.)

Requesting a review of Arnold Bennett's *Journals*.

G180 To Ronald Bottrall   FABER AND FABER, LTD., 24 RUSSELL SQUARE, LONDON, W.C.1   18 May 1932

T. L. s. 1 p. (25.3 × 20.2 cm.)

Acknowledging receipt of "Festivals of Fire," in which Eliot feels the influence of Pound's *Cantos*.

G181 To F. R. Leavis   FABER AND FABER, LTD., 24 RUSSELL SQUARE, LONDON, W.C.1   26 May 1932

T. L. s. 1 p. (24.9 × 20.3 cm.)

Enclosing a check for a subscription to *Scrutiny*.

G182 To Henry Tonks   FABER AND FABER, LTD., 24 RUSSELL SQUARE, LONDON, W.C.1   8 June 1932

T. L. s. 1 p. (25.5 × 20.4 cm.)

Asking if Tonks would consider writing a volume of memoirs and reminiscences.

G183 To Henry Tonks   FABER AND FABER, LTD., 24 RUSSELL SQUARE, LONDON, W.C.1   15 June 1932

T. L. s. 1 p. (25.5 × 20.4 cm.)

Expressing disappointment that Tonks will not consider writing his memoirs.

G184 To Charles Du Bos   FABER AND FABER, LTD., 24 RUSSELL SQUARE, LONDON, W.C.1   15 June 1932

T. L. s. 1 p. (25.5 × 20.3 cm.)

Acknowledging receipt of *Approximations,* and expressing particular interest in the treatment of Baudelaire.

G185 To Geoffrey West [Geoffrey Harry Wells] FABER AND FABER, LTD., 24 RUSSELL SQUARE, LONDON, W.C.1 22 June 1932

T. L. s. 1 p. (25.5 × 20.3 cm.)

Asking West to suggest another title for review since Cassell's will not send a copy of Arnold Bennett's *Journals* to *The Criterion.*

G186 To Eleanor Farjeon THE CRITERION, 24 RUSSELL SQUARE, LONDON, W.C.1 15 July 1932

T. L. s. 1 p. (26.5 × 20.9 cm.)

On the idea that clarity in writing is often merely a deceptive knack of style.

G187 To F. R. Leavis THE CRITERION, 24 RUSSELL SQUARE, LONDON, W.C.1 19 July 1932

T. L. s. 1 p. (25.4 × 20.8 cm.)

Concerning Ronald Bottrall's "Festivals of Fire."

G188 To Richard Church THE CRITERION, 24 RUSSELL SQUARE, LONDON, W.C.1 9 August 1932

T. L. s. 2 pp. (26.6 × 20.9 cm.)

Replying to an inquiry about securing help from Lascelles Abercrombie. Eliot addresses Church "Sir Richard" as a joke.

G189 To Ronald Bottrall THE CRITERION, 24 RUSSELL SQUARE, LONDON, W.C.1 23 August 1932

T. L. s. 1 p. (25.6 × 20.8 cm.)

On publishing "Festivals of Fire."

G190 To G. Wilson Knight FABER AND FABER, LTD., 24 RUSSELL

SQUARE, LONDON, W.C.1   26 August 1932

T. L. s. 3 pp. (25.4 × 20.3 cm.)

Concerning *The Christian Renaissance*, which Eliot has read in manuscript.

G191 To Ronald Bottrall   T. S. ELIOT, B-11 ELIOT HOUSE, CAMBRIDGE [Massachusetts]   26 October 1932

T. L. s. "T.S.E." 1 p (13.7 × 21.6 cm.)

Expressing interest in the revised version of "Festivals of Fire," which he would be glad to see.

G192 To Louis Zukofsky   T. S. ELIOT, B-11 ELIOT HOUSE, CAMBRIDGE [Massachusetts]   28 October 1932

T. L. s. 1 p. (13.9 × 21.7 cm.)

Asking to be reminded what poems he gave Zukofsky permission to include in *An 'Objectivists' Anthology*.

G193 To Louis Zukofsky   T. S. ELIOT, B-11 ELIOT HOUSE, CAMBRIDGE [Massachusetts]   31 October 1932

T. L. s. 1 p. (28 × 21.7 cm.)

Requesting a copy of *An 'Objectivists' Anthology*.

G194 To Ronald Bottrall   T. S. ELIOT, B-11 ELIOT HOUSE, CAMBRIDGE [Massachusetts]   18 November 1932

T. L. s. 1 p. (13.7 × 21.6 cm.) with envelope

Telling of plans to spend Thanksgiving with relatives, but offering to get Bottrall a guest room in Eliot House when he comes.

G195 To Ronald Bottrall   T. S. ELIOT, B-11 ELIOT HOUSE, CAMBRIDGE [Massacusetts]   26 November 1932

T. L. s. "T.S.E." 1 p (13.8 × 21.6 cm.)

Telling Bottrall that they are to dine together that evening with the Master of Leverett House.

G196 To Alida [Monro]   T. S. ELIOT, B-11 ELIOT HOUSE, CAMBRIDGE [Massachusetts]   26 December 1932

T. L. s. "Tom" 1 p. (13.8 × 21.6 cm.)

On Eliot's great activity traveling and lecturing; he will carry Harold Monro's MS to California and try to write the introduction there.

G197 To Alida [Monro]   T. S. ELIOT, B-11 ELIOT HOUSE, CAMBRIDGE [Massachusetts]   5 February 1933

T. L. s. "Tom" 1 p. (28.1 × 21.6 cm.)

Sending the introduction for Monro's *Collected Poems*. Begun in California, scrapped and rewritten, Eliot is still not satisfied. It is difficult, he feels, to write about a contemporary, especially about one who was known personally.

G198 To Ronald Bottrall   T. S. ELIOT, B-11 ELIOT HOUSE, CAMBRIDGE [Massachusetts]   15 February 1933

T. L. s. 1 p. (28 × 21.6 cm.)

Promising to write to Faber and Faber about "Festivals of Fire" which he will recommend for publication in the autumn.

G199 To Ronald Bottrall   T. S. ELIOT, B-11 ELIOT HOUSE, CAMBRIDGE [Massachusetts]   10 April 1933
T. L. s. 1 p. (13.6 × 21.6 cm.)

On having written to recommend Bottrall to the Colonial Office.

G200 To Ronald Bottrall   T. S. ELIOT, B-11 ELIOT HOUSE, CAMBRIDGE [Massachusetts]   4 June 1933

T. L. s. 1 p.(27.9 × 21.5 cm.)

On preparing to leave for England with many unread manuscripts.

G201 To Ronald Bottrall   FABER AND FABER, LTD., 24 RUSSELL SQUARE, LONDON, W.C.1   2 August 1933

T. L. s. 1 p. (25.3 × 21.2 cm.)

About the improbability that Faber and Faber will publish any poetry in the autumn.

G202 To Alida [Monro] SOCIETY OF THE SACRED MISSION. KELHAM THEOLOGICAL COLLEGE. HOUSE OF THE SACRED MISSION, KELHAM, NEWARK, NOTTS. 12 September 1933

A. L. s. "Tom" 2 pp. (21.8 × 17 cm.)

Reporting that he has never received a copy of Harold Monro's *Collected Poems*; and on his absence from London at least through October.

G203 To L. C. Knights FABER AND FABER, LTD., 24 RUSSELL SQUARE, W.C.1 8 October 1933

T. L. s. 1 p. (24.8 × 20.2 cm.)

Declining at present to do a review for *Scrutiny*, but suggesting that it may be possible in the spring.

G204 To Ronald Bottrall FABER AND FABER, LTD., 24 RUSSELL SQUARE, LONDON, W.C.1 24 October 1933

T. L. s. 1 p. (25.4 × 20.3 cm.)

Offering to publish Bottrall's poems in the spring, but suggesting omission of one part at the end.

G205 To Ronald Bottrall FABER AND FABER, LTD., 24 RUSSELL SQUARE, LONDON, W.C.1 31 October 1933

T. L. s. 1 p. (25.3 × 20.2 cm.)

Asking that Bottrall himself remove the undesired dramatic fragment at the end.

G206 To Frederic Prokosch THE CRITERION, 24 RUSSELL SQUARE, LONDON, W.C.1 6 March 1934

T. L. s. 1 p. (25.4 × 20.2 cm.)

On Eliot's pleasure in "The Voyage," which Prokosch sent him.

G207 To George Barker FABER AND FABER, LTD., 24 RUSSELL SQUARE, LONDON, W.C.1   8 March 1934

T. L. s. 1 p. (25.4 × 20.2 cm.)

Commenting on Barker's poems "Elegy Anticipating Death" and "Daedalus."

G208 To F. R. Leavis THE CRITERION, 24 RUSSELL SQUARE, LONDON, W.C.1   16 March 1934

T. L. s. 1 p (24.5 × 20.2 cm.)

Hoping still to contribute to *Scrutiny*, Eliot writes that he is unable to consider doing so until the autumn.

G209 To George Barker   THE CRITERION, 24 RUSSELL SQUARE, LONDON, W.C.1   16 March 1934

T. L. s. 1 p (25.4 × 20.2 cm.)

Expressing great interest in seeing Barker's manuscript of verse.

G210 To John Pudney FABER AND FABER, LTD., 24 RUSSELL SQUARE, LONDON, W.C.1   29 March 1934

T. L. s. 2 pp. (25.4 × 20.3 cm.)

Commenting on a dramatic manuscript and declining to publish it.

G211 To Rayner Heppenstall THE CRITERION, 24 RUSSELL SQUARE, LONDON, W.C.1   6 April 1934

T. L. s. 1 p. (25.4 × 20.2 cm.)

Returning poems submitted for a volume but inviting Heppenstall to offer a few of them to *The Criterion*.

G212 To George Barker   FABER AND FABER, LTD., 24 RUSSELL SQUARE, LONDON, W.C.1   12 April 1934

T. L. s. 1 p. (25.3 × 20.3 cm.)

Expressing interest in Barker's poems, but the desire to publish a larger group for a first volume.

G213 To George Barker FABER AND FABER, LTD., 24 RUSSELL SQUARE, LONDON, W.C.1   17 April 1934

T. L. s. 1 p. (25.4 × 20.3 cm.)

Encouraging Barker to bring more of his poems when he comes to London.

G214 To George Barker FABER AND FABER, LTD., 24 RUSSELL SQUARE, LONDON, W.C.1   18 May 1934

T. L. s. 2 pp. (25.3 × 20.3 cm.)

Commenting on "The Bacchant," and how it should be published.

G215 To [Lillah McCarthy] Lady Keble FABER AND FABER, LTD., 24 RUSSELL SQUARE, LONDON, W.C.1   30 May 1934   TSE/EW

T. L. s. 1 p. (25.4 × 20.4 cm.)

Expressing gratitude for her letter on the choruses from *The Rock*.

G216 To George Barker FABER AND FABER, LTD., 24 RUSSELL SQUARE, LONDON, W.C.1   1 June 1934   TSE/EW

T. L. s. 2 p. (25.3 × 20.4 cm.)

Offering an advance payment for the volume of poems and for the option to publish "The Bacchant."

G217 To George Barker FABER AND FABER, LTD., 24 RUSSELL SQUARE, LONDON, W.C.1   8 June 1934

T. L. s. 1 p. (25.3 × 20.3 cm.)

On the readiness to draw up a contract.

G218 To George Barker FABER AND FABER, LTD., 24 RUSSELL SQUARE, LONDON, W.C.1   29 June 1934   TSE/EW

T. L. s. 1 p. (25.3 × 20.3 cm.)

Sending an advance payment.

G219 To George Barker FABER AND FABER, LTD., 24 RUSSELL SQUARE, LONDON, W.C.1 10 July 1934 TSE/EW

T. L. s. 1 p. (25.3 × 20.3 cm.)

Assuring him that relief of anxieties will make writing less difficult.

G220 To John Pudney THE CRITERION, 24 RUSSELL SQUARE, LONDON, W.C.1 10 July 1934 TSE/EW

T. L. s. 1 p (25.8 × 20.3 cm.)

Expressing a preference for Pudney's poetry over his prose.

G221 To George Barker FABER AND FABER, LTD., 24 RUSSELL SQUARE, LONDON. W.C.1 17 July 1934 TSE/EW

T. L. s. 1 p. (25.3 × 20.3 cm.)

Suggesting a visit if Barker comes to London.

G222 To John Lehmann FABER AND FABER, LTD., 24 RUSSELL SQUARE, LONDON, W.C.1 18 July 1934

T. L. s. 1 p. (25.4 × 20.3 cm.)

Declining permission to publish a selection from *The Rock*.

G223 To Rayner Heppenstall THE CRITERION, 24 RUSSELL SQUARE, LONDON, W.C.1 25 July 1934

T. L. s. 1 p. (25.3 × 20.3 cm.)

Apologizing for delay in making up his mind about Heppenstall's poems.

G224 To John Pudney FABER AND FABER, LTD., 24 RUSSELL SQUARE, W.C.1 29 August 1934

T. L. s. 2 pp. (25.3 × 20.4 cm.)

On what the B.B.C. calls radio drama.

G225 To George Barker FABER AND FABER, LTD., 24 RUSSELL SQUARE, LONDON, W.C.1 20 September 1934 *postmark*

T. P. C. s. "T.S.E." (8.7 × 14.3 cm.)

On two words in Barker's manuscript that are "difficult."

G226 To [Stanley] Nott   FABER AND FABER, LTD., 24 RUSSELL SQUARE, LONDON, W.C.1   9 November 1934

T. L. s. 1 p. (25.4 × 20.3 cm.)

Enclosing a memoir of A. R. Orage, editor of *The New English Weekly* (1932–34). "Orage: Memories" appeared in *The New English Weekly* on 15 November 1934.

G227 To George Barker   FABER AND FABER, LTD., 24 RUSSELL SQUARE, LONDON, W.C.1   4 December 1934

T. L. s. 1 p. (25.3 × 20.3 cm.)

Reporting that he will suggest something that may help Barker economically.

G228 To George Barker   FABER AND FABER, LTD., 24 RUSSELL SQUARE, LONDON, W.C.1   4 December 1934

T. L. s. 1 p. (25.3 × 20.3 cm.)

Giving more detail of economic help being offered to Barker anonymously.

G229 To George Barker   FABER AND FABER, LTD., 24 RUSSELL SQUARE, LONDON, W.C.1   8 December 1934

T. L. s. 2 pp. (25.3 × 20.3 cm.)

Inquiring about Barker's preferred order for the poems which are now ready for the printer. Autograph note signed at the top of the first page: "This is the first ½ of the letter written to me by Eliot after Faber's acceptance of my first book of poems. G.B." The two pages of the letter, then separated, are now together.

G230 To [Lillah McCarthy] Lady Keble   FABER AND FABER, LTD., 24 RUSSELL SQUARE, LONDON, W.C.1   15 January 1935

T. L. s. 1 p. (25.5 × 20.4 cm.)

Declining an invitation to become a vice-president of the Oxford Branch of the English Verse Speaking Association.

G231 To George Barker FABER AND FABER, LTD., 24 RUSSELL SQUARE, LONDON, W.C.1 15 January 1935

T. L. s. 1 p. (25.3 × 20.3 cm.)

Reporting Faber and Faber's desire to publish two prose works, "Documents of Death" and "The Bacchant," in one volume.

G232 To George Barker FABER AND FABER, LTD., 24 RUSSELL SQUARE, LONDON, W.C.1 18 January 1935

T. L. S. 1 p. (25.5 × 20.3 cm.)

Announcing March 14th as the date of publication for Barker's poems.

G233 To [Lillah McCarthy] Lady Keble FABER AND FABER, LTD., 24 RUSSELL SQUARE, LONDON, W.C.1 22 January 1935

T. L. s. 1 p. (25.5 × 20.4 cm.)

Replying to another letter about the English Verse Speaking Association and expressing an attitude toward appointments offered without obligation or responsibility.

G234 To George Barker FABER AND FABER, LTD., 24 RUSSELL SQUARE, LONDON, W.C.1 24 January 1935

T. L. s. 1 p. (25.4 × 20.3 cm.)

Asking Barker to consider a title for the volume which will contain "Documents of Death" and "The Bacchant." The title was to be *Janus* (Faber and Faber, 1935).

G235 To Frederic Prokosch FABER AND FABER, LTD., 24 RUSSELL SQUARE, LONDON, W.C.1 20 February 1935

T. L. s. 1 p. (25.4 × 20.2 cm.)

Expressing pleasure in the printing and in the gift of *Words for Music* (A28).

G236 To Rayner Heppenstall THE CRITERION, 24 RUSSELL SQUARE, LONDON, W.C.1 20 February 1935

T. L. s. 2 pp. (25.3 × 20.3 cm.)

Offering the poems of George Barker for review when they appear.

G237 To Rayner Heppenstall THE CRITERION, 24 RUSSELL SQUARE, LONDON, W.C.1 27 February 1935

T. L. s. 2 pp. (25.4 × 20.3 cm.)

Sending George Barker's poems for review.

G238 To Rayner Heppenstall THE CRITERION, 24 RUSSELL SQUARE, LONDON, W.C.1 11 March 1935

T. L. s. 2 pp. (25.4 × 20.3 cm.)

On Heppenstall's article "The Frankness of the West," and Eliot's own view of the relation between ritual and belief.

G239 To George Barker FABER AND FABER, LTD., 24 RUSSELL SQUARE, LONDON, W.C.1 19 March 1935

T.L.s. 1 p. (25.4 × 20.3 cm.)

On Barker's new poem which Eliot has looked over and found exciting.

G240 To Geoffrey Grigson THE CRITERION, 24 RUSSELL SQUARE, LONDON, W.C.1 22 March 1935

T.L.s. 1 p. (25.4 × 20.2 cm.)

Declining an invitation to write on Hopkins because of the time and effort which it would demand. Grigson was editor of *New Verse*, to which Eliot contributed a brief essay in December 1935 (original script F19).

G241 To George Barker FABER AND FABER, LTD., 24 RUSSELL SQUARE, LONDON, W.C.1 26 March 1935

T. L. s. 1 p. (25.4 × 20.2 cm.)

Inviting Barker to visit and discuss his poem.

G242 To R. J. G. Johnson   FABER AND FABER, LTD., 24 RUSSELL SQUARE, LONDON, W.C.1   1 April 1935

T. L. s. 2 pp. (25.4 × 20.2 cm.)

Reporting on having read Johnson's pamphlet "A New Theatre" with much interest, and commenting on *Sweeney Agonistes*.

G243 To R. J. G. Johnson   FABER AND FABER, LTD., 24 RUSSELL SQUARE, LONDON, W.C.1   9 April 1935

T. L. s. 1 p. (25.4 × 20.2 cm.)

Suggesting other publishers who may be interested in doing "A New Theatre" as a pamphlet.

G244 To George Barker   FABER AND FABER, LTD., 24 RUSSELL SQUARE, LONDON, W.C.1   18 April 1935

T. L. s. 1 p. (25.4 × 20.3 cm.)

Sending the new Pound *Cantos* for Barker's review in *The Criterion*, XIV. 57 (July 1935) 649–51.

G245 To Rayner Heppenstall   THE CRITERION, 24 RUSSELL SQUARE, LONDON, W.C.1   29 April 1935

T. L. s. 2 pp. (25.4 × 20.3 cm.)

Asking for some revision in his review of George Barker's poems.

G246 To Rayner Heppenstall   THE CRITERION, 24 RUSSELL SQUARE, LONDON, W.C.1   3 May 1935

T. L. s. "B. O'G. [Secretary]" with autograph postscript   2 pp. (25.4 × 20.3 cm.)

Expressing satisfaction with Heppenstall's revision of the review of George Barker. Heppenstall's review is in *The Criterion*, XIV. 57 (July 1935) 677–80.

G247 To Rayner Heppenstall   THE CRITERION, 24 RUSSELL SQUARE, LONDON, W.C.1   22 May 1935

T. L. s. 1 p. (25.4 × 20.4 cm.)

Sending payment for a review.

G248 To Frederic Prokosch FABER AND FABER, LTD., 24 RUSSELL
SQUARE, LONDON, W.C.1 4 June 1935

T. L. s. 1 p. (25.4 × 20.2 cm.)

On a novel and poems by Prokosch being considered for publication by
Faber and Faber.

G249 To Richard Church FABER AND FABER, LTD., 24 RUSSELL SQUARE,
LONDON, W.C.1 5 June 1935

T. L. s. 1 p. (25.4 × 20.2 cm.)

Proposing a meeting for lunch and discussion.

G250 To John Lehmann FABER AND FABER, LTD., 24 RUSSELL SQUARE,
LONDON, W.C.1 22 August 1935

T. L. s. 1 p. (25.3 × 20.9 cm.)

Denying permission to use part of *Murder in the Cathedral* for an anthology, and explaining the difficulty at present of giving other permissions because of a forthcoming edition of *Collected Poems.*

G251 To George Barker FABER AND FABER, LTD., 24 RUSSELL SQUARE,
LONDON, W.C.1 3 September 1935

T. L. s. 1 p. (25.4 × 20.9 cm.)

About a poem of Barker's which the B.B.C. was supposed to consider
for recital. Eliot will write again about it to "Siepmann."

G252 To George Barker FABER AND FABER, LTD., 24 RUSSELL SQUARE,
LONDON, W.C.1 10 September 1935

T. L. s. 1 p. (25.5 × 21 cm.)

Reporting the return of a manuscript from the B.B.C. There will be no
recital of poetry for the present.

G253 To George Barker FABER AND FABER, LTD., 24 RUSSELL SQUARE,
LONDON, W.C.1 26 September 1935

T. L. s. 1 p. (25.5 × 20.9 cm.)

Reporting that a bank will make an immediate payment.

G254 To Ronald Bottrall THE CRITERION, 24 RUSSELL SQUARE, LON-
DON. W.C.1 25 October 1935

T. L. s. 2 pp. (25.3 × 20.2 cm.)

Advising Bottrall on the length of a second volume of poems if it is to
help him in the market for poetry.

G255 To Rayner Heppenstall THE CRITERION, 24 RUSSELL SQUARE,
LONDON, W.C.1 12 November 1935

T. L. s. 2 pp. (25.4 × 20.3 cm.)

On Heppenstall's poem "Sebastian (Fragment)," shown to Eliot by
Philip Mairet, editor of *The New English Weekly* (original typescript
with Eliot's marginal comments, F31).

G256 To F. R. Leavis THE CRITERION, 24 RUSSELL SQUARE, LONDON,
W.C.1 16 December 1935

T. L. s. 1 p. (25.1 × 20.3 cm.)

Returning *The Experimental College* by Alexander Meiklejohn with a
comment on its value, together with a reply to Leavis's praise of Eliot's
essay on Marvell.

G257 To Rayner Heppenstall FABER AND FABER, LTD., 24 RUSSELL
SQUARE, LONDON, W.C.1 30 January 1936

T L. s. 1. p. (25.4 × 20.8 cm.)

Offering to publish Heppenstall's book on the dance (*Apology for
Dancing*, Faber & Faber, 1936).

G258 To Rayner Hepppenstall FABER AND FABER, LTD., 24 RUSSELL
SQUARE, LONDON, W.C.1 4 February 1936

T. L. s. 1 p. (25.3 × 20.3 cm.)

Suggesting that Heppenstall's book needs major revision only in the first chapter. Eliot's criticism is developed in the original typescript, F30.

G259 To Richard Church THE CRITERION, 24 RUSSELL SQUARE, LONDON, W.C.1 26 February 1936

T. L. s. 1 p (25.4 × 20.3 cm.)

Asking if Church will review the recent anthologies of poetry.

G260 To Geoffrey Grigson FABER AND FABER, LTD., 24 RUSSELL SQUARE, LONDON, W.C.1 27 March 1936

T. L. s. 2 pp. (28 × 20.7 cm.)

Suggesting that the present is not a good time for a new anthology. Grigson had proposed making one from the contributions to *New Verse*.

G261 To John Lehmann THE CRITERION, 24 RUSSELL SQUARE, LONDON, W.C.1 7 April 1936

T. L. s. 1 p. (25.4 × 20.3 cm.)

Promising to print an apology for a sentence in Janet Adam Smith's review of *The Year's Poetry: 1935* in *The Criterion*, XV. 60 (April 1936) 524. Miss Smith had criticized the editors for not including a chorus from *Murder in the Cathedral*, not knowing that Eliot had denied permission. Eliot apologizes in *The Criterion*, XV. 61 (July 1936) 691.

G262 To Rayner Heppenstall THE CRITERION, 24 RUSSELL SQUARE, LONDON, W.C.1 17 April 1936

T. L. s. 2 pp. (25.4 × 20.3 cm.)

Accepting the article which would be published as "A Context for Leon Bloy" in *The Criterion*, XVI. 62 (October 1936) 43–60.

G263 To Rayner Heppenstall FABER AND FABER, LTD., 24 RUSSELL SQUARE, LONDON, W.C.1 28 April 1936

T. L. s. 2 pp. (25.4 × 20.3 cm.)

Apologizing for delay in the publication date of *Apology for Dancing*.

G264 To Stanley Nott FABER AND FABER, LTD., 24 RUSSELL SQUARE, LONDON, W.C.1 1 May 1936

T. L. s. 1p. (25.4 × 20.7 cm.)

Concerning Faber and Faber's interest in adding the "Douglas Manual" to their list from that of Nott's firm.

G265 To R. [J.] G. Johnson FABER AND FABER, LTD., 24 RUSSELL SQUARE, LONDON, W.C.1 5 May 1936

T. L. s. 1 p. (25.4 × 20.3 cm.)

Replying to Johnson's request that Eliot direct suitable plays to The Group Theatre.

G266 To Stanley Nott THE CRITERION, 24 RUSSELL SQUARE, LONDON, W.C.1 13 May 1936

T. L. s. 1 p. (25.4 × 20.4 cm.)

Accepting an invitation to lunch.

G267 To [one who may consider George Barker for appointment as an academic lecturer] THE CRITERION, 24 RUSSELL SQUARE, LONDON, W.C.1 14 May 1936

T. N. s. 1 p. (25.4 × 20.4 cm.)

A recommendation of Barker as both poet and critic.

G268 To Ronald Bottrall THE CRITERION, 24 RUSSELL SQUARE, LONDON, W.C.1 20 May 1936

T. L. s. 1 p. (25.3 × 20.2 cm.)

Apologizing for publishing "Sermons on Transmutability" without sending Bottrall proof for *The Criterion*, XV. 61 (July 1936) 644–47.

G269 To Rayner Heppenstall FABER AND FABER, LTD., 24 RUSSELL SQUARE, LONDON, W.C.1 29 May 1936

T. L. s. 2 pp. (25.4 × 20.8 cm.)

On Heppenstall's collection of poems "Ad Cor Altum," and the question whether a single writer should attempt to use the forms of both the novel and poetry.

G270 To John Lehmann THE CRITERION, 24 RUSSELL SQUARE, LONDON, W.C.1 6 July 1936

T. L. s. 1 p. (25.3 × 20.3 cm.)

Replying to Lehmann's question about poems for an anthology.

G271 To Rayner Heppenstall FABER AND FABER, LTD., 24 RUSSELL SQUARE, LONDON, W.C.1 10 July 1936

T. L. s. 1 p. (25.3 × 20.8 cm.)

Reporting that the manuscript of Heppenstall's novel is being read with interest, though not by Eliot.

G272 To John Lehmann FABER AND FABER, LTD., 24 RUSSELL SQUARE, LONDON, W.C.1 13 July 1936

T. L. s. with autograph postscript 1 p. (25.2 × 20.8 cm.)

Suggesting consideration of Bottrall, Auden, and Barker for inclusion in the new anthology.

G273 To Rayner Heppenstall FABER AND FABER, LTD., 24 RUSSELL SQUARE, LONDON, W.C.1 23 July 1936

T. L. s. 1 p. (25.3 × 20.8 cm.)

Expressing little interest in publishing a photographic study of ballet.

G274 To Rayner Heppenstall FABER AND FABER, LTD., 24 RUSSELL SQUARE, LONDON, W.C.1 24 July 1936

T. L. s. 1 p. (25.3 × 20.8 cm.)

About Heppenstall's connection with the Adelphi Centre.

G275 To George Barker FABER AND FABER, LTD., 24 RUSSELL SQUARE, LONDON, W.C.1 27 July 1936

T. L. s. 1 p. (25.3 × 20.9 cm.)

On Barker's "Essays on the Theory of Poetry" and Eliot's feeling that Barker's next book should be one of poetry not prose. Barker's prose work *Janus* (1935) was followed by the poem *Calamiterror* (1937).

G276 To George Barker THE CRITERION, 24 RUSSELL SQUARE, LONDON, W.C.1 13 August 1936 TSE/BOD

T. L. s. 2 pp. (25.4 × 20.2 cm.)

Encouraging Barker to continue work on his long poem and suggesting that some clerical job in London may help with expenses without necessarily preventing him from writing.

G277 To George Barker FABER AND FABER, LTD., 24 RUSSELL SQUARE, LONDON, W.C.1 15 November 1936

A. L. s. "T. S. E." 1 p. (18 × 11.4 cm.)

Sending Barker money that may help him continue to work in the country.

G278 To F. L. [i.e. R.] Leavis THE CRITERION, 24 RUSSELL SQUARE, LONDON, W.C.1 10 December 1936

T. L. s. 1 p. (24.4 × 20.2 cm.)

Asking if Leavis would review *Higher Learning in America* by Robert Hutchins.

G279 To George Barker THE CRITERION, 24 RUSSELL SQUARE, LONDON, W.C.1 22 December 1936

T. L. s. "T. S. E." (25.6 × 20.4 cm.)

Inquiring about Barker's ability to continue work on his poem.

G280 To Ronald Bottrall FABER AND FABER, LTD., 24 RUSSELL SQUARE, LONDON, W.C.1 5 January 1937

T. L. s. 1 p. (25.3 × 20.6 cm.)

Reporting on the unfavorable action of the committee at Faber and Faber, though Eliot himself favored publication of Bottrall's new volume of poems.

G281 To [George] Barker THE CRITERION, 24 RUSSELL SQUARE, LONDON, W.C.1 8 January 1937

T. L. s. 1 p. (25.4 × 20.3 cm.)

Expressing regret to have been unable to hear a B. B. C. broadcast recital of Barker's poems. Eliot is going to buy a radio.

G282 To George Barker THE CRITERION, 24 RUSSELL SQUARE, LONDON, W.C.1 9 February 1937

T. L. s. 1 p. (25.3 × 20.2 cm.)

Reporting general approval of the title *Calamiterror* for Barker's new volume of cantos.

G283 To Geoffrey Grigson THE CRITERION, 24 RUSSELL SQUARE, LONDON, W.C.1 19 March 1937

T. L. s. 1 p. (25.7 × 20.2 cm.)

Agreeing gladly to propose again a *New Verse* anthology drawn from Grigson's periodical.

G284 To George Barker THE CRITERION, 24 RUSSELL SQUARE, LONDON, W.C.1 24 March 1937

T. L. s. 2 pp. (25.3 × 20.3 cm.)

Replying to Barker's comment on financial need and to his request of a particular book for review, *Quia Amore Langueo*. Though Eliot now says that the book is not available for review, Barker reviews it in *The Criterion*, XVII. 68 (April 1938), 583.

G285 To Rayner Heppenstall THE CRITERION, 24 RUSSELL SQUARE, LONDON, W.C.1 8 April 1937

T. L. s. 1 p. (25.3 × 20.3 cm.)

Replying to Heppenstall's request that he may review *Revelation*. Eliot does not wish to have it reviewed, because he was a contributor to it.

G286 To Rayner Heppenstall THE CRITERION, 24 RUSSELL SQUARE, LONDON, W.C.1 12 April 1937

T. L. s. 1 p. (25.3 × 20.3 cm.)

Asking if Heppenstall will do a short note on Leon Bloy's *Letters to his Fiancée.*

G287 To Ronald Bottrall THE CRITERION, 24 RUSSELL SQUARE, LONDON, W.C.1 7 May 1937

T. L. s. 1 p. (25.2 × 20.1 cm.)

Expressing regret Eliot could not come to Bottrall's sherry party.

G288 To Rayner Heppenstall THE CRITERION, 24 RUSSELL SQUARE, LONDON, W.C.1 11 May 1937

T. L. s. "Ann Bradby, Secretary to Mr. Eliot." 1 p. (25.3 × 20.3 cm.)

Regarding a copy of *The Destiny of Man* by Berdyaev, which Heppenstall is to review.

G289 To Geoffrey Grigson THE CRITERION, 24 RUSSELL SQUARE, LONDON, W.C.1 26 May 1937

T. L. s. 1 p. (25.3 × 20.2 cm.)

Reporting nothing suitable to offer for Grigson's anthology "The Year's Poetry." Eliot is at work on a play "as anthology-proof as possible."

G290 To Rayner Heppenstall THE CRITERION, 24 RUSSELL SQUARE, LONDON, W.C.1 14 June 1937

T. L. s. 1 p. (25.3 × 20.3 cm.)

Declining to publish Heppenstall's volume of essays, though Eliot has read them with interest and enjoyment.

G291 To George Barker THE CRITERION, 24 RUSSELL SQUARE, LONDON, W.C.1 15 June 1937

T. L. s. "T. S. E." 2 pp. (25.4 × 20.3 cm.)

Suggesting that an essay in *The Criterion* is Barker's best chance of obtaining immediate funds. Barker's essay "Poetry and Reality" appears in *The Criterion*, XVII. 66 (October 1937).

G292 To George Barker THE CRITERION, 24 RUSSELL SQUARE, LONDON,
W.C.1 27 July 1937

T. L. s. 3 pp. (25.4 × 20.4 cm.)

Sending "interim criticism" of the prose work *Jerusalem*, which Eliot
admires for the clarity and lucidity of the images.

G293 To George Barker THE CRITERION, 24 RUSSELL SQUARE, LONDON,
W.C.1 26 September 1937

T. L. s. "T. S. E." 4 pp. (25.4 × 20.3 cm.)

Commenting further on *Jerusalem* and generally on the character of
Barker's "genius."

G294 To Ronald Bottrall THE CRITERION, 24 RUSSELL SQUARE, LONDON,
W.C.1 12 October 1937

T. L. s. 1 p. (25.2 × 20.2 cm.)

Granting permission to use Eliot's name for a job in Florence.

G295 To Rayner Heppenstall THE CRITERION, 24 RUSSELL SQUARE,
LONDON, W.C.1 12 October 1937

T. L. s. 1 p. (25.3 × 20.3 cm.)

Assuring Heppenstall of continued and friendly interest. But Eliot did
not feel the stories recently returned were very successful.

G296 To Mrs. [Lilian Bird] Morley THE CRITERION, 24 RUSSELL
SQUARE, LONDON, W.C.1 18 October 1937

T. L. s. 1 p. (25.3 × 20.3 cm.)

Expressing sympathy on the death of her husband Dr. Morley, father
of Frank Morley and Christopher Morley.

G297 To Ronald Bottrall THE CRITERION, 24 RUSSELL SQUARE, LONDON,
W.C.1 30 November 1937

T. L. s. 1 p. (25.5 × 20.3 cm.)

Congratulating Bottrall on securing the job in Florence.

G298 To Rayner Heppenstall THE CRITERION, 24 RUSSELL SQUARE, LONDON, W.C.1   7 December 1937

T. L. s. 1 p. (25.4 × 20.3 cm.)

Commenting on a subject proposed as being too limited in interest at present for Faber and Faber to publish.

G299 To Rayner Heppenstall THE CRITERION, 24 RUSSELL SQUARE, LONDON, W.C.1   29 December 1937

T. L. s. 2 pp. (25.4 × 20.3 cm.)

Replying to Heppenstall's expressed dissatisfaction with some books he is reviewing. Eliot does not send him poetry for review since he thinks it is better, for a poet's sake, to review another kind of book.

G300 To Rayner Heppenstall THE CRITERION, 24 RUSSELL SQUARE, LONDON, W.C.1   6 January 1938

T. L. s. 1 p. (25.4 × 19.9 cm.)

Acknowledging receipt of *Pelagia*, which Eliot has just begun to read.

G301 To Ronald Bottrall THE CRITERION, 24 RUSSELL SQUARE, LONDON, W.C.1   18 January 1938

T. L. s. 1 p. (25.4 × 20.2 cm.)

Reporting that Faber and Faber will not undertake *Crooked Elipses*, although Eliot did argue in its favor.

G302 To Rayner Heppenstall THE CRITERION, 24 RUSSELL SQUARE, LONDON, W.C.1   18 January 1938

T. L. s. 1 p. (25.4 × 19.9 cm.)

On Mansell Jones as a writer on the subject of education.

G303 To George Barker   THE CRITERION, 24 RUSSELL SQUARE, LONDON, W.C.1   24 January 1938

T. L. s. 5 pp. (25.4 × 20.3 cm.)

On growth and development in a poet. A letter quoted at length in

"T. S. Eliot at Texas," *The Library Chronicle of the University of Texas,*
VIII. 3 (Spring 1967) 25–6.

G304 To Rayner Heppenstall   THE CRITERION, 24 RUSSELL SQUARE,
LONDON, W.C.1   8 February 1938

T. L. s. 2 pp. (25.4 × 20 cm.)

About Heppenstall's play *Pelagia* which Eliot feels unqualified to
criticize because it seems to be written for broadcasting.

G305 To Rayner Heppenstall   THE CRITERION, 24 RUSSELL SQUARE,
LONDON, W.C.1   14 February 1938

T. L. s. 1 p. (25.4 × 19.9 cm.)

Suggesting that if *Pelagia* was not written to be broadcast it should be
redrafted in a purely literary form.

G306 To Rayner Heppenstall   THE CRITERION, 24 RUSSELL SQUARE,
LONDON, W.C.1   22 March 1938

T. L. s. 1 p. (25.4 × 19.9 cm.)

Replying to Heppenstall's offer to translate a Rilke letter. Eliot asks if
the translation would be made from the original German.

G307 To Rayner Heppenstall   THE CRITERION, 24 RUSSELL SQUARE,
LONDON, W.C.1   27 April 1938

T. L. s. "Ann Bradby Secretary to Mr. Eliot" 1 p. (25.5 × 20.3 cm.)

Sending Heppenstall *Purify Your Hearts* for his review of Kierkegaard.

G308 To Richard Church   THE CRITERION, 24 RUSSELL SQUARE, LONDON,
W.C.1   25 May [1938?]

T. L. s. "Tom" 1 p. (25.3 × 20.2 cm.)

Expressing Eliot's appreciation. An autograph note added, initialed by
Church: "I think this was in 1938 when I chaired him at a lecture in the
Sunday Times Exhibition. The reference was to the first Mrs. E."

G309 To Rayner Heppenstall   THE CRITERION, 24 RUSSELL SQUARE,

London, W.C.1   24 June 1938

T. L. s. 1 p. (25.4 × 19.1 cm.)

Regarding a delay in the appearance of the Kierkegaard Journals, which Heppenstall is to review.

G310 To Rayner Heppenstall   THE CRITERION, 24 RUSSELL SQUARE, LONDON, W.C.1   1 July 1938

T. L. s. 2 pp. (25.4 × 20.3 cm.)

Thanking Heppenstall for the review of Kierkegaard which Eliot finds good. It appears in *The Criterion*, XVIII. 70 (October 1938) 107–11.

G311 To Ronald Bottrall   THE CRITERION, 24 RUSSELL SQUARE, LONDON, W.C.1   25 August 1938

T. L. s. 1 p. (25.3 × 20.2 cm.)

Accepting an essay on Byron which Eliot likes very much. "Byron and the Colloquial Tradition" appears in *The Criterion*, XVIII. 71 (January 1939) 204–24.

G312 To Geoffrey Grigson   THE CRITERION, 24 RUSSELL SQUARE, LONDON, W.C.1   26 September 1938

T. L. s. 2 pp. (25.3 × 20.2 cm.)

Asking for a longer and more truly "Grigson" introduction to the *New Verse Anthology*, which Faber and Faber will soon publish.

G313 To Rayner Heppenstall   FABER AND FABER, LTD., 24 RUSSELL SQUARE, LONDON, W.C.1   17 October 1938

T. P. C. s. "Ann Bradby Secretary to Mr. Eliot"   (8.9 × 13.9 cm.)

Changing the date of an appointment.

G314 To Rayner Heppenstall   THE CRITERION, 24 RUSSELL SQUARE, LONDON, W.C.1   27 October 1938

T. L. s. 1 p. (25.4 × 19.9 cm.)

Expressing regret that Heppenstall did not wait to keep the appointment with Eliot after lunch.

G315 To George Barker THE CRITERION, 24 RUSSELL SQUARE, LONDON, W.C.1 28 October 1938

T. L. s. 1 p. (25.4 × 20.3 cm.)

On a new work of Barker's which Eliot has not yet been able to give the close attention that it requires.

G316 To Rayner Heppenstall THE CRITERION, 24 RUSSELL SQUARE, LONDON, W.C.1 1 November 1938

T. L. s. "Ann Bradby Secretary to Mr. Eliot" 1 p. (25.4 × 20.3 cm.)

Arranging an appointment to discuss Heppenstall's poems.

G317 To Geoffrey Grigson FABER AND FABER, LTD., 24 RUSSELL SQUARE, LONDON, W.C.1 16 November 1938

T. L. s. 2 pp. (25.4 × 20.7 cm.)

Replying to Grigson's objection, and repeating Eliot's thought that the *New Verse Anthology* needs a preface that is "more personally Grigson" and less nearly anonymous.

G318 To Rayner Heppenstall THE CRITERION, 24 RUSSELL SQUARE, LONDON, W.C.1 16 December 1938 TSE/AB

T. L. s. 1 p. (25.4 × 19.9 cm.)

Returning Heppenstall's poems because Heppenstall has no copy. Eliot has not yet decided which poems he wants.

G319 To Ronald Bottrall THE CRITERION, 24 RUSSELL SQUARE, LONDON, W.C.1 16 December 1938

T. L. s. 1 p. (25.3 × 20.2 cm.)

Expressing pleasure in Bottrall's new appointment to the School of Oriental Studies [London]. Eliot would like to recommend E. W. F. Tomlin to Bottrall's post in Florence.

G320 To Ronald Bottrall THE CRITERION, 24 RUSSELL SQUARE, LONDON, W.C.1 5 January 1939

T. L. s. 1 p. (25.3 × 20.2 cm.)

Returning poems that were to be printed in *The Criterion,* now brought to an end.

G321 To Rayner Heppenstall Faber and Faber, Ltd., 24 Russell Square, London, W.C.1   13 January 1939   TSE/AB

T. L. s. 1 p. (25.4 × 20.8 cm.)

Commenting on Heppenstall's outline of a plan for a project of work.

G322 To Ronald Bottrall   Faber and Faber, Ltd., 24 Russell Square, London, W.C.1   13 January 1939

T. L. s. 1 p. (20.7 × 25.3 cm.)

Enclosing a copy of a letter from Giovanni Papini, of Florence, who has invited Eliot to speak at a forthcoming conference. Eliot wants advice before sending his reply.

G323 To Ronald Bottrall   Faber and Faber, Ltd., 24 Russell Square, London, W.C.1   8 March 1939   TSE/AB

T. L. s. 1 p. (25.3 × 20.2 cm.)

Expressing desire for a meeting.

G324 To George Barker   Faber and Faber, Ltd., 24 Russell Square, London, W.C.1   20 March 1939   TSE/AB

T. L. s. 1 p. (25.4 × 20.8 cm.)

Raising no objection to Barker's allowing a friend in Manchester to publish one of his poems, "Elegy on Spain."

G325 To Philip Mairet   T. S. Eliot, 24 Russell Square, London, W.C.1 [other parts of *The Criterion* letterhead cancelled]   4 April 1939

T. L. s. "T. S. E." 1 p. (25.5 × 20.3 cm.)

Sending a first contribution to *The New English Weekly,* and expressing the thought that the first, because it will be more noticed, ought to be the best that one can do. Eliot calls it "Commentary" but Mairet, as editor, gives it another title. "That Poetry is made with Words" appears in *The New English Weekly,* XV.2 (27 April 1939) 27–8.

G326 To [George] Barker Faber and Faber, Ltd., 24 Russell Square, London, W.C.1 12 April 1939

T. L. s. "T. S. E." 1 p. (25.4 × 20.8 cm.)

Promising a copy of *The Family Reunion*, requested by Barker.

G327 To [J. B.] Priestley Faber and Faber, Ltd., 24 Russell Square, London, W.C.1 3 May 1939

T. L. s. 1 p. (25.5 × 20.8 cm.)

Expressing appreciation for the work done at the Mask Theatre in producing *The Family Reunion*.

G328 To Henry Treece Faber and Faber, Ltd., 24 Russell Square, London, W.C.1 6 July 1939 TSE/AB

T. L. s. 1 p. (25.4 × 20.8 cm.)

Commenting on a long poem by Treece and suggesting that he publish in periodicals until he is better known and has published a larger body of work.

G329 To Stanley Nott Faber and Faber, Ltd., 24 Russell Square, London, W.C.1 16 October 1939 TSE/AB

T. L. s. 1 p. (25.4 × 20.8 cm.)

Expressing Eliot's wish of a brighter prospect for Nott in New York than could be seen in London at present.

G330 To George Barker Faber and Faber, Ltd., 24 Russell Square, London, W.C.1 20 October 1939

T. L. s. 1 p. (17.5 × 20.8 cm.)

Raising a few questions about Barker's poems, which Eliot has gone through carefully again.

G331 To [Cyril] Connolly and [Stephen] Spender T. S. Eliot, 24 Russell Square, London, W.C.1 [other parts of the *Criterion* letterhead cancelled] 29 March 1940

T. L. s. 1 p. (25.3 × 20.2 cm.)

Expressing thanks for their "testimonial" of March 28th.

G332 To J. V. Healy FABER AND FABER, LTD., 24 RUSSELL SQUARE, LONDON, W.C.1 2 April 1940 TSE/AB

T. L. s. 1 p. (25.5 × 20.9 cm.)

Replying that Ezra Pound will, if he wishes, answer the charge that the *Cantos* falsify history in representing Benjamin Franklin's attitude to Jews.

G333 To J. V. Healy FABER AND FABER, LTD., 24 RUSSELL SQUARE, LONDON, W.C.1 10 May 1940

T. L. s. with autograph revision 1 p. (25.5 × 20.9 cm.)

Commenting on the sentence in *After Strange Gods* that Healy has called anti-semitic, and enclosing a copy of a letter from Ezra Pound.

G334 To J. V. Healy FABER AND FABER, LTD., 24 RUSSELL SQUARE, LONDON, W.C.1 19 June 1940

T. L. s. 1 p. (25.5 × 20.9 cm.)

Regretting the violent tone of *After Strange Gods* but standing by the statement in it concerning Jews.

G335 To John Lehmann FABER AND FABER, LTD., 24 RUSSELL SQUARE, LONDON, W.C.1 11 July 1940

T. L. s. 1 p. (25.4 × 20.8 cm.)

Granting permission for reprinting three Faber and Faber poems in *Penguin New Writing* if a reasonable fee is paid.

G336 To Stanley Nott FABER AND FABER, LTD., 24 RUSSELL SQUARE, LONDON, W.C.1 4 October 1940

T. L. s. 1 p. (25.4 × 20.7 cm.)

On the possibility of Faber and Faber's publishing three books by Frank Lloyd Wright.

G337 To [Ronald] Bottrall THE CRITERION, 24 RUSSELL SQUARE, LONDON, W.C.1 18 November 1940

T. L. s. 1 p. (25.3 × 20.2 cm.)

On Eliot's recent experience as air-raid warden. Now living in Surrey, he visits London one or two nights a week to do business and pick up manuscripts that require attention.

G338 To E. H. Blakeney   FABER AND FABER, LTD., 24 RUSSELL SQUARE, LONDON, W.C.1   7 December 1940

T. L. s. 1 p. (25.3 × 20.7 cm.)

Welcoming Blakeney's offer to send his book of poems entitled "My Cats."

G339 To E. H. Blakeney   THE CRITERON, 24 RUSSELL SQUARE, LONDON, W.C.1   4 January 1941

T. L. s. 1 p. (25.3 × 20.1 cm.)

Expressing pleasure in Blakeney's book on cats.

G340 To [Philip] Mairet   A QUARTERLY REVIEW, 24 RUSSELL SQUARE, LONDON, W.C.1   [*The Criterion* has been dropped from the letterhead by the printer]   5 January 1941

T. L. s. "T. S. E." with autograph note in margin 2 pp. (25.5 ×20.4 cm.)

Enclosing an early draft of *The Dry Salvages*. It will be published by Mairet, in revised form, in *The New English Weekly* on February 27th. Eliot comments on education in reply to Mairet's recent letter.

G341 To Richard Church   Shamley Wood, Shamley Green, Guildford [Surrey]   6 February 1941

T. L. s. 1 p. (25.4 × 20.3 cm.)

Expressing pleasure in remarks by Church on Eliot's recent work. According to an autograph note in the margin, signed R[ichard]. C[hurch]., Eliot alludes to an article in *The Fortnightly*, reprinted in *Eight for Immorality* (1941). Shamley Green in Surrey is "a community of nuns C[hurch]. of E[ngland]."

G342 To John Lehmann   FABER AND FABER, LTD., 24 RUSSELL SQUARE, LONDON, W.C.1   7 February 1941

T. L. s. 1 p. (25.4 × 20.8 cm.)

Replying to the inquiry of January 27th about reprinting in *Penguin New Writing* W. H. Auden poems which had originally appeared in that series.

G343 To John Lehmann FABER AND FABER, LTD., 24 RUSSELL SQUARE, LONDON, W.C.1 11 February 1941

T. L. s. "L. M. Melton Secretary to Mr. T. S. Eliot" 1 p. (17.5 × 20.8 cm.)

Asking Lehmann to get in touch with "Mr. Stewart, our Manager," since Eliot is still in the country.

G344 To Philip Mairet Shamley Wood, Shamley Green, Guilford [Surrey] 15 February 1941

T. L. s. "T. S. E." 2 pp. 25.4 × 20.4 cm.)

Inquiring about the receipt of corrected proof for *The Dry Salvages*, and quoting the last six lines as Eliot now wishes them to appear. Variants from the printed versions in punctuation only. Earlier versions are listed above as F11 and F12. This letter illustrated in reduced facsimile in *An Exhibition . . . of T. S. Eliot* (University of Texas at Austin, 1961), p. 25.

G345 To [Philip] Mairet THE CRITERION, 24 RUSSELL SQUARE, LONDON, W.C.1 18 February 1941

T. L. s. "T.S.E." 1 p. (25.4 × 20.3 cm.)

Naming five persons in the United States and seven in England, to whom copies of *The Dry Salvages* are to be sent.

G346 To [Philip] Mairet Shamley Wood, Shamley Green, Guildford [Surrey] 21 February 1941

T. L. s. "T. S. E." 2 pp. (25.4 × 20.3 cm.)

On a series of broadcast talks in which Eliot and Mairet are participating, especially on the great difficulty of making oneself rightly understood.

G347 To [Philip] Mairet THE CRITERION, 24 RUSSELL SQUARE, LONDON,

W.C.1   10 March 1941

T. L. s. "T. S. E." 1 p. (25.4 × 20.3 cm.)

More on the broadcasts and the problem of making one's meaning understood.

G348 To [F. R.] Leavis   THE CRITERION, 24 RUSSELL SQUARE, LONDON, W.C.1   2 May 1941

T. L. s. 1 p. (24.5 × 20.3 cm.)

On a forthcoming visit to Cambridge where Eliot hopes he may talk with Leavis.

G349 To Henry Treece   FABER AND FABER, LTD., 24 RUSSELL SQUARE, LONDON, W.C.1   6 June 1941   TSE/CBS

T. L. s. 1 p. (25.4 × 20.3 cm.)

Expressing a brief critical appreciation of Treece's poems. Faber and Faber published the volume Eliot speaks of in *Invitation and Warning* (1942).

G350 To Henry Treece   FABER AND FABER, LTD., 24 RUSSELL SQUARE, LONDON, W.C.1   12 June 1941

T. L. s. 1 p. (25.4 × 20.8 cm.)

On the poems of Treece to be published.

G351 To Henry Treece   FABER AND FABER, LTD., 24 RUSSELL SQUARE, LONDON, W.C.1   21 June 1941

T. L. s. 1 p. (25.4 × 20.7 cm.)

Expressing personal approval of the title, *Invitation and Warning*; and on the order of the poems and the desired length of the book.

G352 To Henry Treece   FABER AND FABER, LTD., 24 RUSSELL SQUARE, LONDON, W.C.1   9 July 1941

T. L. s. 1 p. (25.4 × 20.8 cm.)

On the receipt of revisions from Treece, and the possible need to omit some poems to reduce the length of the book.

G353 To Henry Treece FABER AND FABER, LTD., 24 RUSSELL SQUARE, LONDON, W.C.1 20 July 1941

T. L. s. 1 p. (25.4 × 20.7 cm.)

On the need to shorten the volume by twenty pages and Eliot's preferred way of doing so.

G354 To Henry Treece FABER AND FABER, LTD., 24 RUSSELL SQUARE, LONDON, W.C.1 24 July 1941

T. L. s. with autograph postscript 1 p. (25.4 × 20.7 cm.)

On two proposals by Treece: a volume of his own stories and a volume on the work of Herbert Read.

G355 To Ronald Bottrall THE CRITERION, 24 RUSSELL SQUARE, LONDON, W.C.1 30 July 1941

T. L. s. 1 p. (25.4 × 20.2 cm.)

Replying to Bottrall's inquiry whether Faber and Faber might reprint a selection of his poems in the Sesame Series.

G356 To [Ronald] Bottrall THE CRITERION, 24 RUSSELL SQUARE, LONDON, W.C.1 "from Tyglyn Aeron, Cilian Aeron, near Lampeter, Cardiganshire" 5 September 1941

T. L. s. 1 p. (25.3 × 20.2 cm.)

On Michael Roberts, and possibly William Empson, coming to work for the B. B. C. in London.

G357 To Ronald Bottrall FABER AND FABER, LTD., 24 RUSSELL SQUARE, LONDON, W.C.1 7 October 1941

T. L. s. 1 p. (25.2 × 20.5 cm.)

Wishing Bottrall success on his mission to Stockholm.

G358 To Richard Cobden-Sanderson FABER AND FABER, LTD., 24 RUSSELL SQUARE, LONDON, W.C.1 23 October 1941

T. L. s. "T. S. E." 1 p. (25.3 × 20.3 cm.)

On a life of Donne by "Miss Hardy," which was sent through Cobden-

Sanderson, and which Eliot thinks cannot be published at the present time.

G359 To [Philip] Mairet THE CRITERION, 24 RUSSELL SQUARE, LONDON, W.C.1   17 November 1941

T. L. s. "T S E" 1 p. (25.4 × 20.3 cm.)

Concerning recent articles on education in *The New English Weekly*, and the recent note on the "muffled tone of English discussion."

G360 To [Henry] Treece   FABER AND FABER, LTD., 24 RUSSELL SQUARE, LONDON, W.C.1   18 November 1941

T. L. s. 1 p. (25.5 × 20.8 cm.)

Suggesting that Treece may expect proof for *Invitation and Warning* in less than a month; and welcoming the offer to send *Kingdom Come*, a periodical begun in 1939 in "wartime Oxford." Treece is now one of its three editors.

G361 To Henry Treece   FABER AND FABER, LTD., 24 RUSSELL SQUARE, LONDON, W.C. 1   3 December 1941

T.L.s. 1 p. (25.5 × 20.4 cm.)

Declining to contribute to a series entitled "Art and Democracy" in *Kingdom Come*.

G362 To Richard Church   FABER AND FABER, LTD., 24 RUSSELL SQUARE, LONDON, W.C. 1   11 December 1941

T.L.s. 1 p. (25.4 × 20.3 cm.)

Welcoming the possibility that Edwin Muir may send his poems to Faber and Faber.

G363 To Ronald Gregor Smith   FABER AND FABER, LTD., 24 RUSSELL SQUARE, LONDON, W.C. 1   19 February 1942

T.L.s. 1 p. (25.4 × 20.3 cm.)

Acknowledging receipt of a manuscript from Gregor Smith whom Eliot is pleased to learn was the translator of a "remarkable" book by Martin Buber.

G364 To Richard Church THE CRITERION, 24 RUSSELL SQUARE, LON-DON, W.C. 1 "Easter [5 April] 1942"

T.L.s. 1 p. (25.4 × 20.2 cm.)

Expressing pleasure that Church sent Edwin Muir to Faber and Faber, and the hope that some day an edition of his selected poems can be published. *Selected Poems* by Edwin Muir appeared in 1965 with a preface by T. S. Eliot. Church sent Muir to Eliot because Church's recommendation for Muir at J. M. Dent had been overruled.

G365 To Ronald Gregor Smith FABER AND FABER, LTD., 24 RUSSELL SQUARE, LONDON, W.C. 1 3 June 1942

T.L.s. 1 p. (25.4 × 20.7 cm.)

On having read Smith's essay *Personal History* with interest, but finding it not suitable for a general publisher.

G366 To Ronald Bottrall 24 Russell Square [London,] W.C. 1 30 June 1942

T.L.s. 1 p. (20.6 × 26.7 cm.)

Promising to write again after he has had more time to "absorb" the poem which Bottrall has sent.

G367 To Henry Treece FABER AND FABER, LTD., 24 RUSSELL SQUARE, LONDON, W.C. 1 22 July 1942

T.L.s. 1 p. (25.3 × 20.6 cm.)

Accepting for publication a book of essays on Herbert Read, including one by Treece.

G368 To John Lehmann FABER AND FABER, LTD., 24 RUSSELL SQUARE, LONDON, W.C. 1 27 August 1942

T.L.s. 1 p. (17.8 × 20.5 cm.)

Expressing thanks for *New Writing and Daylight*, and special appreciation of Helen Gardner's article "The Recent Poetry of T. S. Eliot." The value which Eliot placed on Helen Gardner's treatment of his work is noted by Mary Trevelyan (J33).

G369 To Henry Treece FABER AND FABER, LTD., 24 RUSSELL SQUARE, LONDON, W.C. 1 31 August 1942

T.L.s. 1 p. (25.4 × 20.4 cm.)

Commenting on *Corkscrews and Footrules*, essays by Treece which Eliot is sure Faber and Faber wants to publish.

G370 To Louis MacNeice FABER AND FABER, LTD., 24 RUSSELL SQUARE, LONDON, W.C. 1 31 August 1942

T.L.s. "T.S.E." 1 p. (17.7 × 20.5 cm.)

Expressing eagerness to see the verse play by MacNeice, *Christopher Columbus*.

G371 To Henry Treece FABER AND FABER, LTD., 24 RUSSELL SQUARE, LONDON, W.C. 1 10 September 1942

T.L.s. 1 p. (25.2 × 20.4 cm.)

Expressing Eliot's willingness to read Treece's collection of stories, even though they are not typed.

G372 To F. R. Leavis FABER AND FABER, LTD., 24 RUSSELL SQUARE, LONDON, W.C. 1 10 September 1942

T.L.s. 1 p. (24.9 × 20.4 cm.)

Giving permission to publish some new poems by Ronald Bottrall.

G373 To Ronald [Bottrall] Shamley Wood, Shamley Green, Guildford [Surrey] 7 October 1942

T.L.s. "T.S.E." 1 p. (25.4 × 20.3 cm.)

Asking for a talk about *Farewell and Welcome*, particularly about Part III.

G374 To Henry Treece FABER AND FABER, LTD., 24 RUSSELL SQUARE, LONDON, W.C. 1 12 November 1942

T.L.s. 1 p. (25.5 × 20.5 cm.)

Advising him strongly not to permit Tambimuttu to publish a booklet of Treece's poems in the Poetry London series.

G375 To Henry Treece FABER AND FABER, LTD., 24 RUSSELL SQUARE, LONDON, W.C. 1   18 November 1942

T.L.s. 1 p. (17.8 × 20.4 cm.)

Approval for the volume on Herbert Read of an essay by H. W. Häusermann translated from German.

G376 To Ronald Bottrall FABER AND FABER, LTD., 24 RUSSELL SQUARE, LONDON, W.C. 1   9 December 1942

T.L.s. "Tom" 1 p. (20.3 × 17.3 cm.)

On Eliot's liking *Farewell and Welcome,* but Faber and Faber having decided against publishing the volume.

G377 To Louis MacNeice FABER AND FABER, LTD., 24 RUSSELL SQUARE, LONDON, W.C. 1   18 December 1942

T.L.s. "T.S.E." 1 p. (25.4 × 20.4 cm.)

Desiring to see the twenty poems which MacNeice has spoken of before deciding if they should be published as a volume.

G378 To Henry Treece FABER AND FABER, LTD., 24 RUSSELL SQUARE, LONDON, W.C. 1   18 December 1942

T.L.s. 1 p. (25.4 × 20.4 cm.)

On various topics, in reply to Treece, including the question whether a new group of ten poems by Treece should be published as a pamphlet.

G379 To Henry Treece FABER AND FABER, LTD., 24 RUSSELL SQUARE, LONDON, W.C. 1   21 January 1943

T.L.s. 1 p. (17.8 × 20.4 cm.)

Inquiring whether Treece is Welsh by birth or ancestry.

G380 To F. R. Leavis FABER AND FABER, LTD., 24 RUSSELL SQUARE, LONDON, W.C. 1   12 February 1943

T.L.s. 1 p. (17.8 × 20.4 cm.)

Explaining that Eliot is unable to recommend the poems by "Loveless" which were presented as having been recommended by Leavis. This appears to be a hoax, though neither Eliot nor Leavis treats it openly as one.

G381 To Edith Sitwell FABER AND FABER, LTD., 24 RUSSELL SQUARE, LONDON, W.C. 1 15 February 1943

T.L.s. "Tom" 1 p. (25.4 × 20.4 cm.)

On plans for a public reading in which Eliot will participate.

G382 To Henry Treece FABER AND FABER, LTD., 24 RUSSELL SQUARE, LONDON, W.C. 1 16 February 1943

T.L.s. 1 p. (25.5 × 20.5 cm.)

Concerning essays and poems by Treece, and the book on Herbert Read which is now postponed for autumn publication.

G383 To F. R. Leavis FABER AND FABER, LTD., 24 RUSSELL SQUARE, LONDON, W.C. 1 17 February 1943

T.L.s. 1 p. (24.9 × 20.4 cm.)

Concerning the poems by "Loveless" which Eliot sent to Leavis to be returned to the author.

G384 To Ronald Bottrall FABER AND FABER, LTD., 24 RUSSELL SQUARE, LONDON, W.C. 1 24 March 1943

T.L.s. 2 pp. (20.7 × 20 cm.)

On Eliot's friendship and respect for F. R. Leavis and *Scrutiny*.

G385 To Henry Treece FABER AND FABER, LTD., 24 RUSSELL SQUARE, LONDON, W.C. 1 31 March 1943

T.L.s. 1 p. (20.7 × 20.1 cm.)

On Eliot's desire to include Treece in an anthology of contemporary Welsh verse to be edited by Keidrych Rhys.

G386 To Louis MacNeice FABER AND FABER, LTD., 24 RUSSELL SQUARE, LONDON, W.C.1 7 April 1943

T. L. s. 1 p. (21.8 × 20.3 cm.)

Concerning MacNeice's verse play *Christopher Columbus,* and the introduction which MacNeice has added.

G387 To Osbert Sitwell FABER AND FABER, LTD., 24 RUSSELL SQUARE, LONDON, W.C.1   28 April 1943

T. L. s. "Tom" 1 p. (20.6 × 17.7 cm.)

About having taken part, at Sitwell's request, in an affair for a charitable purpose.

G388 To Philip Mairet FABER AND FABER, LTD., 24 RUSSELL SQUARE, LONDON, W.C.1   5 May 1943

T. L. s. 1 p. (20.8 × 17.8 cm.)

Expressing Eliot's desire to publish *Lettre aux Anglais* in translation. It was recommended by Mairet.

G389 To Richard Church FABER AND FABER, LTD., 24 RUSSELL SQUARE, LONDON, W.C.1   24 May 1943

T. L. s. 1 p. (20.7 × 17.7 cm.)

Acknowledging the gift of Church's *Twentieth Century Psalter,* and commenting on its title and metrical forms.

G390 To Osbert Sitwell FABER AND FABER, LTD., 24 RUSSELL SQUARE, LONDON, W.C.1   27 May 1943

T. L. s. "T. S. E." 1 p. (20.2 × 17.6 cm.)

On Eliot's pleasure in finding a reason not to give a poetry reading at Tunbridge Wells.

G391 To Henry Treece FABER AND FABER, LTD., 24 RUSSELL SQUARE, LONDON, W.C.1   23 July 1943

T. L. s. 2 pp. (25.4 × 21 cm.)

On Treece's proposal to make an anthology of Royal Air Force poems, and more particularly on Treece's own development in his career as a writer.

G392 To Henry Treece FABER AND FABER, LTD., 24 RUSSELL SQUARE,
LONDON, W.C.1   11 August 1943

T. L. s. with autograph postscript 2 pp. (25.5 × 21 cm.)

On books by Treece being written or planned for publication.

G393 To [Philip] Mairet FABER AND FABER, LTD., 24 RUSSELL SQUARE,
LONDON, W.C.1   16 August 1943

T. L. s. "T. S. E." 1 p. (20.3 × 17.7 cm.)

On plans for a course of lectures and the problem of receptivity or
resistance in the audience.

G394 To Henry Treece FABER AND FABER, LTD., 24 RUSSELL SQUARE,
LONDON, W.C.1   19 August 1943

T. L. s. 1 p. (25.5 × 21.1 cm.)

On a frontispiece for the Herbert Read volume and on the possible
future publication of *Corkscrews and Footrules*.

G395 To Henry Treece FABER AND FABER, LTD., 24 RUSSELL SQUARE,
LONDON, W.C.1   2 September 1943

T. L. s. 1 p. (20.4 × 17.8 cm.)

On the title for the Herbert Read volume, and on plans for the Air
Force anthology.

G396 To Henry Treece FABER AND FABER, LTD., 24 RUSSELL SQUARE,
LONDON, W.C.1   8 September 1943

T. L. s. 1 p. (25.4 × 21 cm.)

On *Corkscrews and Footrules* and its proper place in Treece's development and career as a writer.

G397 To Henry Treece FABER AND FABER, LTD., 24 RUSSELL SQUARE,
LONDON, W.C.1   22 September 1943

T. L. s. 1 p. (20.3 × 17.7 cm.)

On distributing through Treece the royalty to contributors to the
Herbert Read volume.

G398 To W. F. J[ackson]. Knight Faber and Faber, Ltd., 24 Russell Square, London, W.C.1 26 October 1943

T. L. s. 1 p. (20.3 × 17.7 cm.)

On devising a constitution for the Virgil Society.

G399 To Henry Treece Faber and Faber, Ltd., 24 Russell Square, London, W.C.1 17 November 1943

T. L. s. 1 p. (20.4 × 17.7 cm.)

Promising a letter of introduction to Robert Frost and recommending John Crowe Ransom as an American writer on education.

G400 To Henry Treece Faber and Faber, Ltd., 24 Russell Square, London, W.C.1 30 November 1943 TSE/MDG

T. L. s. 1 p. (25.5 × 20.5 cm.)

Enclosing a letter to Robert Frost and suggesting how Treece may make contact with John Crowe Ransom.

G401 To Robert Frost Faber and Faber, Ltd., 24 Russell Square, London, W.C.1 30 November 1943 TSE/MDG

T. L. s. 1 p. (25.5 × 20.4 cm.)

Introducing Treece as a young friend, poet, and editor. Treece was editor of *Transformation* and co-editor of *Kingdom Come*.

G402 To Henry Treece Faber and Faber, Ltd., 24 Russell Square, London, W.C.1 9 February 1944

T. L. s. with autograph corrections 2 pp. (25.5 × 21 cm.)

Commenting on a new group of poems by Treece.

G403 To Henry Treece Faber and Faber, Ltd., 24 Russell Square, London, W.C.1 15 March 1944

T. L. s. with autograph postscript 1 p. (25.4 × 21 cm.)

On Treece's poems and his proposal to write an essay on *Four Quartets*.

G404 To Ronald Bottrall FABER AND FABER, LTD., 24 RUSSELL SQUARE, LONDON, W.C.1 16 March 1944

T. L. s. "T. S. E." 1 p. (25.3 × 20.9 cm.)

Rejecting a proposal to publish a volume of poems in ottava rima by Byron.

G405 To Henry Treece FABER AND FABER, LTD., 24 RUSSELL SQUARE, LONDON, W.C.1 23 March 1944

T. L. s. 1 p. (20.4 × 17.5 cm.)

Approving the title *The Black Seasons.*

G406 To Henry Treece FABER AND FABER, LTD., 24 RUSSELL SQUARE, LONDON, W.C.1 27 April 1944

T. L. s. "T. S. Eliot" by an unidentified secretary 1 p. (20.4 × 17.5 cm.)

On the need to reduce the length of *The Black Seasons.*

G407 To George Barker FABER AND FABER, LTD., 24 RUSSELL SQUARE, LONDON, W.C.1 17 May 1944

T. L. s. 1 p. (20.4 × 17.5 cm.)

On Barker's new poems and Eliot's objection to *American Poems* as a title.

G408 To George Barker FABER AND FABER, LTD., 24 RUSSELL SQUARE, LONDON, W.C.1 8 June 1944

T. L. s. 1 p. (20.9 × 17.7 cm.)

Approving *The Altars of Dereliction* as a title.

G409 To Henry Treece FABER AND FABER, LTD., 24 RUSSELL SQUARE, LONDON, W.C.1 15 June 1944

T. L. s. 1 p. (20.3 × 17.5 cm.)

On Eliot's readiness to do a volume of ninety-six pages, which leaves room for two or three more pages than had been planned.

G410 To George Barker Faber and Faber, Ltd., 24 Russell Square, London, W.C.1   17 June 1944

T. L. s. 1 p. (20.9 × 17.7 cm.)

On the willingness despite hesitation to accept as a title *Word in a Bag of Waters*.

G411 To George Barker Faber and Faber, Ltd., 24 Russell Square, London, W.C.1   9 July 1944

T. L. s. 1 p. (25.5 × 20.5 cm.)

Accepting the title *Eros in Dogma*.

G412 To Henry Treece Faber and Faber, Ltd., 24 Russell Square, London, W.C.1   14 July 1944

T. L. s. 1 p. (20.4 × 17.5 cm.)

On Eliot's inability, in the absence of his secretary, to find other poems of Treece.

G413 To John Lehmann Faber and Faber, Ltd., 24 Russell Square, London, W.C.1   17 August 1944

T. L. s. 1 p. (20.4 × 17.5 cm.)

On dates proposed for the appearance of *Four Quartets*; and Eliot's lack of desire to write any verse since *Little Gidding*.

G414 To Edith [Sitwell] Shamley Green, Guildford [Surrey] 28 August 1944

T. L. s. 1 p. (20.5 × 17.5 cm.)

Eliot's praise of *Green Song*.

G415 To Henry Treece Faber and Faber, Ltd., 24 Russell Square, London, W.C.1   8 September 1944

T. L. s. 1 p. (20.4 × 17.5 cm.)

On Eliot's inability at present to write anything about his methods of working, a topic suggested by Treece.

G416 To Ronald Bottrall FABER AND FABER, LTD., 24 RUSSELL SQUARE, LONDON, W.C.1 20 September 1944

T. L. s. "T. S. E." 1 p. (17.4 × 20.3 cm.)

Giving Eliot's personal permission to reprint five poems in a Bonniers anthology which Bottrall is preparing to publish in Stockholm.

G417 To Stanley Nott FABER AND FABER, LTD., 24 RUSSELL SQUARE, LONDON, W.C.1 24 October 1944

T. L. s. 1 p. (20.4 × 17.5 cm.)

Arranging to meet for lunch on one of the three days in the middle of the week, when Eliot is normally in London.

G418 To Ronald Bottrall FABER AND FABER, LTD., 24 RUSSELL SQUARE, LONDON, W.C.1 23 November 1944

T. L. s. "T. S. E." 1 p. (20.3 × 17.4 cm.)

Arranging to meet for lunch.

G419 To A[rthur]. V. Moore FABER AND FABER, LTD., 24 RUSSELL SQUARE, LONDON, W.C.1 3 January 1945

T. L. s. 1 p. (20.4 × 17.5 cm.)

Sending a borrowed copy of Ezra Pound's *Jefferson and/or Mussolini* which may be useful in Pound's defense.

G420 To Stanley Nott FABER AND FABER, LTD., 24 RUSSELL SQUARE, LONDON, W.C.1 5 January 1945

T. L. s. "T. S. Eliot/M. L." 2 pp. (20.4 × 17.5 cm.)

Returning *The Dance of Shiva* by A. K. Coomaraswamy, which Faber and Faber are now unable to reissue because of a congested program for some time in the future.

G421 To Ronald [Bottrall] FABER AND FABER, LTD., 24 RUSSELL SQUARE, LONDON, W.C.1 14 January 1945

T. L. s. "T. S. E." 1 p. (20.4 × 17.4 cm.)

OLD POSSUM'S BOOK
OF PRACTICAL CATS

to Miss Mary Trevelyan
Thanks a million

O. P.

Miss Mary Trevelyan
Is like Godfrey of Bouillon.
For his name means pottage
And her name means cottage.
(Remove, if you will,
The elegant varnish
Provided by Cornish,
It means "public house
*   under the hill".)*

Inscribed half title of the first edition of *Old Possum's Book of Practical Cats*, 1939,
with a poem, also in Eliot's hand, on card pasted below. A34a(4)

Apologizing for the need to postpone meeting for lunch because of illness.

G422 To Stanley Nott   FABER AND FABER, LTD., 24 RUSSELL SQUARE, LONDON, W.C.1   6 February 1945

T. L. s. 1 p. (20.3 × 17.5 cm.)

Inviting Nott to send his manuscript of a diary kept on visits to the United States.

G423 To Edith [Sitwell]   24 RUSSELL SQUARE, [LONDON,] W.C.1 25 February 1945

T. L. s. "Tom" 1 p. (20.3 × 17.3 cm.)

Replying to a letter about an article in *The Spectator* by Sheila Shannon.

G424 To [Philip] Mairet   [THE VIRGIL SOCIETY letterhead cancelled] 25 February 1945

T. L. s. "T. S. E." 1 p. (20.5 × 16.4 cm.)

Commenting on a letter from Herbert Read to Mairet as editor of *The New English Weekly*, on a recent article by Montgomery Belgion.

G425 To W. F. Jackson Knight   FABER AND FABER, LTD., 24 RUSSELL SQUARE, LONDON, W.C.1   13 March 1945

T. L. s. 1 p. (20.3 × 17.5 cm.)

On Eliot's long-standing preference for Virgil over Homer.

G426 To John Lehmann   FABER AND FABER, LTD., 24 RUSSELL SQUARE, LONDON, W.C.1   3 April 1945

T. L. s. "T. S. E." 1 p. (20.4 × 17.5 cm.)

Expressing appreciation for *The Penguin New Writing*, especially for the article by John Heath-Stubbs.

G427 To Rayner Heppenstall   FABER AND FABER, LTD., 24 RUSSELL SQUARE, LONDON, W.C.1   30 May 1945

T. L. s. 1 p. (20.4 × 17.5 cm.)

On the possibility of employment for Heppenstall who is about to return to civilian life.

G428 To Ronald Gregor Smith FABER AND FABER, LTD., 24 RUSSELL SQUARE, LONDON, W.C.1 1 June 1945

T. L. s. 1 p. (20.4 × 17.5 cm.)

Concerning Smith's autobiographical novel which Eliot has read in manuscript.

G429 To Stanley Nott FABER AND FABER, LTD., 24 RUSSELL SQUARE, LONDON, W.C.1 1 June 1945

T. L. s. 2 pp. (20.4 × 17.5 cm.)

Declining to publish Nott's diary though Eliot found it interesting. He doubts whether there is sufficient general interest now in the impressions of a British visitor to the United States in that period, before and just after they entered the war.

G430 To Edith [Sitwell] FABER AND FABER, LTD., 24 RUSSELL SQUARE, LONDON, W.C.1 25 June 1945

T. L. s. "Tom" 1 p. (20.1 × 17.3 cm.)

On Eliot's obligation to attend a meeting to introduce Frederick G. Melcher, an important person in the publishing world of New York.

G431 To [W. F.] Jackson Knight 24 Russell Square, W.C.1 25 June 1945

T. L. s. 1 p. (20.4 × 16.5 cm.)

Concerning the choice of a new president for the Virgil Society.

G432 To W. F. Jackson Knight FABER AND FABER, LTD., 24 RUSSELL SQUARE, LONDON, W.C.1 11 July 1945

T. L. s. 1 p. (20.5 × 17.5 cm.)

Returning a typescript for further work on it.

G433 To Henry Treece FABER AND FABER, LTD., 24 RUSSELL SQUARE,

THE DRY SALVAGES

I

I do not know much about gods; but I think that the river
Is a strong brown god—sullen, untamed and intractable,
Patient to some degree, at first recognised as a frontier;
Useful, untrustworthy, as a conveyor of commerce;
Then only a problem confronting the builder of bridges.
The problem once solved, the brown god is almost forgotten
By the dwellers in cities—ever, however, implacable,
Keeping his seasons and rages, destroyer, reminder
Of what men choose to forget. Unhonoured, unpropitiated
By worshippers of the machine, but waiting, watching and
    waiting.
His rhythm was present in the nursery bedroom,
In the rank ailanthus of the April dooryard,
In the smell of grapes on the autumn table,
And the evening circle in the winter gaslight.

The river is within us, the sea is all about us;
The sea is the land's edge also, the granite
Into which it reaches, the beaches where it tosses
Its hints of earlier and other creation:
The starfish, the ~~hermit~~ crab, the whale's backbone;
The pools where it offers to our curiosity
The more delicate algae and the sea anemone.
It tosses up our losses, the torn seine,

horseshoe /
T.S.E.

[7]

Initialed correction of "hermit" to "horseshoe" in the first edition of
The Dry Salvages, 1941. A39(4)

To J S Eliot:
a token of remembrance
& with all good wishes
from W J. de la Mare
April 25 1948

To Light you to Bed

Here at his hornbook sits a drowsy child
Lit by a guttering candle's fickle beams
So heavy is his eye each letter seems
An imp endowed with grins & antics will.
But at his open window, large & mild.
The moon doth stream from far away; he deems
That she may there upon the land of dreams
Where letters unto sense are reconciled
So in the silence doth he sit & learn;
So learns he tribulation & dismay.
For, though to shut his eyes & dream he yearn,—
There is many a weary mile to Z from A.
O woe Taskmaster, spare his mazed head,
And send his moonstruck scholar safe to bed!

Christmas 1897

Autograph manuscript of Walter de la Mare's sonnet to Eliot, 1948, inscribed on fly leaf of *The Traveller* and bearing Eliot's marginal notes critical of the romantic diction. Reproduction permission granted by the Society of Authors, agents for the Walter de la Mare Estate. F36

LONDON, W.C.1   2 August 1945

T. L. s. 1 p. (20.6 × 17.5 cm.)

Thanking Treece for a letter of congratulations.

G434 To Edith Sitwell   FABER AND FABER, LTD., 24 RUSSELL SQUARE,
LONDON, W.C.1   17 August 1945

T. L. s. "Tom" 1 p. (20.6 × 17.5 cm.)

On Eliot's sorrow to hear of the recent accident suffered by Miss Sitwell.

G435 To Ronald Bottrall   FABER AND FABER, LTD., 24 RUSSELL SQUARE,
LONDON, W.C.1   17 August 1945

T. L. s. "T. S. E." 1 p. (20.5 × 17.4 cm.)

On having given *Poetry London* permission to reprint from *Festivals
of Fire.*

G436 To Philip Mairet   FABER AND FABER, LTD., 24 RUSSELL SQUARE,
LONDON, W.C.1   24 August 1945

T. L. s. "T S E" 1 p. (20.3 × 17.5 cm.)

On Eliot's reaction to news of the atom bomb.

G437 To Ronald Duncan   FABER AND FABER, LTD., 24 RUSSELL SQUARE,
LONDON, W.C.1   16 November 1945

T. L. s. 1 p. (20.5 × 17.5 cm.)

Acknowledging receipt of a Canto by Pound, and expressing the desire
to publish all the Cantos together, if the poem is not endless.

G438 To Henry Treece   FABER AND FABER, LTD., 24 RUSSELL SQUARE,
LONDON, W.C.1   8 February 1946

T. L. s. 1 p. (20.5 × 17.6 cm.)

On Eliot's not having been in touch with Bertrand Russell for more than
twenty years.

G439 To Ronald Duncan   FABER AND FABER, LTD., 24 RUSSELL SQUARE,

London, W.C.1   25 February 1946

T. L. s. 2 pp. (20.4 × 17.3 cm.)

On H. E. Herlitschka as a possible translator of *This Way to the Tomb* into German, and on Duncan's *Rape of Lucrece*, which Eliot wishes to publish.

G440 To Henry Treece   Faber and Faber, Ltd., 24 Russell Square, London, W.C.1   26 March 1946

T. L. s. 2 pp. (20.5 × 17.6 cm.)

Praising Treece's *Elegy* as a sustained and moving poem, but raising questions about publishing the entire new group as a volume to follow *The Black Seasons*.

G441 To Edith Sitwell   Faber and Faber, Ltd., 24 Russell Square, London, W.C.1   28 March 1946

T. L. s. "Tom" 1 p. (20.2 × 17.3 cm.)

On a forthcoming visit to Salisbury.

G442 To Edith Sitwell   Faber and Faber, Ltd., 24 Russell Square, London, W.C.1   3 April 1946

T. L. s. 1 p. (20.4 × 17.3 cm.)

Enclosing for signature a letter affirming Ezra Pound's service to literature.

G443 To Henry Treece   Faber and Faber, Ltd., 24 Russell Square, London, W.C.1   4 April 1946

T. L. s. 1 p. (20.4 × 17.5 cm.)

Returning poems for some rearrangement, but agreeing that this group of Treece's poems should be published now as a book.

G444 To Ronald Duncan   Faber and Faber, Ltd., 24 Russell Square, London, W.C.1   4 April 1946

T. L. s. 1 p. (20.5 × 17.5 cm.)

Inquiring whether Duncan now has anything to do with the direction

to Mary Trevelyan
in all simplicity:
T. S. Eliot
5.xi.48

Inscribed fly leaf of the first edition of *Notes Towards the Definition of Culture*,
1948. A51a(1)

Several published versions of *The Waste Land* and *Murder in the Cathedral,*
as described here or in Gallup.

of *Scythe*, of which he was formerly the editor.

G445 To Cyril Connolly FABER AND FABER, LTD., 24 RUSSELL SQUARE, LONDON, W.C.1 15 May 1946

T. L. s. 1 p. (20.7 × 17.5 cm.)

Promising to write or speak to people about help for James Joyce.

G446 To George Barker FABER AND FABER, LTD., 24 RUSSELL SQUARE, LONDON, W.C.1 6 August 1946

T. L. s. 1 p. (20.4 × 17.8 cm.)

Inquiry about Barker's trip to New York and whether he will return to England.

G447 To Marion van Dorn [Mrs. E. McKnight Kauffer] 19 Carlyle Mansions, Cheyne Walk [London], S.W.3 8 August 1946

T. L. s. "Tom" 1 p. (27.9 × 21.3 cm.)

Asking Marion van Dorn to return *Take Three Tenses*, which Eliot left at her party in New York. He promised to read it, because it is said to be based on *Four Quartets*.

G448 To Henry Treece FABER AND FABER, LTD., 24 RUSSELL SQUARE, LONDON, W.C.1 20 August 1946

T. L. s. 2 pp. (20.4 × 17.8 cm.)

Asking what arrangement of poems Treece intends for *The Haunted Garden*.

G449 To Ronald Bottrall FABER AND FABER, LTD., 24 RUSSELL SQUARE, LONDON, W.C.1 20 August 1946

T. L. s. "Tom" 1 p. (20.3 × 17.2 cm.)

Unable to accept Bottrall's invitation to a cocktail party.

G450 To Miss R. L. Mixner FABER AND FABER, LTD., 24 RUSSELL SQUARE, LONDON, W.C.1 9 September 1946 TSE/MDG

T. L. s. 1 p. (20.9 × 17.7 cm.)

Acknowledging receipt of two cartons of cigarettes, one for Walter de la Mare.

G451 To Henry Treece FABER AND FABER, LTD., 24 RUSSELL SQUARE, LONDON, W.C.1 13 September 1946 TSE/MDG

T. L. s. 1 p. (20.9 × 17.7 cm.)

On the terms for publishing Treece's volume *The Haunted Garden*.

G452 To Philip Mairet FABER AND FABER, LTD., 24 RUSSELL SQUARE, LONDON, W.C.1 13 September 1946 TSE/MDG

T. L. s. 2 pp. (20.9 × 17.7 cm.)

On Eliot's resignation from the Board of *The Christian News Letter*; and a recommendation to Mairet of two American periodicals, *The Commonweal* and *Politics*.

G453 To [Henry] Treece FABER AND FABER, LTD., 24 RUSSELL SQUARE, LONDON, W.C.1 16 September 1946

T. L. s. 2 pp. (20.8 × 17.7 cm.)

On Treece's *Ivan Morgan*, an opera libretto, and on the relations of verse, music, and speech written for the stage.

G454 To Ronald Duncan FABER AND FABER, LTD., 24 RUSSELL SQUARE, LONDON, W.C.1 17 September 1946

T. L. s. 1 p. (20.4 × 17.7 cm.)

On the decision of a group in New York that a book on Ezra Pound would not be helpful to him now.

G455 To Henry Treece FABER AND FABER, LTD., 24 RUSSELL SQUARE, LONDON, W.C.1 22 October 1946

T. L. s. 1 p. (20.8 × 17.8 cm.)

Thanking him for a copy of *How I See Apocalypse*.

G456 To Mrs. [Ezra] Pound FABER AND FABER, LTD., 24 RUSSELL SQUARE, LONDON, W.C. 1 13 November 1946

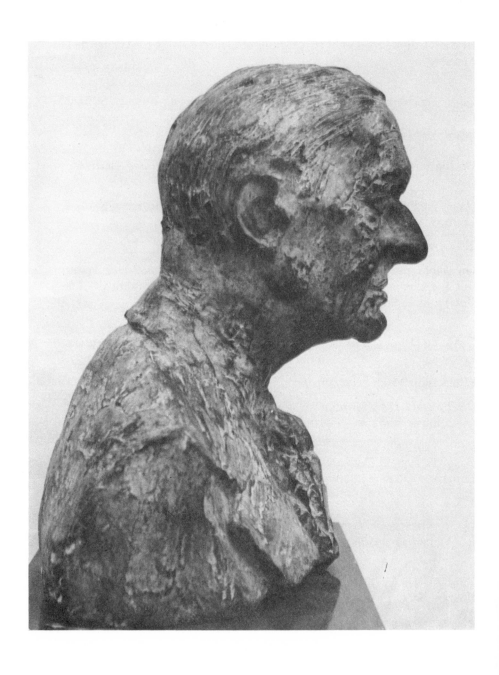

Jacob Epstein's *T. S. Eliot Portrait Bust*, cast in bronze, 1953. K8

T. L. s. "To[m]" 1 p. (20.8 × 17.8 cm.)

On his inability to act from London on a problem which Mrs. Pound has written about.

G457 To F. R. Leavis FABER AND FABER, LTD., 24 RUSSELL SQUARE, LONDON, W.C.1 21 November 1946

T. L. s. 1 p. (20.7 × 17.8 cm.)

Enclosing a letter requested to recommend James Smith, who authored essays in *Scrutiny* on Metaphysical poetry, Elizabethan drama, and other topics.

G458 To [Mary Trevelyan] FROM MESSRS. FABER AND FABER, 24 RUSSELL SQUARE, LONDON, W.C.1 [1946]

T. N. 1 p. (14 × 10.4 cm.)

Sending, "With Mr. Eliot's compliments," *The Era of Atomic Power*, Report of a Commission appointed by the British Council of Churches (London 1946).

G459 To Henry Treece FABER AND FABER, LTD., 24 RUSSELL SQUARE, LONDON, W.C.1 22 January 1947

T. L. s. 1 p. (20.7 × 17.8 cm.)

On having forwarded proofs of *The Haunted Garden*, which will be published March 21st.

G460 To Ronald Duncan FABER AND FABER, LTD., 24 RUSSELL SQUARE, LONDON, W.C.1 23 January 1947

T. L. s. "T.S.E." 1 p. (20.3 × 17.7 cm.)

Suggesting that the Cantos by Ezra Pound which Duncan has just sent are far below the level of those which Eliot has already seen. He is impatient to see a final text.

G461 To Arland Ussher FABER AND FABER, LTD., 24 RUSSELL SQUARE, LONDON, W.C.1 31 January 1947

T. L. s. 2 pp. (20.4 × 17.7 cm.)

Commenting on a collection of essays by Ussher, a contributor to *The New English Weekly*, and the author of *The Twilight of the Ideas and Other Essays* (1948).

G462 To Edward Field FABER AND FABER, LTD., 24 RUSSELL SQUARE, LONDON, W.C.1 17 March 1947

T. L. s. 1 p. (20.3 × 17.6 cm.) with envelope

Eliot's denial of anti-Semitism in any of his poetry.

G463 To George Barker FABER AND FABER, LTD., 24 RUSSELL SQUARE, LONDON, W.C.1 27 March 1947

T. L. s. 7 pp. (20.3 × 17.7 cm.)

Offering critical notes on diction and idiom in *The Degradations of Guatemozin*.

G464 To W. F. Jackson Knight FABER AND FABER, LTD., 24 RUSSELL SQUARE, LONDON, W.C.1 3 April 1947

T. L. s. 1 p. (20.3 × 17.7 cm.)

Sending clippings requested.

G465 To Marion van Dorn [Mrs. E. McKnight Kauffer] FABER AND FABER, LTD., 24 RUSSELL SQUARE, LONDON, W.C.1 "Easter Sunday [6 April] 1947"

T. L. s. "Tom" 1 p. (20.4 × 17.6 cm.)

On Eliot's plans for a visit to the United States.

G466 To [Philip] Mairet 24 RUSSELL SQUARE, LONDON, W.C.1 "Easter Monday [7 April] 1947"

T. L. s. "T.S.E." 2 pp. (20.5 × 17.6 cm.)

On a conversation with Mrs. Orage and Richard Orage about determining the policy and content of *The New English Weekly*. Orage preceded Mairet as editor.

G467 To Henry Treece FABER AND FABER, LTD., 24 RUSSELL SQUARE,

Sir Gerald Kelly's oil, *T. S. Eliot in My Studio*, completed in 1965 but begun some years earlier. K11

London, W.C.1   10 April 1947

T. L. s. 2 pp. (20.4 × 17.7 cm.)

On a novel recently submitted by Treece, and on the possible future publication of *The Haunted Garden* in the United States.

G468 To Henry Treece Faber and Faber, Ltd., 24 Russell Square, London, W.C.1   18 April 1947

T. L. s. 1 p. (20.4 × 17.7 cm.)

On the Japanese edition of Eliot's essays.

G469 To William Turner Levy   41 Kirkland Street, Cambridge 38, Massachusetts   15 May 1947

T. L. s. 1 p. (26.7 × 20.3 cm.)

Thanking Levy for an interesting letter and offering to meet him in London. Cited in *Affectionately, T. S. Eliot* by William Turner Levy and Victor Scherle (Philadelphia and New York: J. B. Lippincott Company), p. 10.

G470 To Marion van Dorn [Mrs. E. McKnight Kauffer]   84 Prescott Street, Cambridge, Massachusetts   7 June 1947

T. L. s. "Tom" 1 p. (27.9 × 21.4 cm.)

On plans to see her in New York. Eliot will arrive on June 13th.

G471 To W. F. Jackson Knight   Faber and Faber, Ltd., 24 Russell Square, London, W.C.1   1 July 1947

T. L. s. 1 p. (20.3 × 17.6 cm.)

Thanking Jackson Knight for a pocket-size volume of Sophocles in Greek.

G472 To [T. I. F. Armstrong] The Literary Digest, 1 Furnivall Street, London, E. C. 4   Faber and Faber, Ltd., 24 Russell Square, London, W.C.1   22 August 1947

T. L. s. "Mary Bland (Mrs.) Secretary to Mr. T. S. Eliot" 1 p. (20.2 × 17.6 cm.)

Expressing no objection in principle to printing a condensed version of "The Significance of Charles Williams." Armstrong edited *The Literary Digest* under the name of John Gawsworth.

G473 To Philip Mairet   FABER AND FABER, LTD., 24 RUSSELL SQUARE, LONDON, W.C.1   29 September 1947

T. L. s. "T. S. E." 1 p. (20.3 × 17.6 cm.)

Declining to prepare anything on existentialism.

G474 To Henry Treece   FABER AND FABER, LTD., 24 RUSSELL SQUARE, LONDON, W.C.1   17 October 1947

T. L. s. 2 pp. (25.6 × 20.5 cm.)

Commenting on *The Haunted Garden* and its place in Treece's career as an author.

G475 To Philip Mairet   FABER AND FABER, LTD., 24 RUSSELL SQUARE, LONDON, W.C.1   24 October 1947

T. L. s. "T. S. E." 1 p. (20.7 × 17.8 cm.)

Sending German pamphlets for Mairet's possible use in *The New English Weekly.*

G476 To Henry Treece   FABER AND FABER, LTD., 24 RUSSELL SQUARE, LONDON, W.C.1   28 October 1947

T. L. s. 2 pp. (25.6 × 20.4 cm.)

On Treece's recent development, with a comment especially on "Caractacus."

G477 To F. R. Leavis   FABER AND FABER, LTD., 24 RUSSELL SQUARE, LONDON, W.C.1   31 October 1947

T. L. s. 1 p. (20.7 × 17.8 cm.)

On Eliot's letter to the editor of *Scrutiny* concerning a review by H. A. Mason (XV. 1 [December 1947] 56).

G478 To [Philip] Mairet   24 RUSSELL SQUARE, [London,] W.C.1

23 December 1947

T. L. s. "T. S. E." 2 pp. (18.2 × 11.3 cm.)

Of Eliot's movements across Europe for the British Council.

G479 To [J. B.] Priestley   24 RUSSELL SQUARE, LONDON, W.C.1
3 January 1948

T. L. s. 1 p. (18.1 × 11.3 cm.)

Expressing pleasure in Priestley's verbal portrait of Walter de la Mare.

G480 To Ronald Duncan   24 RUSSELL SQUARE, LONDON, W.C.1   7
January 1948

T. L. s. 1 p. (18.1 × 11.5 cm.)

Thanking Duncan for a telegram of congratulations. Referring to the
award of the Order of Merit?

G481 To Henry Treece   24 RUSSELL SQUARE, LONDON, W.C.1
7 January 1948

T. L. s. 1 p. (18 × 11.5 cm.)

Thanking Treece for a telegram of congratulations.

G482 To Mr. and Mrs. Keidrych Rhys   24 RUSSELL SQUARE, LONDON,
W.C.1   8 January 1948

T. L. s. 1 p. (18.1 × 11.3 cm.)

Expressing thanks for their postcard of congratulations.

G483 To L. A. G. Strong   24 RUSSELL SQUARE, LONDON, W.C.1
14 January 1948

T. L. s. 1 p. (18.2 × 11.3 cm.)

Thanking Strong for a letter of congratulations.

G484 To Peter Russell   FABER AND FABER, LTD., 24 RUSSELL SQUARE,
LONDON, W.C.1   21 January 1948

T. L. s. 1 p. (26.3 × 20.7 cm.)

On the question whether a book should be written on Ezra Pound's Cantos.

G485 To Henry Treece   FABER AND FABER, LTD., 24 RUSSELL SQUARE, LONDON, W.C.1   29 January 1948

T. L. s. 1 p. (26.4 × 20.8 cm.)

On Treece's dedicating to Eliot a book of selections from Swinburne.

G486 To Philip Mairet   24 RUSSELL SQUARE, LONDON, W.C.1 "Sunday" [January 1948?]

A. L. s. "T. S. E." 1 p. (18.1 × 11.3 cm.)

Questioning whether *The New English Weekly* should print "O. M." after Eliot's name. He has just been awarded the Order of Merit, but he asks if some people may not think that "O. M." stands for Oswald Moseley the British Fascist.

G487 To Ashley Dukes   OXFORD AND CAMBRIDGE UNIVERSITY CLUB, PALL MALL, LONDON, S.W.1   "Ash Wednesday [10 February] 1948"

A. L. s. "T. S. E." 2 pp. (17.4 × 11.3 cm.)

Expressing pleasure in the Shrove Tuesday dinner party given by Dukes.

G488 To Peter Russell   FABER AND FABER, LTD., 24 RUSSELL SQUARE, LONDON, W.C.1   10 February 1948

T. L. s. 1 p. (20.7 × 17.6 cm.)

On the publication of Pound's *Cantos* in New York and London.

G489 To Ronald Bottrall   FABER AND FABER, LTD., 24 RUSSELL SQUARE, LONDON, W.C.1   12 February 1948

T. L. s. "T. S. E." 2 pp. (26.4 × 20.8 cm.)

On *Palisades of Fear*, which Eliot is returning with marginal comments. The typescript with Eliot's comments is F37.

G490 To Peter Russell   FABER AND FABER, LTD., 24 RUSSELL SQUARE, LONDON, W.C.1   16 February 1948

T. L. s. 1 p. (20.7 ×17.6 cm.)

Sending Eliot's 1945 article on Pound in Italian translation since a copy of the English version is not at hand.

G491 To Henry Treece   FABER AND FABER, LTD., 24 RUSSELL SQUARE, LONDON, W.C.1   16 February 1948

T. L. s. 1 p. (20.7 × 17.6 cm.)

On Treece's intended dedication of the Swinburne work to Eliot.

G492 To Philip Mairet   FABER AND FABER, LTD., 24 RUSSELL SQUARE, LONDON, W.C.1   16 February 1948

T. L. s. "T. S. E." 1 p. (20.2 × 17.6 cm.)

Enclosing and commenting on the review which appeared in *The New English Weekly* on March 4th, under the title "Our Culture."

G493 To Philip Mairet   FABER AND FABER, LTD., 24 RUSSELL SQUARE, LONDON, W.C.1   23 February 1948

T. L. s. "T. S. E." 1 p. (20.7 × 17.6 cm.)

Asking Mairet if he will give his opinion of a manuscript concerning a biological and agrarian approach to social problems.

G494 To George Barker   FABER AND FABER, LTD., 24 RUSSELL SQUARE, LONDON, W.C.1   4 March 1948

T. L. s. 1 p. (25.3 × 20.2 cm.)

On the tactical question of publishing a new poem by Barker separately before the appearance of *News of the World*.

G495 To Barbara Cooper   FABER AND FABER, LTD., 24 RUSSELL SQUARE, LONDON, W.C.1   8 April 1948

T. L. s. 1 p. (20.2 × 17.6 cm.)

Granting permission to reprint "Cultural Diversity and European Unity" in an English number of *Prisma*, a periodical published in South Germany.

G496 To Ronald Bottrall   FABER AND FABER, LTD., 24 RUSSELL SQUARE, LONDON, W.C.1   8 April 1948

T. L. s. "Tom" 1 p. (25.3 × 20.3 cm.)

On Eliot's present restricted plans for travel.

G497 To W. F. Jackson Knight   FABER AND FABER, LTD., 24 RUSSELL SQUARE, LONDON, W.C.1.   3 May 1948

T. L. s. 1 p. (20.7 × 17.5 cm.)

Replying to an inquiry about poems submitted by "Mr. Whitehouse."

G498 To W. F. Jackson Knight   FABER AND FABER, LTD., 24 RUSSELL SQUARE, LONDON, W.C.1   4 May 1948

T. L. s. 1 p. (20.6 × 17.5 cm.)

On Eliot's personal interest in the subject which Jackson Knight has chosen for the presidential address to the Virgil Society.

G499 To Philip Mairet   FABER AND FABER, LTD., 24 RUSSELL SQUARE, LONDON, W.C.1   11 May 1948

T. L. s. "T.S.E." 1 p. (25.4 × 20.4 cm.)

Asking for advice on a suggestion that Faber publish in translation some of Goethe's scientific writing.

G500 To Philip Mairet   FABER AND FABER, LTD., 24 RUSSELL SQUARE, LONDON, W.C.1   22 May 1948

T. L. s. "T.S.E." 1 p. (25.5 × 20.4 cm.)

Declining the invitation to reply to an article in *The New English Weekly* which seems to attack Eliot's thought as "reactionary."

G501 To Peter Russell   FABER AND FABER, LTD., 24 RUSSELL SQUARE, LONDON, W.C.1   27 May 1948

T. L. s. 1 p. (26.4 × 20.8 cm.)

On the relation of Pound's Canto VIII to *The Waste Land*. Pound saw *The Waste Land* in a draft copy in January 1922.

G502 To Peter Russell   FABER AND FABER, LTD., 24 RUSSELL SQUARE, LONDON, W.C.1   31 May 1948

T. L. s. "Mary Bland (Mrs.) Secretary to Mr. T. S. Eliot"   1 p. (20.2 × 17.5 cm.)

Sending a copy of *Cronos*, with an article on Pound by Harold Watts.

G503 To Henry Treece   FABER AND FABER, LTD., 24 RUSSELL SQUARE, LONDON, W.C.1   1 June 1948

T. L. s. "T.S.E." 1 p. (20.7 × 17.5 cm.)

Expressing interest in listening to Treece's play which the B.B.C. is to broadcast June 7th.

G504 To Austin Clarke   FABER AND FABER, LTD., 24 RUSSELL SQUARE, LONDON, W.C.1   14 June 1948

T. L. s. 1 p. (20.7 × 17.5 cm.)

On the recent production of *Sweeney Agonistes* in Dublin.

G505 To Henry Treece   FABER AND FABER, LTD., 24 RUSSELL SQUARE, LONDON, W.C.1   21 June 1948

T. L. s. 1 p. (20.7 × 17.8 cm.)

Promising to recommend Treece for a job with the B.B.C.

G506 To Marion van Doorn [sic] [Mrs. E. McKnight Kauffer]   FABER AND FABER, LTD., 24 RUSSELL SQUARE, LONDON, W.C.1   28 July 1948

T. L. s. "Tom" (20.7 × 17.5 cm.)

On Eliot's forthcoming arrival in New York.

G507 To Marion van Doorn [sic] [Mrs. E. McKnight Kauffer]   FABER AND FABER, LTD., 24 RUSSELL SQUARE, LONDON, W.C.1   15 August 1948

T. L. s. "Tom" 1 p. (20.7 × 17.5 cm.) with envelope

Welcoming the possibility of meeting at the dock in New York, before going to Princeton.

G508 To Ronald [Bottrall] FABER AND FABER, LTD., 24 RUSSELL SQUARE, LONDON, W.C.1   16 August 1948

T. L. s. "T.S.E." 1 p. (25.4 × 20.3 cm.)

Introducing Linda Melton to Bottrall in Rome.

G509 To Peter Russell FABER AND FABER, LTD., 24 RUSSELL SQUARE, LONDON, W.C.1   10 September 1948

T. L. s. "Mary Bland (Mrs.) Secretary to Mr. T. S. Eliot" 1 p. (20.4 × 17.6 cm.)

On some pamphlets enclosed, and "Alfred Venison," suspected as a pseudonym of Ezra Pound.

G510 To Ronald Bottrall   FABER AND FABER, LTD., 24 RUSSELL SQUARE, LONDON, W.C.1   14 September 1948

T. L. s. 1 p. (25.4 × 20.3 cm.)

Expressing thanks for the letter about Linda Melton, and promising to see Allen Tate about the publication of Bottrall in America.

G511 To Philip Mairet FABER AND FABER, LTD., 24 RUSSELL SQUARE, LONDON, W.C.1   20 September 1948

T. L. s. 1 p. (205.4 × 20.3 cm.)

On Mairet's receiving a review copy of *The Pisan Cantos* published in New York, before the Faber edition has appeared.

G512 To Henry Treece FABER AND FABER, LTD., 24 RUSSELL SQUARE, LONDON, W.C.1   21 September 1948

T. L. s. 1 p. (20.7 × 17.6 cm.)

On a manuscript of plays by Treece which Eliot will read after his return from America.

G513 To William Turner Levy THE INSTITUTE FOR ADVANCED STUDY, PRINCETON, NEW JERSEY   7 October 1948

T. L. s. 1 p. (28.1 × 21.7 cm.)

Asking particularly to be remembered to the Mark van Dorens. Cited in *Affectionately, T. S. Eliot*, p. 16.

G514 To William Turner Levy   THE INSTITUTE FOR ADVANCED STUDY, PRINCETON, NEW JERSEY   13 October 1948

T. L. s. 1 p. (16.6 x 14 cm.)

Promising to write when more settled and free so that Levy can come down for lunch. Cited in *Affectionately, T. S. Eliot*, p. 16.

G515 To Mrs. S. Van R. Crosby   INSTITUTE FOR ADVANCED STUDY, PRINCETON, NEW JERSEY   8 November 1948

T. L. s. 1 p. (27.9×26.6 cm.)

Expressing thanks for congratulations.

G516 To Julien Cornell [Princeton, New Jersey]   24 November 1948

T. L. carbon copy 1 p. (28×21.6 cm.)

On Eliot's visit to Pound at St. Elizabeth's Hospital. This letter is printed in *The Trial of Ezra Pound* by Julien Cornell (New York 1966), pp. 110–11.

G517 To Peter Russell   FABER AND FABER, LTD., 24 RUSSELL SQUARE, LONDON, W.C. 1   15 December 1948

T. L. s. 1 p. (20.7×17.5 cm.)

Inviting a visit to discuss a number of questions raised by Russell.

G518 To Peter Russell   FABER AND FABER, LTD., 24 RUSSELL SQUARE, LONDON, W.C.1   23 December 1948

T. L. s. 1 p. (20.7×17.5 cm.)

On [David?] Soper's study which was recommended by Wyndham Lewis.

G519 To [Philip] Mairet   FABER AND FABER, LTD., 24 RUSSELL SQUARE, LONDON, W.C.1   "St. John Evangelist [27 December]: 1948"

T. L. s. "T.S.E." 1 p. (20.6×17.5 cm.)

Sending an obituary note on Michael Roberts.

G520 To Ronald [Bottrall] FABER AND FABER, LTD., 24 RUSSELL SQUARE, LONDON, W.C.1 30 December 1948

T. L. s. 2 pp. (20.6 × 17.4 cm.)

On Eliot's commitment to complete a play for Martin Browne before next summer.

G521 To Peter Russell FABER AND FABER, LTD., 24 RUSSELL SQUARE, LONDON, W.C.1 8 February 1949

T. L. s. 1 p. (25.5 × 20.4 cm.)

On the question of Faber and Faber's reprinting the work of Ezra Pound.

G522 To Henry Treece FABER AND FABER, LTD., 24 RUSSELL SQUARE, LONDON, W.C.1 8 February 1949

T. L. s. 1 p. (25.6 × 20.4 cm.)

On the possibility of publishing plays by Treece.

G523 To Philip Mairet FABER AND FABER, LTD., 24 RUSSELL SQUARE, LONDON, W.C.1 21 February 1949

T. L. s. 1 p. (25.4 × 20.3 cm.)

On the review in *The New English Weekly*, February 17th, of *Deviation into Sense*, published by Faber and Faber.

G524 To William Turner Levy FABER AND FABER, LTD., 24 RUSSELL SQUARE, LONDON, W.C.1 23 February 1949

T. L. s. with autograph postscript 1 p. (20.8 × 17.6 cm.)

Expressing thanks for a Christmas parcel which arrived late because of the strike. Cited in *Affectionately, T. S. Eliot*, p. 17.

G525 To Peter Russell FABER AND FABER, LTD., 24 RUSSELL SQUARE, LONDON, W.C.1 14 March 1949

T. L. s. 1 p. (25.5 × 20.2 cm.)

On the birthday volume for Ezra Pound, and Eliot's desire to print all the Cantos in one volume.

G526 To Peter Russell FABER AND FABER, LTD., 24 RUSSELL SQUARE, LONDON, W.C.1   16 March 1949

T. L. s. 1 p. (25.5 × 20.3 cm.)

On Eliot's inability to commit himself this year to talk to the Pound Circle.

G527 To Peter Russell FABER AND FABER, LTD., 24 RUSSELL SQUARE, LONDON, W.C.1   31 March 1949

T. L. s. 1 p. (25.5 × 20.3 cm.)

On Fabers' unwillingness to undertake distribution of a magazine projected by Russell.

G528 To Philip Mairet FABER AND FABER, LTD., 24 RUSSELL SQUARE, LONDON, W.C.1   4 April 1949

T. L. s. "T. S. E." 1 p. (25.6 × 20.1 cm.)

On Eliot's having missed a meeting of Chandos.

G529 To William Turner Levy FABER AND FABER, LTD., 24 RUSSELL SQUARE, LONDON, W.C.1   11 April 1949

T. L. s. 1 p. (20.7 × 17.5 cm.)

Thanking Levy for his letter and Easter gift. Cited in *Affectionately, T. S. Eliot*, p. 17.

G530 To Philip Mairet FABER AND FABER, LTD., 24 RUSSELL SQUARE, LONDON, W.C.1   Easter [17 April] 1949

T. L. s. "T. S. E." 1 p. (25.6 × 20.1 cm.)

Asking if Mairet will look at a lengthy manuscript by G. I. Gurdjieff.

G531 To Philip Mairet FABER AND FABER, LTD., 24 RUSSELL SQUARE, LONDON, W.C.1   21 April 1949

T. L. s. "T. S. E." 1 p. (25.6 × 20.1 cm.)

Thanking Mairet for agreeing to look at the work by Gurdjieff.

G532 To Philip Mairet FABER AND FABER, LTD., 24 RUSSELL SQUARE, LONDON, W.C.1 11 June 1949

T. L. s. "T. S. E." 1 p. (25.6 × 20.1 cm.)

Asking if Mairet will report on another book in the same field as Gai Eaton's *The Richest Vein*, which Mairet read earlier.

G533 To F. R. Leavis FABER AND FABER, LTD., 24 RUSSELL SQUARE, LONDON, W.C.1 12 July 1949

T. L. s. 1 p. (24.9 × 20.3 cm.)

Acknowledging Leavis's recommendations of John Speirs's manuscript, *Chaucer the Maker*, published by Faber and Faber in 1951.

G534 To Edith Sitwell FABER AND FABER, LTD., 24 RUSSELL SQUARE, LONDON, W.C.1 4 August 1949

T. L. s. "Mary Bland Secretary to Mr. T. S. Eliot" 1 p. (20.8 × 17.5 cm.)

Acknowledging receipt of a letter in Eliot's absence.

G535 To G. Wilson Knight FABER AND FABER, LTD., 24 RUSSELL SQUARE, LONDON, W.C.1 12 August 1949

T. L. s. 1 p. (25.4 × 20.3 cm.)

Of the book on Homer being written by W. F. Jackson Knight.

G536 To Philip Mairet 24 RUSSELL SQUARE, LONDON, W.C.1 19 August 1949

T. L. s. "T. S. E." 1 p. (20.7 × 17.8 cm.)

Acknowledging receipt and expressing concern about a letter from [Wyndham?] Lewis which Mairet had sent to Eliot.

G537 To Edith [Sitwell] 24 RUSSELL SQUARE, LONDON, W.C.1 28 August 1949

T. L. s. "Tom" 1 p. (20.6 × 17.7 cm.)

On the parties which Eliot attended recently in Edinburgh with Scottish dramatists and Scottish poets.

G538 To Edith Sitwell 24 Russell Square, London, W.C.1
1 September 1949

T. L. s. "Tom" 1 p. (20.4 × 17.5 cm.)

Accepting an invitation.

G539 To Henry Sherek Faber and Faber, ltd., 24 Russell Square,
London, W.C.1 20 September 1949

T. L. s. 2 pp. (25.5 × 20.4 cm.)

Replying to Sherek's proposal about producing *The Cocktail Party* in
New York.

G540 To Edith [Sitwell] 24 Russell Square, London, W.C.1 20
September 1949

T. L. s. "Tom" 1 p. (20.2 × 17.5 cm.)

On receiving a copy of *The Canticle of the Rose.*

G541 To Edith [Sitwell] Faber and Faber, ltd., 24 Russell Square,
London, W.C.1 26 September 1949

T. L. s. "Tom" 1 p. (20.6 × 17.3 cm.)

Declining an invitation to lunch.

G542 To Philip Mairet Faber and Faber, Ltd., 24 Russell Square,
London, W.C.1 29 September 1949

T. L. s. "T.S.E." 1 p. (20.8 × 17.7 cm.)

Asking him to read and report on a new book by Langmead Casserley.

G543 To W. F. Jackson Knight Faber and Faber, Ltd., 24 Russell
Square, London, W.C.1 20 October 1949

T. L. s. 1 p. (25.4 × 20.3 cm.)

Expressing regret that he is unable to take the chair for Jackson Knight when Knight delivers the Presidential address to the Virgil Society.

G544 To Philip Mairet FABER AND FABER, LTD., 24 RUSSELL SQUARE, LONDON, W.C.1 24 October 1949

T. L. s. "T.S.E." 1 p. (20.8 × 17.6 cm.)

About the *Christian Frontier* scheme.

G545 To M[ary]. Trevelyan FABER AND FABER, LTD., 24 RUSSELL SQUARE, LONDON, W.C.1 26 October 1949 *postmark*

T. P. C. (8.5 × 13.8 cm.)

To remind her to see "Ghosh," and promising a copy of Helen Gardner's *Art of T. S. Eliot.*

G546 To Henry Treece FABER AND FABER, LTD., 24 RUSSELL SQUARE, LONDON, W.C.1 26 October 1949

T. L. s. 2 pp. (25.4 x 20.3 cm.)

On the possibility of publishing Treece's plays.

G547 To William Turner Levy FABER AND FABER, LTD., 24 RUSSELL SQUARE, LONDON, W.C.1 28 October 1949

T. L. s. "Valerie Fletcher Secretary to Mr. T. S. Eliot" 1 p. (20.7 × 17.6 cm.)

Acknowledging arrival of a Christmas food parcel.

G548 To Denis ApIvor FABER AND FABER, LTD., 24 RUSSELL SQUARE, LONDON, W.C.1 12 December 1949

T. L. s. 2 pp. (25.5 × 20.4 cm.)

On the musical setting for *The Hollow Men.*

G549 To Henry Treece FABER AND FABER, LTD., 24 RUSSELL SQUARE, LONDON, W.C.1 29 December 1949

T. L. s. 2 pp. (25.4 × 20.3 cm.)

On publishing certain plays by Treece.

G550 To William Turner Levy FABER AND FABER, LTD., 24 RUSSELL SQUARE, LONDON, W.C.1 3 January 1950

T. L. s. 2 pp. (20.7 × 17.5 cm.)

On Eliot's forthcoming voyage to South Africa, chiefly for rest and relaxation. Cited in *Affectionately, T. S. Eliot*, pp. 17–18.

G551 To [Henry] Sherek 26 January 1950

T. copy of Western Union Cablegram from "FABBAF"

Accepting contract for recording *The Cocktail Party.*

G552 To Henry Sherek FABER AND FABER, LTD., 24 RUSSELL SQUARE, LONDON, W.C.1 6 March 1950 TSE/MDG

T. L. s 1 p. (26.6 × 17.5 cm.)

Acknowledging receipt of advance payment for recording of *The Cocktail Party.*

G553 To Edith [Sitwell] 24 RUSSELL SQUARE, LONDON, W.C.1 11 March 1950

T. L. s. "Tom" 1 p. (20.6 × 17.7 cm.)

Concerning affairs of mutual friends.

G554 To [Maria Cristina] Chambers FABER AND FABER, LTD., 24 RUSSELL SQUARE, LONDON, W.C.1 20 March 1950

T. L. s. in photocopy 1 p. (20.3 × 18 cm.)

Thanking her for praise of *The Cocktail Party.*

G555 To Henry Sherek FABER AND FABER, LTD., 24 RUSSELL SQUARE, LONDON, W.C.1 24 March 1950

T. L. unsigned after the close "Yours sincerely" 2 pp. (25.4 × 20.4 cm.)

Rejecting a proposal of John Chapman about *The Cocktail Party.*

G556 To George Barker FABER AND FABER, LTD., 24 RUSSELL SQUARE, LONDON, W.C.1 24 March 1950

T. L. s. 1 p. (20.8 × 17.5 cm.)

Expressing pleasure in Barker's new book *News of the World* and promising to inquire about an award from the Royal Society of Literature.

G557 To Henry Treece   FABER AND FABER, LTD., 24 RUSSELL SQUARE, LONDON, W.C.1   30 March 1950

T. L. s. "Valerie Fletcher Secretary to Mr. Eliot" 1 p. (20.7 × 17.5 cm.)

Giving permission to use Eliot's name as a reference.

G558 To Henry Sherek   FABER AND FABER, LTD., 24 RUSSELL SQUARE, LONDON, W.C.1   11 April 1950

T. L. s. 2 pp. (25.4 × 20.3 cm.)

Expressing interest in the German translation of *The Family Reunion* and in the success of a recent production in Düsseldorf.

G559 To Mark Reinsberg   FABER AND FABER, LTD., 24 RUSSELL SQUARE, LONDON, W.C.1   19 April 1950

T. L. s. 1 p. (20.7 × 17.5 cm.) with envelope

On Eliot's very slight acquaintance with Margaret Anderson.

G560 To George Barker   FABER AND FABER, LTD., 24 RUSSELL SQUARE, LONDON, W.C.1   15 May 1950

T. L. s. 2 pp. (25.4 × 20.3 cm.)

On the expectation that Faber eventually will publish Barker's collected poems. *Collected Poems 1930–1955* was published in 1957.

G561 To Ronald Duncan   FABER AND FABER, LTD., 24 RUSSELL SQUARE, LONDON, W.C.1   16 May 1950

T. L. s "Tom" 2 pp. (25.4 × 20.2 cm.)

On Eliot's considering Suhrkamp as the publisher of his work in German.

G562 To George Barker   FABER AND FABER, LTD., 24 RUSSELL SQUARE, LONDON, W.C.1   17 May 1950

T. P. C. s. "Valerie Fletcher Secretary to Mr. Eliot" (8.4 × 13.8 cm.)

Reporting that Barker's books *Calamiterror* and *Eros in Dogma* are still in print.

G563 To Henry Sherek FABER AND FABER, LTD., 24 RUSSELL SQUARE, LONDON, W.C.1   1 June 1950

T. L. s. 1 p. (25.4 × 20.3 cm.)

Gratefully accepting Sherek's suggestion that Eliot use an accountant.

G564 To Philip Mairet FABER AND FABER, LTD., 24 RUSSELL SQUARE, LONDON, W.C.1   1 June 1950

T. L. s. "T. S. E." with autograph postscript 1 p. (25.5 × 20 cm.)

Asking his opinion of publishing a book on Alberta.

G565 To Henry Treece FABER AND FABER, LTD., 24 RUSSELL SQUARE, LONDON, W.C.1   8 June 1950

T. L. s. 1 p. (20.7 × 17.5 cm.)

On the forthcoming production of Treece's play *The Barkeley Tragedy*.

G566 To Henry Treece FABER AND FABER, LTD., 24 RUSSELL SQUARE, LONDON, W.C.1   22 June 1950

T. L. s. 1 p. (25.4 × 20.3 cm.)

On a new volume of poems by Treece which Eliot has given one reading, and now wishes to wait a few weeks before tackling again.

G567 To Henry Sherek FABER AND FABER, 24 RUSSELL SQUARE, LONDON, W.C.1   17 July 1950

T. L. s. "Tom" 1 p. (25.4 × 20.4 cm.)

On Eliot's desire to attend the hundredth performance of *The Cocktail Party*, especially to bid farewell to Rex Harrison.

G568 To G. Wilson Knight FABER AND FABER, LTD., 24 RUSSELL SQUARE, LONDON, W.C.1   15 August 1950

T. L. s. 1 p. (20.6 × 17.5 cm.)

Replying to Wilson Knight's question about the propriety of his allusion to Eliot in the introduction to *The Imperial Theme*.

G569 To Henry Sherek   FABER AND FABER, LTD., 24 RUSSELL SQUARE, LONDON, W.C.1   21 August 1950

T. L. s. 1 p. (20.8 × 17.5 cm.)

Agreeing to Sherek's subletting rights for the Irish production of *The Cocktail Party*.

G570 To Klaus W. Jonas   FABER AND FABER, LTD., 24 RUSSELL SQUARE, LONDON, W.C.1   29 August 1950

T. L. s. 1 p. (20.9 × 17.6 cm.)

Declining an invitation to contribute to a volume of criticism on Somerset Maugham.

G571 To Edith Sitwell   FABER AND FABER, LTD., 24 RUSSELL SQUARE, LONDON, W.C.1   29 August 1950

T. L. s. "Tom" 1 p. (25.5 × 20.4 cm.)

Concerning Kenneth Patchen.

G572 To William Turner Levy   FABER AND FABER, LTD., 24 RUSSELL SQUARE, LONDON, W.C.1   31 August 1950

T. L. s. 1 p. (20.8 × 17.5 cm.)

On Eliot's plan to go directly to Chicago early in December, but to stop in New York several nights before his return voyage. Cited in *Affectionately, T. S. Eliot*, p. 18.

G573 To Edith [Sitwell]   24 RUSSELL SQUARE, LONDON, W.C.1   2 September 1950

T. L. s. "Tom" 1 p. (20.5 × 17.7 cm.)

Accepting an inscribed copy of *A Book of the Winter*.

G574 To Geoffrey Barry   FABER AND FABER, LTD., 24 RUSSELL SQUARE,

LONDON, W.C.1 5 September 1950

T. L. s. 1 p. (20.3 × 17.5 cm.)

Inviting Barry to lunch.

G575 To Geoffrey Barry FABER AND FABER, LTD., 24 RUSSELL SQUARE, W.C.1 11 September 1950

T. L. s. "Valerie Fletcher Secretary to Mr. Eliot" 1 p. (20.3 × 17.5 cm.)

Arranging to meet for lunch at 1 o'clock Friday.

G576 To William Turner Levy FABER AND FABER, LTD., 24 RUSSELL SQUARE, LONDON, W.C.1 14 September 1950

T. L. s. with autograph correction 1 p. (20.6 × 17.5 cm.)

Asking Levy to convey Eliot's condolences to Robinson Jeffers.

G577 To William Turner Levy THE UNIVERSITY OF CHICAGO, CHICAGO 37, ILLINOIS 20 October 1950

T. L. s. 1 p. (27.3 × 21.6 cm.)

On Eliot's sympathy for Robinson Jeffers upon the loss of his wife, and for the distress which he suffered during the past year or two.

G578 To Henry Sherek THE UNIVERSITY OF CHICAGO, CHICAGO 37, ILLINOIS 1 November 1950

T. L. s. "Tom" 1 p. (26.6 × 18.4 cm.)

About an unlicensed production of *The Cocktail Party* in Mexico City.

G579 To Rayner Heppenstall FABER AND FABER, LTD., 24 RUSSELL SQUARE, LONDON, W.C.1 8 November 1950

T. L. s. "Valerie Fletcher Secretary to Mr. Eliot" 1 p. (20.6 × 17.5 cm.)

Acknowledging receipt of a letter during Eliot's absence.

G580 To Christopher Morley THE UNIVERSITY OF CHICAGO, CHICAGO 37, ILLINOIS 10 November 1950

T. L. s. "Tom" 1 p. (27.3 × 21.6 cm.)

Of the controversy over a possible Sherlock Holmes exhibition at the Festival of Britain in 1951.

G581 To William Turner Levy FABER AND FABER, LTD., 24 RUSSELL SQUARE, LONDON, W.C.1 15 November 1950

T. L. s. "Valerie Fletcher Secretary to Mr. Eliot" 1 p. (20.6 × 17.5 cm.)

Thanking Levy for the food parcel which arrived during Eliot's absence.

G582 To Henry Sherek 13 Kirkland Street, Cambridge 38, Massachusetts 29 November 1950 TSE/hc

T. Air Letter s. "Tom" (30.4 × 18.5 cm.)

Expressing surprise that Sherek does not control right for all English-speaking productions of *The Cocktail Party*.

G583 To Rayner Heppenstall FABER AND FABER, LTD., 24 RUSSELL SQUARE, LONDON, W.C.1 28 December 1950

T. L. s. 1 p. (25.4 × 20.3 cm.)

Replying to the inquiry about recording *Ash-Wednesday* for broadcast.

G584 To Geoffrey Barry FABER AND FABER, LTD., 24 RUSSELL SQUARE, LONDON, W.C.1 12 January 1951

T. L. s. 1 p. (20.3 × 17.4 cm.)

Expressing thanks for a Christmas parcel.

G585 To Henry Sherek FABER AND FABER, LTD., 24 RUSSELL SQUARE, LONDON, W.C.1 16 January 1951

T. L. s. "Tom" 1 p. (20.6 × 17.5 cm.)

On attending the final performance of *The Cocktail Party*, February 10th.

G586 To Rayner Heppenstall FABER AND FABER, LTD., 24 RUSSELL SQUARE, LONDON, W.C.1 7 February 1951

T. L. s. 1 p. (20.6 × 17.5 cm.)

Asking what the B.B.C. might pay for the planned recording of *Ash-Wednesday*.

G587 To Henry Sherek FABER AND FABER, LTD., 24 RUSSELL SQUARE, LONDON, W.C.1 22 February 1951

T. L. s. "Tom" 1 p. (20.6 × 17.5 cm.)

On the doctor's order to restrict Eliot's engagements.

G588 To William Turner Levy FABER AND FABER, LTD., 24 RUSSELL SQUARE, LONDON, W.C.1 12 March 1951

T. L. s. with autograph postscript 1 p. (20.6 × 17.5 cm.)

On Eliot's being kept several days in a clinic, and the plan to go South, either to Spain or Italy. Cited in *Affectionately, T. S. Eliot*, p. 23.

G589 To Terence Tiller FABER AND FABER, LTD., 24 RUSSELL SQUARE, LONDON, W.C.1 21 May 1951

T. L. s. 1 p. (20.4 × 17.7 cm.)

On plans for recording *Ash-Wednesday*.

G590 To Edith [Sitwell] 24 RUSSELL SQUARE, [LONDON,] W.C.1 9 June 1951

T. L. s. "Tom" 1 p. (20.6 × 17.7 cm.)

On Bernard Shaw.

G591 To Henry Treece FABER AND FABER, LTD., 24 RUSSELL SQUARE, W.C.1 26 June 1951

T. L. s. with autograph correction 2 pp. (25.4 × 20.4 cm.)

Commenting on poems for the new volume by Treece.

G592 To Ronald Bottrall FABER AND FABER, LTD., 24 RUSSELL SQUARE, W.C.1 3 July 1951

T. L. s. "Tom" 1 p. (25.3 × 20.1 cm.)

Replying to Bottrall's question about being unrepresented in *The Faber Book of Modern Verse.*

G593 To Ronald Bottrall   FABER AND FABER, LTD., 24 RUSSELL SQUARE, LONDON, W.C.1   9 July 1951

T. L. s. "Tom" 1 p. (20.3 × 17.6 cm.)

Promising to recall Bottrall's name to whoever revises *The Faber Book of Modern Verse* in the future.

G594 To Henry Treece   FABER AND FABER, LTD., 24 RUSSELL SQUARE, LONDON, W.C.1   9 July 1951

T. L. s. 1 p. (20.4 × 17.4 cm.)

Expressing hope of producing Treece's book in early spring.

G595 To Louis Zukofsky   FABER AND FABER, LTD., 24 RUSSELL SQUARE, LONDON, W.C.1   18 July 1951

T. L. s. 1 p. (25.4 × 20.4 cm.)

On Zukofsky's story *Ferdinand.*

G596 To Henry Treece   FABER AND FABER, LTD., 24 RUSSELL SQUARE, LONDON, W.C.1   18 July 1951

T. L. s. with autograph correction 1 p. (25.5 × 20.3 cm.)

On the possibility of publishing a play commissioned for performance at Lincoln Cathedral in 1953.

G597 To Henry Treece   FABER AND FABER, LTD., 24 RUSSELL SQUARE, LONDON, W.C.1   1 August 1951

T. L. s. with autograph correction 1 p. (25.5 × 20.3 cm.)

On revisions by Treece for the new volume of his poems.

G598 To Henry Sherek   FABER AND FABER, LTD., 24 RUSSELL SQUARE, LONDON, W.C.1   31 August 1951

T. L. s. "Tom" 1 p. (20.4 × 17.7 cm.)

Of plans for a holiday in Switzerland.

G599 To Geoffrey Barry FABER AND FABER, LTD., 24 RUSSELL SQUARE, LONDON, W.C.1 4 October 1951

T. L. s. 1 p. (25.4 × 20.4 cm.)

On Eliot's pleasure with the reception of *The Cocktail Party* in South Africa.

G600 To Henry Sherek FABER AND FABER, LTD., 24 RUSSELL SQUARE, LONDON, W.C.1 9 October 1951

T. L. s. 1 p. (25.5 × 24.3 cm.)

Expressing thanks for clippings on *The Cocktail Party*.

G601 To Louis Zukofsky FABER AND FABER, LTD., 24 RUSSELL SQUARE, LONDON, W.C.1 10 October 1951

T. L. s. 1 p. (25.4 × 20.3 cm.)

On Zukofsky's question whether Faber might publish a volume of his collected poems.

G602 To Edith Sitwell FABER AND FABER, LTD., 24 RUSSELL SQUARE, LONDON, W.C.1 22 October 1951

T. L. s. "Tom" 1 p. (20.3 × 17.5 cm.)

On William Carlos Williams.

G603 To Edith Sitwell FABER AND FABER, LTD., 24 RUSSELL SQUARE, LONDON, W.C.1 13 November 1951

T. L. s. "Tom" 1 p. (25.5 × 20.3 cm.)

Commenting on allusions to himself in the autobiography of William Carlos Williams

G604 To Louis Zukofsky FABER AND FABER, LTD., 24 RUSSELL SQUARE, LONDON, W.C.1 21 November 1951

T. L. s. 1 p. (20.5 × 17.8 cm.)

On possibly meeting Zukofsky and his wife when Eliot visits New York in May or June.

G605 To Philip Mairet FABER AND FABER, LTD., 24 RUSSELL SQUARE, LONDON, W.C.1 21 November 1951

T. L. s. 1 p. (20.6 × 17.5 cm.)

Apologizing for the tone of a recent message explaining that he could not attend a meeting of Chandos.

G606 To Philip Mairet FABER AND FABER, LTD., 24 RUSSELL SQUARE, LONDON, W.C.1 28 November 1951 *postmark*

T. P. C. s. "T. S. E." (8.6 × 14.1 cm.)

Commenting on André Gide and on anyone's attempt to set a measure for sincerity.

G607 To G. Wilson Knight FABER AND FABER, LTD., 24 RUSSELL SQUARE, LONDON, W.C.1 13 December 1951

T. L. s. 2 pp. (25.4 × 20.3 cm.)

Reporting that Faber and Faber probably could not reprint *The Christian Renaissance* in a cheap edition.

G608 To G. Wilson Knight FABER AND FABER, LTD., 24 RUSSELL SQUARE, LONDON, W.C.1 27 December 1951

T. L. s. 1 p. (20.4 × 17.4 cm.)

Regretfully confirming the opinion already expressed about reprinting *The Christian Renaissance*.

G609 To Henry Treece FABER AND FABER, LTD., 24 RUSSELL SQUARE, LONDON, W.C.1 30 December 1951

T. L. s. 2 pp. (25.4 × 20.4 cm.)

On Treece's complaint about the blurb which Eliot had written for Treece's new book of poems.

G610 To Henry Sherek FABER AND FABER, LTD., 24 RUSSELL SQUARE,

LONDON, W.C.1   3 January 1952

T. L. s. "Tom" 1 p. (20.4 × 17.7 cm.)

Thanking Sherek for clippings and for a copy of Sherek's correspondence with *Time*.

G611 To William Turner Levy   FABER AND FABER, LTD., 24 RUSSELL SQUARE, LONDON, W.C.1   16 January 1952

T. L. s. 1 p. (25.4 × 20.3 cm.)

Thanking Levy for gifts of food, and expressing interest in his letters and activities. Cited in *Affectionately, T. S. Eliot*, p. 24.

G612 To Henry Treece   FABER AND FABER, LTD., 24 RUSSELL SQUARE, LONDON, W.C.1   23 January 1952

T. L. s. 1 p. (20.3 × 17.6 cm.)

On Eliot's continued interest in Treece's play despite the collapse of plans for a production in Lincoln Cathedral.

G613 To Ronald Bottrall   FABER AND FABER, LTD., 24 RUSSELL SQUARE, LONDON, W.C.1   7 February 1952

T. L. s. "Tom" 1 p. (20.2 × 17.5 cm.)

Declining to publish Bottrall's new poems.

G614 To Henry Treece   FABER AND FABER, LTD., 24 RUSSELL SQUARE, LONDON, W.C.1   19 February 1952

T. L. s. 1 p. (25.4 × 20.4 cm.)

On reading Treece's talk on modern poetry and on some of its details concerning individual poets between 1913 and 1918.

G615 To Ronald Duncan   FABER AND FABER, LTD., 24 RUSSELL SQUARE, LONDON, W.C.1   26 February 1952

T. L. s. "Tom" 1 p. (20.3 × 17.6 cm.)

On the possibility of Stein's producing one of Fredo's operas at Covent Garden.

G616 To Ronald Duncan FABER AND FABER, LTD., 24 RUSSELL SQUARE, LONDON, W.C.1 4 March 1952

T. L. s. "Tom" with autograph addition 1 p. (25.4 × 20.3 cm.)

On Eliot's gratitude to Duncan for writing at length on Fredo's opera; and Eliot's desire to publish Duncan's *Don Juan* when it is produced on the stage.

G17 To William Turner Levy FABER AND FABER, LTD., 24 RUSSELL SQUARE, LONDON, W.C.1 4 March 1952

T. L. s. 1 p. (25.4 × 20.3 cm.)

On the news of Reinhold Niebuhr's illness. Cited in *Affectionately, T. S. Eliot*, p. 25.

G618 To John Lehmann FABER AND FABER, LTD., 24 RUSSELL SQUARE, LONDON, W.C.1 7 April 1952

T. L. s. "Tom" 1 p. (20.3 × 17.7 cm.)

Declining an invitation to write for the B.B.C. New Soundings Programme an account of his experience in editing a literary avant-garde magazine.

G619 To Louis Zukofsky HARCOURT, BRACE AND COMPANY, INC. 383 MADISON AVENUE, NEW YORK 17 N.Y. 6 May 1952

T. L. s. 1 p. (28 × 21.6 cm.)

On Eliot's being able to meet not in Brooklyn but in Manhattan.

G620 To Henry Sherek FABER AND FABER, LTD., 24 RUSSELL SQUARE, LONDON, W.C.1 5 June 1952

T. L. s. "Tom" 1 p. (25.4 × 20.4 cm.)

Opposing the idea of making *The Cocktail Party* into a film.

G621 To Philip Mairet FABER AND FABER, LTD., 24 RUSSELL SQUARE, LONDON, W.C.1 12 June 1952

T. L. s. "T. S. E." 2 pp. (25.6 × 20 cm.)

Thanking Mairet for the current issue of *Frontier* containing an intelligent article on *Murder in the Cathedral*. *The Frontier* (Oxford) superseded *The Christian News-Letter* from 1950 to 1952.

G622 To Henry Treece FABER AND FABER, LTD., 24 RUSSELL SQUARE, LONDON, W.C.1 12 June 1952

T. L. s. 1 p. (25.5 × 20.4 cm.)

On Eliot's view that Faber and Faber have a moral claim to an option on prose fiction written by poets whom they publish.

G623 To Ronald Duncan FABER AND FABER, LTD., 24 RUSSELL SQUARE, LONDON, W.C.1 17 June 1952

T. L. s. "Tom" 1 p. (25.4 × 20.3 cm.)

On Ezra Pound's relation to Lawrence Pollinger and to Arthur V. Moore.

G624 To Henry Treece FABER AND FABER, LTD., 24 RUSSELL SQUARE, LONDON, W.C.1 25 June 1952

T. L. s. 1 p. (20.3 × 17.6 cm.)

Agreeing now that the complaint against Treece in the letter of June 12th had no foundation.

G625 To Henry Treece FABER AND FABER, LTD., 24 RUSSELL SQUARE, LONDON, W.C.1 7 July 1952

T. L. s. 1 p. (20.3 × 17.6 cm.)

Declining to think that a prize awarded to Treece would be subject to a publisher's commission.

G626 To Ronald Duncan FABER AND FABER, LTD., 24 RUSSELL SQUARE, LONDON, W.C.1 22 July 1952

T. L. s. "Tom" 1 p. (20.2 × 17.6 cm.)

Accepting an invitation to tea on the 31st.

G627 To William Turner Levy FABER AND FABER, LTD., 24 RUSSELL

Square, London, W.C.1 22 July 1952

T. Air Letter s. with autograph revision 1 p. (24.4 × 20 cm.)

On Reinhold Niebuhr's illness and future work. Cited in *Affectionately,
T. S. Eliot*, p. 31.

G628 To George Barker Faber and Faber, Ltd., 24 Russell Square,
London, W.C.1 29 July 1952

T. L. s. "T.S.E." 1 p. (20.3 × 17.6 cm.)

Concerning an appointment which Barker seeks at Leeds University.

G629 To George Barker Faber and Faber, Ltd., 24 Russell Square,
London, W.C.1 11 August 1952

T. L. s. "T. S. E." 1 p. (20.2 × 17.6 cm.)

On Eliot's not presenting Barker's name at Leeds because the fellow-
ship is already accepted by John Heath-Stubbs.

G630 To Henry Treece Faber and Faber, Ltd., 24 Russell Square,
London, W.C.1 15 August 1952

T. L. s. 2 pp. (25.4 × 20.3 cm.)

On the *Berkeley Tragedy* by Treece. Title differently spelled in G565.

G631 To Ronald Bottrall Faber and Faber, Ltd., 24 Russell Square,
London, W.C.1 18 August 1952

T. L. s. "Tom" 1 p. (20.2 × 17.5 cm.)

On Charles Tomlinson's collection of essays by various persons, which
Eliot feels does not make a volume.

G632 To Ronald Duncan Faber and Faber, Ltd., 24 Russell Square,
London, W.C.1 17 September 1952

T. L. s. "Tom" 1 p. (20.3 × 17.6 cm.)

On Duncan's *Don Juan*, which Eliot wants in the final text when established between Ronald Duncan and the producer.

G633 To William Turner Levy Faber and Faber, Ltd., 24 Russell

SQUARE, LONDON, W.C.1   3 October 1952

T. Air Letter s. 1 p. (24.4 × 20 cm.)

Thanking him for an aromatic cheese which was sent, Eliot suspects, for his birthday (26 September).

G634 To Ronald Duncan   FABER AND FABER, LTD., 24 RUSSELL SQUARE, LONDON, W.C.1   13 October 1952

T. L. s. "Tom" 1 p. (20.4 × 17.6 cm.)

On publishing *Don Juan* by the spring of 1954, regardless of theatrical production, so that it will not appear too closely after *The Rape of Lucretia.*

G635 To Geoffrey Barry   FABER AND FABER, LTD., 24 RUSSELL SQUARE, LONDON, W.C.1   15 October 1952

T. Air Letter s. (24.3 × 19.9 cm.)

On the appeal to young readers of Rupert Brooke and A. E. Housman.

G636 To Ronald Duncan   FABER AND FABER, LTD., 24 RUSSELL SQUARE, LONDON, W.C.1   18 October 1952

T. L. s. "Tom" with autograph addition 1 p. (20.3 × 17.6 cm.)

Replying to a question about whom to meet in America, Eliot thinks first of Marianne Moore, Mr. and Mrs. Edward McKnight Kauffer, Robert Giroux, Huntington Cairns, Katherine Biddle, and Conrad Aiken.

G637 To Robert Giroux   FABER AND FABER, LTD., 24 RUSSELL SQUARE, LONDON, W.C.1   18 October 1952

T. L. s. "Tom" 1 p. (20.1 × 17.5 cm.)

Introducing Robert Duncan as a friend, a poet, and a dramatist.

G638 To Henry Sherek   FABER AND FABER, LTD., 24 RUSSELL SQUARE, LONDON, W.C.1   28 October 1952

T. L. s. "Tom" 2 pp. (25.4 × 20.3 cm.)

On the idea of producing three plays at the Edinburgh Festival of 1953
—*The Family Reunion, The Cocktail Party*, and Eliot's new play.

G639 To Robert H. Bagley FABER AND FABER, LTD., 24 RUSSELL SQUARE, LONDON, W.C.1 3 November 1952

T. Air Letter s. 1 p. (24.3 × 19.9 cm.)

Refusing permission to film "The Love Song of J. Alfred Prufrock."

G640 To Philip Mairet FABER AND FABER, LTD., 24 RUSSELL SQUARE, LONDON, W.C.1 18 November 1952 TSE/MDG

T. L. s. 1 p. (20.4 × 17.7 cm.)

Inviting Mairet to dinner on December 2nd.

G641 To William Turner Levy FABER AND FABER, LTD., 24 RUSSELL SQUARE, LONDON, W.C.1 2 December 1952

T. Air Letter s. 1 p. (24.3 × 20 cm.)

Expressing interest in publishing Reinhold Niebuhr in England. Cited in *Affectionately, T. S. Eliot*, p. 32.

G642 To Edith Sitwell FABER AND FABER, LTD., 24 RUSSELL SQUARE, LONDON, W.C.1 12 December 1952

T. Air Letter s. "Tom (T. S. Eliot)" (24 × 19.9 cm.)

Inviting her to suggest a more suitable choice of her poems than the Faber anthologists have made.

G643 To Henry Sherek FABER AND FABER, LTD., 24 RUSSELL SQUARE, LONDON, W.C.1 12 December 1952

T. L. s. "Tom" 1 p. (25.4 × 20.3 cm.)

On Eliot's willingness to cut the text of *The Confidential Clerk*, cutting (though painful) being easier than amplifying.

G644 To William Turner Levy FABER AND FABER, LTD., 24 RUSSELL SQUARE, LONDON, W.C.1 15 December 1952

T. Air Letter s. 1 p. (24.4 × 20 cm.)

Expressing hope to publish Reinhold Niebuhr. Cited in *Affectionately, T. S. Eliot*, p. 33.

G645 To Philip Mairet FABER AND FABER, LTD., 24 RUSSELL SQUARE, LONDON, W.C.1 17 December 1952

T. L. s. with autograph postscript 1 p. (20.4 × 17.7 cm.)

Thanking Mairet for the December *Frontier* with the article by Michael Tippett.

G646 To Mrs. Jacob Levy 19 Carlyle Mansions, Cheyne Walk, London, S.W.3 27 December 1952

T. Air Letter s. 1 p. (24.4 × 19.8 cm.)

Thanking Mrs. Levy for gifts of food, especially the fudge. Cited in *Affectionately, T. S. Eliot*, p. 33–4.

G647 To R[onald] Duncan [1952?]

A. N. s. "T. S. E."

Written on a copy of *The New Leader*, January 28, 1952, and inquiring about an article entitled "India's New Gandhi," on Acharya Vinobha Bhave.

G648 To Edith Sitwell FABER AND FABER, LTD., 24 RUSSELL SQUARE, LONDON, W.C.1 2 January 1953

T. Air Letter s. "Tom" (24 × 19.8 cm.)

On the new choice of her poems by [John] Heath-Stubbs and [David] Wright for a Faber anthology.

G649 To Reinhold Niebuhr FABER AND FABER, LTD., 24 RUSSELL SQUARE, LONDON, W.C.1 7 January 1953

T. Air Letter s. 1 p. (24.3 × 19.9 cm.)

Thanking Niebuhr for *The Irony of American History*.

G650 To Ronald Bottrall FABER AND FABER, LTD., 24 RUSSELL SQUARE,

London, W.C.1   13 January 1953

T. L. s. "Tom" 1 p. (20.2 × 17.6 cm.)

On the Italian translation of *Four Quartets*.

G651 To Henry Sherek   FABER AND FABER, LTD., 24 RUSSELL SQUARE, LONDON, W.C.1   6 February 1953

T. L. s. "T. S. E." 1 p. (20.3 × 17.6 cm.)

On casting roles in *The Confidential Clerk*; Act III will be ready for typing this week.

G652 To Henry Sherek   FABER AND FABER, LTD., 24 RUSSELL SQUARE, LONDON, W.C.1   10 February 1953

T. L. s. "T. S. E." 1 p. (20.3 × 17.6 cm.)

On Sherek's suggestion of Peter Gray for a role in *The Confidential Clerk*.

G653 To Charles Norman   FABER AND FABER, LTD., 24 RUSSELL SQUARE, LONDON, W.C.1   25 February 1953

T. L. s. 1 p. (20.3 × 17.6 cm.)

On Norman's poems and the difficulty of publishing an American poet who has not already built up a public in the United States.

G654 To George Barker   FABER AND FABER, LTD., 24 RUSSELL SQUARE, LONDON, W.C.1   26 February 1953

T. L. s. 2 pp. (25.4 × 20.3 cm.)

Questioning details of diction in "A Vision of Beasts and Gods" which Faber will publish in 1954.

G655 To [Henry Sherek]   FROM MESSRS. FABER AND FABER, 24 RUSSELL SQUARE, LONDON, W.C.1   20 March 1953 [stamped as the date of receipt]

T. Note (14.3 × 10.2 cm.) with newspaper clipping

Enclosing a newspaper clipping of March 13th on Arthur Miller's conflict with the legal profession over *The Crucible*. Eliot will take the same attitude as Miller.

G656 To Henry Sherek FABER AND FABER, LTD., 24 RUSSELL SQUARE, LONDON, W.C.1 25 March 1953

T. L. s. "Tom" 2 pp. (20.3 × 17.6 cm.)

Agreeing that no part of *The Confidential Clerk* should be shown on television before the opening at Edinburgh.

G657 To Mrs. J[acob]. Levy 24 RUSSELL SQUARE, LONDON, W.C.1 27 March 1953

T. Air Letter s. 1 p. (24.3 × 20 cm.)

On Eliot's plan to visit St. Louis early in April and his hope of having a short visit with the Levys as he passes through New York.

G658 To Ashley Dukes FABER AND FABER, LTD., 24 RUSSELL SQUARE, LONDON, W.C.1 2 April 1953

T. L. s. "Tom" 1 p. (20.3 × 17.6 cm.)

Agreeing to attend and perhaps speak briefly on May 14th when Eliot's bust by Jacob Epstein will be shown.

G659 To Henry Sherek FABER AND FABER, LTD., 24 RUSSELL SQUARE, LONDON, W.C.1 2 April 1953

T. L. s. "Tom" 2 pp. (25.4 × 20.4 cm.)

Authorizing a television performance of a selection from *The Confidential Clerk*.

G660 To Mrs. J[acob]. Levy 19 Carlyle Mansions, Cheyne Walk, London, S.W.3 Easter Monday [6 April] 1953

T. Air Letter s. 1 p. (24.3 × 19.9 cm.)

Thanking Mrs. Levy for gifts.

G661 To Henry Sherek FABER AND FABER, LTD., 24 RUSSELL SQUARE, LONDON, W.C.1 7 April 1953

T. L. s. "Tom" 1 p. (20.3 × 17.6 cm.)

Thanking Sherek for the telegram of good wishes after the opening of *Murder in the Cathedral* at the Old Vic.

G662 To Henry Sherek FABER AND FABER, LTD., 24 RUSSELL SQUARE, LONDON, W.C.1   8 April 1953

T. L. s. "Tom" 2 pp. (25.4 × 20.4 cm.)

Asking for a meeting with Sherek and Martin Browne to run through the text of *The Confidential Clerk* and agree upon alterations.

G663 To Geoffrey Barry FABER AND FABER, LTD., 24 RUSSELL SQUARE, LONDON, W.C.1   21 April 1953

T. Air Letter s. (24.2 × 20 cm.)

Expressing regret that Barry cannot see the very good production of *Murder in the Cathedral* at the Old Vic.

G664 To Tom Scott FABER AND FABER, LTD., 24 RUSSELL SQUARE, LONDON, W.C.1   21 May 1953

T. L. s. 1 p. (20.4 × 17.6 cm.)

On Scott's translations of Villon, which Eliot encouraged and is pleased with.

G665 To William [Turner Levy] MRS. HENRY WARE ELIOT, 84 PRESCOTT STREET, CAMBRIDGE 38 MASSACHUSETTS   20 June 1953

T. L. s. 1 p. (17.8 × 16.1 cm.)

On Eliot's plan to arrive in New York on the 28th and leave for London the following day. Cited in *Affectionately, T. S. Eliot*, p. 34

G666 To Henry Sherek FABER AND FABER, LTD., 24 RUSSELL SQUARE, LONDON, W.C.1   15 July 1953

T. L. s. 2 pp. (25.5 × 20.5 cm.)

Criticizing Ian Hunter's proposal to make a recording of selections from *The Confidential Clerk*.

G667 To Philip Mairet FABER AND FABER, LTD., 24 RUSSELL SQUARE, LONDON, W.C.1 29 July 1953

T. L. s. "T. S. E." 1 p. (20.4 × 17.7 cm.)

Welcoming Mairet to a dress rehearsal August 24th of *The Confidential Clerk*.

G668 To Henry Sherek FABER AND FABER, LTD., 24 RUSSELL SQUARE, LONDON, W.C.1 30 July 1953

T. L. s. "Tom" 2 pp. (25.5 × 20.5 cm.)

Expressing hope that the B.B.C. will send its critic to Edinburgh and not try to produce *The Confidential Clerk* with its own performers.

G669 To Henry Sherek FABER AND FABER, LTD., 24 RUSSELL SQUARE, LONDON, W.C.1 6 August 1953

T. L. s. "Tom" 1 p. (20.3 × 17.6 cm.)

Concerning requests for the script of *The Confidential Clerk*.

G670 To Henry Sherek FABER AND FABER, LTD., 24 RUSSELL SQUARE, LONDON, W.C.1 21 September 1953 TSE/MDG

T. L. s. "Tom" 2 pp. (20.4 × 17.7 cm.)

On Sherek's telegram and the carnations, and on the party which Eliot gave after the first performance of *The Confidential Clerk*.

G671 To Mrs. Jacob Levy 19 Carlyle Mansions, Cheyne Walk, London, S.W.3 5 October 1953

T. Air Letter s. 1 p. (24.3 × 20.1 cm.)

On Eliot's birthday gifts and on his feelings upon reaching the age of 65. Cited in *Affectionately, T. S. Eliot*, pp. 44–5.

G672 To Henry Sherek FABER AND FABER, LTD., 24 RUSSELL SQUARE, LONDON, W.C.1 19 October 1953

T. L. s. "Tom" 1 p. (20.3 × 17.6 cm.)

On questions of producing *The Confidential Clerk* in America.

G673 To Ronald Duncan FABER AND FABER, LTD., 24 RUSSELL SQUARE, W.C.1 20 October 1953

T. L. s. "Tom" 1 p. (25.5 × 20.5 cm.)

Replying to an invitation to be a "Vice-President of the Taw and Torrige Festival Society."

G674 To William Turner Levy FABER AND FABER, LTD., 24 RUSSELL SQUARE, LONDON, W.C.1 14 December 1953

T. L. s. 2 pp. (25.4 × 20.3 cm.)

On Levy's book *William Barnes*; and on the word-play of *The Pogo Papers* by Walt Kelly. Cited in *Affectionately, T. S. Eliot*, pp. 45–7.

G675 To Mrs. [Jacob] Levy 24 RUSSELL SQUARE, [LONDON] W.C.1 20 December 1953

T. L. s. 2 pp. (20.6 × 17.7 cm.)

Thanking Mrs. Levy for gifts.

G676 To Marianne Moore 24 RUSSELL SQUARE, LONDON, W.C.1 23 December 1953

T. L. s. "Tom" 2 pp. (25.5 × 20.4 cm.)

Replying to a letter on Gertrude Flynn as an actress; and explaining in some detail why Faber and Faber do not wish to publish Marianne Moore's complete translation of *The Fables of La Fontaine*.

G677 To Geoffrey Barry 24 RUSSELL SQUARE, LONDON, W.C.1 18 February 1954

T. L. s. 2 pp. (20.5 × 17.7 cm.)

On the verse of "Miss de Zoete" which Barry asked Eliot to read.

G678 To Henry Sherek FABER AND FABER, LTD., 24 RUSSELL SQUARE, LONDON, W.C.1 17 March 1954

T. L. s. "Tom" 3 pp. (25.4 × 20.4 cm.)

On the reception of *The Confidential Clerk* in New York.

G679 To Hector MacQuarrie   17 March 1954

T. L. carbon copy 1 p. (25.2 × 20.2 cm.)

Replying to the inquiry about broadcasting *The Confidential Clerk* in South Africa.

G680 To C. E. Carrington FABER AND FABER, LTD., 24 RUSSELL SQUARE, LONDON, W.C.1   19 March 1954

T. L. s. with autograph revision 1 p. (25.4 × 20.4 cm.)

On Kipling and literary traditions. Carrington was writing *Rudyard Kipling: His Life and Work* (London, 1955).

G681 To Marianne Moore FABER AND FABER, LTD., 24 RUSSELL SQUARE, LONDON, W.C.1   23 March 1954

T. Air Letter s. "Tom" 2 pp. (24.4 × 20 cm.)

Expressing appreciation of the rights to make a selection from Marianne Moore's translations of La Fontaine.

G682 To Samuel L. Hynes FABER AND FABER, LTD., 24 RUSSELL SQUARE, LONDON, W.C.1   23 March 1954

T. L. s. 1 p. (25.4 × 20.4 cm.) with envelope

On Eliot's early acquaintance with the works of T. E. Hulme.

G683 To C. E. Carrington FABER AND FABER, LTD., 24 RUSSELL SQUARE, LONDON, W.C.1   26 March 1954

T. L. s. with autograph postscript 1 p. (25.5 × 20.4 cm.)

On Carrington's application to Kipling of Eliot's thought in *The Three Voices of Poetry*.

G684 To Henry Sherek FABER AND FABER, LTD., 24 RUSSELL SQUARE, LONDON, W.C.1   29 March 1954

T. L. s. "Tom" 1 p. (25.5 × 20.3 cm.)

On John Lehmann's broadcast review March 28th of *The Confidential Clerk*.

G685 To Marianne Moore 19 Carlyle Mansions, Cheyne Walk, London, S.W.3 10 April 1954

T. Air Letter s. "Tom" 1 p. (24.5 × 19.9 cm.)

On Marianne Moore's opinion of *The Confidential Clerk* as the best of Eliot's plays.

G686 To Marianne Moore Faber and Faber, Ltd., 24 Russell Square, London, W.C.1 11 May 1954

T. Air Letter s. "Tom" 1 p. (24.4 × 20 cm.)

Reassuring Marianne Moore about his health.

G687 To William Turner Levy Faber and Faber, Ltd., 24 Russell Square, London, W.C.1 11 May 1954

T. Air Letter s. 1 p. (24.4 × 20 cm.)

On the misleading reports concerning Eliot's health and Eliot's gratitude for letters, flowers, and food sent by the Levys. Cited in *Affectionately, T. S. Eliot*, p. 48.

G688 To William Turner Levy 19 Carlyle Mansions, Cheyne Walk, London, S.W.3 Whit Sunday [6 June] 1954

T. Air Letter s. with autograph postscript 1 p. (24.5 × 20 cm.)

On the use of time in youth and middle age.

G689 To Edith [Sitwell] Faber and Faber, Ltd., 24 Russell Square, London, W.C.1 11 June 1954

T. L. s. "Tom" 1 p. (25.4 × 20.3 cm.)

On Edith Sitwell's being honored by the Queen.

G690 To Philip Mairet Faber and Faber, Ltd., 24 Russell Square, London, W.C.1 16 June 1954

T. L. s. 1 p. (25.5 × 20 cm.)

On Mairet's discussion of [Frithjof] Schuon who, Eliot thinks, ought to be studied and answered by theologians, students of religion, and philosophers interested in the theory of knowledge.

G691 To Marianne Moore FABER AND FABER, LTD., 24 RUSSELL SQUARE, LONDON, W.C.1   16 June 1954

T. Air Letter s. "Tom" 1 p. (24.4 × 20 cm.)

Thanking Marianne Moore for the gift of her *La Fontaine*.

G692 To Edith [Sitwell] FABER AND FABER, LTD., 24 RUSSELL SQUARE, LONDON, W.C.1   19 June 1954

T. L. s. "Tom" 1 p. (25.6 × 20.1 cm.)

On the arrival tomorrow of Eliot's sister, who will spend three weeks on the Isle of Wight.

G693 To Cid Corman FABER AND FABER, LTD., 24 RUSSELL SQUARE, LONDON, W.C.1   21 June 1954

T. Air Letter s. 1 p. (24.4 × 20 cm.)

Replying to Corman's inquiry about publishing translations of the work of Gottfried Benn.

G694 To Henry Sherek FABER AND FABER, LTD., 24 RUSSELL SQUARE, LONDON, W.C.1   29 June 1954

T. L. s. "Tom" 2 pp. (20.4 × 17.6 cm.)

Thanking Sherek for the detective story, *The Daughter of Time*, about Richard III; and on the casting of roles for the Paris Festival and the English tour of *The Confidential Clerk*.

G695 To Tom Scott FABER AND FABER, LTD., 24 RUSSELL SQUARE, LONDON, W.C.1   30 June 1954

T. L. s. 1 p. (20.3 × 17.6 cm.)

On having read Scott's poems in the Scottish language with interest, but with imperfect knowledge.

G696 To Henry Sherek FABER AND FABER, LTD., 24 RUSSELL SQUARE, LONDON, W.C.1   27 July 1954

T. L. s. "Tom" 1 p. (25.5 × 20.4 cm.)

Returning *The Daughter of Time* by Miss Mackintosh which Eliot has read with interest because of his sympathy for the Yorkist cause.

G697 To Philip Mairet   FABER AND FABER, LTD., 24 RUSSELL SQUARE, LONDON, W.C.1   28 July 1954

T. L. s. 1 p. (25.6 × 20.5 cm.)

Thanking Mairet for the inscribed copy of [André] Benoit's book [*Le Batême Chrétien au Seconde Siècle*?] and promising not to read it until they have talked about it.

G698 To Marianne Moore   24 Russell Square, London, W.C.1   31 July 1954

T. Air Letter s. "Tom" 1 p. (24.3 × 20 cm.)

On their friend Edward McKnight Kauffer and the problem of alcoholism.

G699 To Henry Sherek   FABER AND FABER, LTD., 24 RUSSELL SQUARE, LONDON, W.C.1   18 August 1954

T. L. s. "Tom" 1 p. (25.5 × 20.4 cm.)

Returning the play *Un Nomme Judas* which Eliot has read at Sherek's request.

G700 To William Turner Levy   24 Russell Square, London, W.C.1   21 August 1954

T. Air Letter s. 1 p. (24.4 × 20 cm.)

On " 'aesthetic' high churchmanship" in contrast to that which comes from an inward movement toward ritual forms; and on reading Paul Tillich, *Systematic Theology*, Vol. I. Cited in *Affectionately, T. S. Eliot*, pp. 49–50.

G701 To Tom Scott   FABER AND FABER, LTD., 24 RUSSELL SQUARE, LONDON, W.C.1   25 August 1954

T. L. s. 2 pp. (25.4 × 20.4 cm.)

On Scott's poems in Lallans, which Eliot feels he can judge less confidently than poems in French, though more than poems in German.

G702 To Philip Mairet FABER AND FABER, LTD., 24 RUSSELL SQUARE, LONDON, W.C.1 25 August 1954

T. L. s. "T. S. E." 1 p. (20.4 × 17.7 cm.)

On first impressions of Benoit's book which seems to Eliot superior to all Western attempts to treat psychology with pseudo-scientific objectivity.

G703 To Philip Mairet FABER AND FABER, LTD., 24 RUSSELL SQUARE, LONDON, W.C.1 1 September 1954

T. L. s. "T. S. E." with autograph correction 1 p. (20.4 × 17.3 cm.)

On Eliot's concern with Benoit's book.

G704 To William Turner Levy 19 Carlyle Mansions, Cheyne Walk, London, S.W.3 St. Luke [18 October]: 1954

T. Air Letter s. 1 p. (24.4 × 19.8 cm.)

Expressing gratitude for the gift of cheese and ham; and describing Eliot's good health and his anxiety to finish the Goethe address for Hamburg. Cited in *Affectionately, T. S. Eliot*, pp. 52–3.

G705 To Marion [Mrs. E. McKnight Kauffer] 19 Carlyle Mansions, Cheyne Walk, London, S.W.3 31 October 1954

T. Air Letter s. "Tom" (24.2 × 19.8 cm.)

On the death of Edward McKnight Kauffer.

G706 To Marion [Mrs. E. McKnight Kauffer] 19 Carlyle Mansions, Cheyne Walk, London, S.W.3 7 November 1954

T. Air Letter s. "Tom" 1 p. (24.3 × 20 cm.)

On the difficulty of understanding the truth about oneself, much less about another person.

G707 To Marianne [Moore] 7 November 1954

T. L. 1 p. (25.9 × 21.5 cm.)

On Edward McKnight Kauffer; after 1946 he seemed beyond the reach of human contact.

G708 To William Turner Levy   19 Carlyle Mansions, Cheyne Walk, London, S.W.3   7 November 1954

T. Air Letter s. 1 p. (24.5 × 20 cm.)

Gratefully acknowledging Levy's remembrance of Edward McKnight Kauffer; and sending the "Ariel" Christmas poem which Eliot does not consider very well executed. Cited in *Affectionately, T. S. Eliot*, p. 53.

G709 To Denis Goacher   FABER AND FABER, LTD., 24 RUSSELL SQUARE, LONDON, W.C.1   1 December 1954

T. L. s. 1 p. (20.4 × 17.6 cm.)

Inviting Goacher to visit to discuss a proposal with regard to the work of Ezra Pound.

G710 To Philip Mairet   FABER AND FABER, LTD., 24 RUSSELL SQUARE, LONDON, W.C.1   10 December 1954

T. L. s. 1 p. (20.4 × 17.7 cm.)

On Mairet's disturbing recent letter and Eliot's desire to meet for dinner to discuss it.

G711 To William Turner Levy   19 Carlyle Mansions, Cheyne Walk, London, S.W.3   27 December 1954

T. Air Letter s. 1 p. (24.5 × 20 cm.)

On the gift of a tile which reminds Eliot of an engraved portrait of Lincoln which hung in Eliot's childhood home. A grandfather who had been active in the Civil War knew Lincoln slightly. Cited in *Affectionately, T. S. Eliot*, p. 54.

G712 To Maurice Carpenter   FABER AND FABER, LTD., 24 RUSSELL SQUARE, LONDON, W.C.1   7 January 1955

T. L. s. 1 p. (24.7 × 19.6 cm.)

On the news of Coker Court, the manor house in East Coker, Somerset.

G713 To Marion [Mrs. E. McKnight Kauffer]   19 Carlyle Mansions, Cheyne Walk, London, S.W.3   16 January 1955

T. Air Letter s. "Tom" (24.2 × 20 cm.)

Replying to a question about visiting the cemetery together where Edward McKnight Kauffer is buried.

G714 To Philip Mairet   FABER AND FABER, LTD., 24 RUSSELL SQUARE, LONDON, W.C.1   15 March 1955

T. L. s. "T. S. E." 2 pp. (25.6 × 20.4 cm.)

On Benoit's book which Eliot continues to study.

G715 To Philip Mairet   FABER AND FABER, LTD., 24 RUSSELL SQUARE, LONDON, W.C.1   23 March 1955

T. L. s. "T. S. E." 1 p. (25.5 × 20.3 cm.)

On Benoit's psychology and the poverty in it of hagiology, rites, and customs. Eliot senses a similar poverty in Irving Babbitt's Buddhism and Ezra Pound's Confucianism.

G716 To Ronald Duncan   FABER AND FABER, LTD., 24 RUSSELL SQUARE, LONDON, W.C.1   28 March 1955

T. L. s. "Valerie Fletcher Secretary to Mr. Eliot" 1 p. (20.3 × 17.6 cm.)

Giving permission to use three poems from *Practical Cats* in the *Punch Revue*, if arrangements are made with Mr. Sautoy.

G717 To Marion [Mrs. E. McKnight Kauffer]   19 Carlyle Mansions, Cheyne Walk, London, S.W.3   3 April 1955

T. Air Letter s. "Tom" (24.3 × 19.7 cm.)

Promising to get in touch with Mrs. Kauffer when he arrives in New York.

G718 To Philip Mairet   24 RUSSELL SQUARE, LONDON, W.C.1   Easter Monday [11 April] 1955

T. L. s. 1 p. (20.6 × 17.8 cm.)

On the possibility that Eliot may join Mairet's pilgrimage to Walsingham.

G719 To William Turner Levy   19 Carlyle Mansions, Cheyne Walk, London, S.W.3   Easter Monday [11 April] 1955

T. Air Letter s. 1 p. (24.5 × 19.8 cm.)

Replying to the request that Eliot secure a crucifix for Levy; and Eliot remarking on three of his own given by friends. Cited in *Affectionately, T. S. Eliot*, p. 55.

G720 To Philip Mairet   Faber and Faber, Ltd., 24 Russell Square, London, W.C.1   25 April 1955

T. L. s. "T. S. E." 1 p. (20.4 × 17.8 cm.)

On the facsimile of a portrait drawing of Goethe given to Eliot by Mairet. Eliot wishes to allude to it in his speech on Goethe in Hamburg.

G721 To William Turner Levy   Faber and Faber, Ltd., 24 Russell Square, London, W.C.1   2 May 1955

T. Air Letter s. 1 p. (24.2 × 19.9 cm.)

On plans to meet with Levy's family and with the Niebuhrs.

G722 To William Turner Levy   Faber and Faber, Ltd., 24 Russell Square, London, W.C.1   30 June 1955

T. Air Letter s. 1 p. (24.1 × 19.8 cm.)

On Franklin D. Roosevelt's Christianity, and the brotherhood of man. Cited in *Affectionately, T. S. Eliot*, pp. 74–5.

G723 To Ronald Duncan   Faber and Faber, Ltd., 24 Russell Square, London, W.C.1   27 June 1955

T. L. s. "Tom" 1 p. (20.3 × 17.6 cm.)

Thanking Duncan for an inscribed book, but expressing concern about four major errors and three minor ones in the quotation from the *Inferno*, after the dedication of "The Death of Satan."

G724 To George Barker FABER AND FABER, LTD., 24 RUSSELL SQUARE, LONDON, W.C.1 18 July 1955

T. L. s. "T. S. E." 1 p. (20.3 × 17.6 cm.)

Condolence for the death of Barker's mother, and recalling the sonnet about her published in *Eros in Dogma* (1944).

G725 To William Turner Levy FABER AND FABER, LTD., 24 RUSSELL SQUARE, LONDON, W.C.1 19 July 1955

T. Air Letter s. 1 p. (24.1 × 19.8 cm.)

Thanking Levy for an informative letter, especially about Mr. and Mrs. Franklin D. Roosevelt. Cited in *Affectionately, T. S. Eliot*, p. 75.

G726 To Ronald Duncan FABER AND FABER, LTD., 24 RUSSELL SQUARE, LONDON, W.C.1 27 July 1955

T. L. s. "Tom" 1 p. (20.3 × 17.6 cm.)

Acknowledging receipt of part of Duncan's poem *Judas*, which Eliot feels unable to criticize until he has seen the whole.

G727 To Philip Mairet FABER AND FABER, LTD., 24 RUSSELL SQUARE, LONDON, W.C.1 28 July 1955

T. L. s. with autograph postscript 2 pp. (25.6 × 20.4 cm.)

Expressing curiosity about Mairet's pilgrimmage to Walsingham, and also about Billy Graham's recent visit to London.

G728 To William Turner Levy 19 Carlyle Mansions, Cheyne Walk, London, S.W.3 "St. Stephen [2 August]: 1955"

T. Air Letter s. 1 p. (24.4 × 19.9 cm.)

Thanking Levy for the gift of three cats made of ornamental wire. Cited in *Affectionately, T. S. Eliot*, pp. 76–7.

G729 To Cid Corman FABER AND FABER, LTD., 24 RUSSELL SQUARE, LONDON, W.C.1 5 August 1955

T. L. s. "Valerie Fletcher Secretary to Mr. Eliot" 1 p. (20.2 × 17.6 cm.) with envelope

Expressing doubt whether Eliot will be able to write an essay requested.

G730 To Edith [Sitwell]   c/o J. K. Clement, 1 Rue de L'Eveche, Geneva   10 August 1955

A.L.s. "Tom" 2 pp. (20.5 × 14.4 cm.)

Declining an invitation and expressing a desire to meet in the autumn.

G731 To Henry Treece   FABER AND FABER, LTD., 24 RUSSELL SQUARE, LONDON, W.C.1   20 September 1955

T.L.s. 2 pp. (25.4 × 20.3 cm.)

On the question of publishing a collected edition of Treece's poems.

G732 To Philip Mairet   FABER AND FABER, LTD., 24 RUSSELL SQUARE, LONDON, W.C.1   20 September 1955

T.L.s. 2 pp. (20.4 × 17.7 cm.)

Expressing the desire to read two books which Mairet has alluded to. But the number of books to be read now seems overwhelming, a feeling which Eliot never suffered from when he was young.

G733 To Philip Mairet   FABER AND FABER, LTD., 24 RUSSELL SQUARE, LONDON, W.C.1   17 October 1955   TSE/VWG

T.L.s. "T.S.E." 1 p. (20.3 × 17.8 cm.)

About [Martin] Jarrett-Kerr and his book [*Studies in Literature and Belief?*].

G734 To Ronald Duncan   FABER AND FABER, LTD., 24 RUSSELL SQUARE, LONDON, W.C.1   17 October 1955   TSE/VWG

T.L.s. 2 pp. (20.2 × 17.6 cm.)

On the treatment of Christ and the Apostles in Duncan's poem *Judas*.

G735 To Henry Treece   FABER AND FABER, LTD., 24 RUSSELL SQUARE, LONDON, W.C.1   18 October 1955

T.L.s. 1 p. (25.4 × 20.3 cm.)

Reporting the decision not to publish at the present time a volume of Treece's collected poems.

G736 To Philip Mairet FABER AND FABER, LTD., 24 RUSSELL SQUARE, LONDON, W.C.1 2 November 1955

T. L. s. 1 p. (20.4 × 17.7 cm.)

On S. L. Bethell's career and his death.

G737 To Henry Sherek FABER AND FABER, LTD., 24 RUSSELL SQUARE, LONDON, W.C.1 7 November 1955

T. L. s. "Tom" 1 p. (25.4 × 20.3 cm.)

On Eliot's use of a tradesman's vocabulary in German.

G738 To Ronald Duncan FABER AND FABER, LTD., 24 RUSSELL SQUARE, LONDON, W.C.1 8 November 1955

T. L. s. "Tom" 1 p. (20.3 × 17.6 cm.)

Returning a letter about *Judas,* and promising to get an outside reader's opinion.

G739 To Ronald Duncan FABER AND FABER, LTD., 24 RUSSELL SQUARE, LONDON, W.C.1 15 November 1955

T. L. s. "Tom" 1 p. (20.3 × 17.6 cm.)

Reporting an outside reader's judgment on *Judas,* and advising against publication.

G740 To Mrs. Jacob Levy 19 Carlyle Mansions, Cheyne Walk, London, S.W.3 27 November 1955

T. Air Letter s. 1 p. (24.5 × 20 cm.)

Thanking Mrs. Levy for a large box of candy.

G741 To Mrs. [Richard] Cobden-Sanderson FABER AND FABER, LTD., 24 RUSSELL SQUARE, LONDON, W.C.1 30 November 1955

T. L. s. "Tom" 1 p. (20.2 × 17.6 cm.)

On Mrs. Cobden-Sanderson's request of books for Lady Robinson.

G742 To Henry Sherek FABER AND FABER, LTD., 24 RUSSELL SQUARE, LONDON, W.C.1 7 December 1955

T. L. s. "Tom" 1 p. (25.5 × 20.3 cm.)

On the interview which Eliot gave to Sue Cardozo because of his very pleasant memory of meeting Justice Cardozo twenty-three years ago.

G743 To Philip Mairet FABER AND FABER, LTD., 24 RUSSELL SQUARE, LONDON, W.C.1 4 January 1956

T. L. s. "T.S.E." 1 p. (20.4 × 17.6 cm.)

Arranging to meet for either lunch or dinner.

G744 To Henry Sherek FABER AND FABER, LTD., 24 RUSSELL SQUARE, LONDON, W.C.1 9 January 1956

T. L. s. "Tom" 1 p. (20.3 × 17.7 cm.)

Asking Sherek to read the translation of a play by a Spanish friend Luis Escobar Kirkpatrick, formerly Director of the National Theatre in Madrid.

G745 To George Barker FABER AND FABER, LTD., 24 RUSSELL SQUARE, LONDON, W.C.1 13 March 1956

T. L. s. "T.S.E." 1 p. (25.4 × 20.3 cm.)

Expressing appreciation of Barker's play *The Seraphina*.

G746 To Denis Goacher FABER AND FABER, LTD., 24 RUSSELL SQUARE, LONDON, W.C.1 22 March 1956

T. L. s. 2 pp. (25.4 × 20.3 cm.)

Acknowledging receipt of a pamphlet about Pound, and of a letter to be addressed to the President of the United States.

G747 To Geoffrey Barry FABER AND FABER, LTD., 24 RUSSELL SQUARE, LONDON, W.C.1 29 March 1956

T. P. C. s. "Valerie Fletcher Secretary to Mr. Eliot" (8.6 × 14 cm.)

Inviting Barry to tea on April 5th.

G748 To Philip Mairet   FABER AND FABER, LTD., 24 RUSSELL SQUARE, LONDON, W.C.1   4 April 1956

T. L. s. "T.S.E." 2 pp. (25.6 × 20.4 cm.)

Of an article on sociology in the *Times Literary Supplement*, March 30th; and on Aldous Huxley.

G749 To Ronald Duncan   FABER AND FABER, LTD., 24 RUSSELL SQUARE, LONDON, W.C.1   4 April 1956

T. L. s. 1 p. (20.3 × 17.6 cm.)

Apologizing for not answering an invitation to the opening of "The Mulberry Bush."

G750 To Marion [Mrs. E. McKnight Kauffer]   FABER AND FABER, LTD., 24 RUSSELL SQUARE, LONDON, W.C.1   14 April 1956

T. L. s. "Tom" 1 p. (20.3 × 17.6 cm.)

On Eliot's going directly to Minneapolis upon arrival in America.

G751 To William Turner Levy   19 Carlyle Mansions, Cheyne Walk, London, S.W.3   14 April 1956

T. Air Letter s. with autograph additions   1 p. (24.6 × 20 cm.)

Thanking Levy for an Easter parcel of bacon and cheese. Cited in *Affectionately, T. S. Eliot*, p. 77.

G752 To Henry Sherek   FABER AND FABER, LTD., 24 RUSSELL SQUARE, LONDON, W.C.1   22 June 1956

A. L. s. "Tom" 3 pp. (20.3 × 17.7 cm.)

Acknowledging Sherek's condolence for the death of Eliot's sister, aged eighty-five.

G753 To Philip Mairet   FABER AND FABER, LTD., 24 RUSSELL SQUARE,

London, W.C.1   28 June 1956

T. L. s. 2 pp. (20.4 × 17.7 cm.)

Thanking Mairet for the remarks on Eliot's Goethe lecture.

G754 To William Turner Levy   FABER AND FABER, LTD., 24 RUSSELL SQUARE, LONDON, W.C.1   2 July 1956

T. L. s. 2 pp. (25.4 × 20.4 cm.)

On Levy's selection of poems by Mark van Doren which Eliot will ask a colleague to study first; and on Eliot's view of Franklin D. Roosevelt. Cited in *Affectionately, T. S. Eliot*, p. 90.

G755 To Henry Sherek   FABER AND FABER, LTD., 24 RUSSELL SQUARE, LONDON, W.C.1   23 July 1956

T. L. s. "Tom" 1 p. (20.3 × 17.6 cm.)

On Eliot's feeling against selling film rights of either *The Cocktail Party* or *The Confidential Clerk*.

G756 To Ashley Dukes   FABER AND FABER, LTD., 24 RUSSELL SQUARE, LONDON, W.C.1   26 July 1956

T. L. s. "Tom" 2 pp. (20.2 × 17.6 cm.)

About securing an apartment for mutual friends.

G757 To William Turner Levy   19 Carlyle Mansions, Cheyne Walk, London, S.W.3   4 August 1956

T. Air Letter s. 1 p. (24.5 × 19.9 cm.)

On varied topics: the place of Milton in a series on Anglicanism and Literature, Rosamund Tuve's book on Herbert, and the reputation of Angus Wilson. Cited in *Affectionately, T. S. Eliot*, pp. 92–3.

G758 To Henry Sherek   FABER AND FABER, LTD., 24 RUSSELL SQUARE, LONDON, W.C.1   10 August 1956

T. L. s. "Tom" 1 p. (20.3 × 17.7 cm.)

Offering to show drafts of two acts for a new play.

G759 To George Barker FABER AND FABER, LTD., 24 RUSSELL SQUARE, LONDON, W.C.1 17 September 1956

T. L. s. "Tom" 2 pp. (25.4 × 20.3 cm.)

On "True Confession," which Eliot wishes to omit from Barker's *Collected Poems*.

G760 To Philip Mairet FABER AND FABER, LTD., 24 RUSSELL SQUARE, LONDON, W.C.1 19 September 1956

T. L. s. "T. S. E." 1 p. (25.5 × 20.4 cm.)

On Eliot's present plan to complete the play he is working on, and then to devote his time to rewriting lectures on education delivered in 1950 at Chicago.

G761 To William Turner Levy 19 Carlyle Mansions, Cheyne Walk, London, S.W.3 28 September 1956

T. Air Letter s. 1 p. (24.5 × 20 cm.)

On the Last Supper of Salvador Dali; and on the rifling of Tarot packs for the Hanged Man because of Eliot's allusion in *The Waste Land*. Cited in *Affectionately, T. S. Eliot*, pp. 93–4.

G762 To Henry Sherek FABER AND FABER, LTD., 24 RUSSELL SQUARE, LONDON, W.C.1 1 October 1956 TSE/VWG

T. L. s. "Tom" 1 p. (20.4 × 17.7 cm.)

On a letter received from the program manager of Station WOWO, Ft. Wayne, Indiana, who wishes to broadcast the Decca recording of *The Cocktail Party*.

G763 To George Barker FABER AND FABER, LTD., 24 RUSSELL SQUARE, LONDON, W.C.1 1 October 1956 TSE/VWG

T. L. s. "Tom" 1 p. (20.4 × 17.7 cm.)

Thanking Barker for his acceptance of Faber and Faber's decision. The following note appears in Barker's *Collected Poems*: "One long poem, *The True Confessions of George Barker*, which Mr. Barker wished to include in this volume, has been omitted at the publisher's request." The poem appeared separately in 1959, not published by Faber and Faber.

G764 To George Barker FABER AND FABER, LTD., 24 RUSSELL SQUARE, LONDON, W.C.1 9 October 1956

T. L. s. "Tom" 1 p. (20.3 × 17.7 cm.)

Expressing regret that Eliot did not hear *The Seraphina,* broadcast on October 4th. It was published in *Two Plays* (Faber and Faber, 1958).

G765 To Henry [Sherek] 24 RUSSELL SQUARE, LONDON, W.C.1 15 October 1956

A. L. s. "Tom" 2 pp. (17.8 × 11.5 cm.)

Arranging a meeting to discuss Eliot's new play.

G766 To Henry Sherek FABER AND FABER, LTD., 24 RUSSELL SQUARE, LONDON, W.C.1 17 October 1956

T. L. s. "Tom" 1 p. (20.3 × 17.7 cm.)

Asking for information about The Foundation Theatre Society.

G767 To Philip Mairet FABER AND FABER, LTD., 24 RUSSELL SQUARE, LONDON, W.C.1 31 October 1956

T. L. s. "T. S. E." 1 p. (25.5 × 20.3 cm.)

Commenting on the source of the line, "Garlic and sapphires in the mud," and on the nature of meaning in poetry.

G768 To William Turner Levy FABER AND FABER, LTD., 24 RUSSELL SQUARE, LONDON, W.C.1 8 November 1956

T. Air Letter s. 1 p. (24.3 × 20.1 cm.)

On Mark van Doren's poems.

G769 To Henry [Sherek] FABER AND FABER, LTD., 24 RUSSELL SQUARE, LONDON, W.C.1 12 November 1956

A. L. s. "Tom" 2 pp. (20.2 × 17.6 cm.)

Accepting an invitation to lunch, and commenting on an actor for the role of Claverton.

G770 To William Turner Levy FABER AND FABER, LTD., 24 RUSSELL SQUARE, LONDON, W.C.1 21 November 1956

T. L. s. 1 p. (20.2 × 17.6 cm.)

On the illness of Levy's father. Cited in *Affectionately, T. S. Eliot*, pp. 95–6.

G771 To Henry Sherek FABER AND FABER, LTD., 24 RUSSELL SQUARE, LONDON, W.C.1 5 December 1956

T. L. s. "Tom" 1 p. (20.3 × 17.3 cm.)

Returning *Milchwald* with a comment on translations into German.

G772 To Henry [Sherek] FABER AND FABER, LTD., 24 RUSSELL SQUARE, LONDON, W.C.1 22 December 1956

A. L. s. "Tom" 2 pp. (20.3 × 17.6 cm.)

On the impossibility of completing his play in time for the Edinburgh Festival in 1957.

G773 To Edith [Sitwell] 24 RUSSELL SQUARE, LONDON, W.C.1 "Sunday" [1956]

A. L. s. "Tom" 2 pp. (20.4 × 17.6 cm.)

Declining an invitation to dinner.

G774 To Richard Church FABER AND FABER, LTD., 24 RUSSELL SQUARE, LONDON, W.C.1 1 January 1957

T. L. s. "Tom Eliot" 1 p. (20.5 × 17.3 cm.)

On seeing Church's name in the annual Honours List.

G775 To Henry Sherek FABER AND FABER, LTD., 24 RUSSELL SQUARE, LONDON, W.C.1 7 February 1957

T. L. s. "Tom" 1 p. (20.3 × 17.6 cm.)

On the likelihood that Eliot will complete his new play only in time for the 1958 Festival.

G776 To Henry Sherek FABER AND FABER, LTD., 24 RUSSELL SQUARE, LONDON, W.C.1   17 February 1957

T. L. s. "Tom" 1 p. (20.3 × 17.6 cm.)

Accepting an invitation to lunch.

G777 To Rayner Heppenstall FABER AND FABER, LTD., 24 RUSSELL SQUARE, LONDON, W.C.1   22 February 1957

T. L. s. 1 p. (20.3 × 17.7 cm.)

On the question of publishing an anthology of French poems in translation which had been broadcast in the Third Programme over the past six years.

G778 To [Charles] Norman FABER AND FABER, LTD., 24 RUSSELL SQUARE, LONDON, W.C.1   13 March 1957

T. L. s. "Natalie Balke-Foote Secretary to Mr. Eliot" 1 p. (20.3 × 17.6 cm.)

Giving permission to include a poem by Eliot in Norman's next book.

G779 To Henry Sherek FABER AND FABER, LTD., 24 RUSSELL SQUARE, LONDON, W.C.1   29 March 1957

T. L. s. "Tom" with autograph revision 1 p. (25.4 × 20.3 cm.)

On a verse play which Sherek has asked Eliot to read.

G780 To Tom Scott FABER AND FABER, LTD., 24 RUSSELL SQUARE, LONDON, W.C.1   29 March 1957

T. L. s. 1 p. (24.4 × 20.4 cm.)

On Scott's difficulties as a young poet, which Eliot compares with his own experience.

G781 To William Turner Levy FABER AND FABER, LTD., 24 RUSSELL SQUARE, LONDON, W.C.1   8 April 1957

T. Air Letter s. "'Tom" 1 p. (24.2 × 20 cm.)

Expressing interest in the plan for a series of Cathedral Lectures, and

Eliot's willingness to comment on the lecture which Levy will give.

G782 To William Turner Levy   3 Kensington Court Gardens, London, W.8   22 April 1957   *postmark*

T. Air Letter s. "Tom" 1 p. (24.4 x 20 cm.)

Thanking Levy for the promised gift, and speaking of Eliot's great happiness in marriage. Cited in *Affectionately, T. S. Eliot*, pp. 98–99.

G783 To Charles Norman   FABER AND FABER, LTD., 24 RUSSELL SQUARE, LONDON, W.C.1   1 May 1957

T. Air Letter s. 1 p. (24.2 × 20 cm.)

Expressing thanks for a copy, which Eliot did not have, of lines which he wrote in 1940 for an exhibition of photographs.

G784 To Henry Sherek   3 Kensington Court Gardens, London, W.8   3 May 1957

T. L. s. "Tom" with autograph postscript 2 pp. (25.4 × 20.3 cm.)

On the relations of author, producer (or director), and actor in staging a play; and on the stage directions of George Bernard Shaw.

G785 To Louis Zukofsky   FABER AND FABER, LTD., 24 RUSSELL SQUARE, London, W.C.1   9 May 1957

T. Air Letter s. 1 p. (24.2 × 20 cm.)

Inviting Zukofsky to visit when he comes to London.

G786 To William Turner Levy   3 Kensington Court Gardens, London, W.8   18 May 1957

T. Air Letter s. "Tom" 1 p. (24.5 × 20 cm.)

Thanking Levy for the wedding gift. Cited in *Affectionately, T. S. Eliot*, pp. 99–100.

G787 To R. A. Scott-James   FABER AND FABER, LTD., 24 RUSSELL SQUARE, LONDON, W.C.1   18 June 1957

T. L. s. 1 p. with autograph correction (25.4 × 20.3 cm.) with envelope

On Mrs. Wyndham Lewis's straitened circumstances since the death of her husband.

G788 To Philip Mairet FABER AND FABER, LTD., 24 RUSSELL SQUARE, LONDON, W.C.1 20 June 1957

T. L. s. 1 p. (25.6 × 20.4 cm.)

On Middleton Murray, about whom Mairet is to write a booklet for the British Council Series.

G789 To William Turner Levy FABER AND FABER, LTD., 24 RUSSELL SQUARE, LONDON, W.C.1 22 June 1957

T. Air Letter s. "Tom" 1 p. (24.2 × 20 cm.)

Expressing approval of the lecture Levy has prepared on the work of Eliot.

G790 To Harvey Breit FABER AND FABER, LTD., 24 RUSSELL SQUARE, LONDON, W.C.1 21 August 1957

T. Air Letter s. 1 p. (24.1 × 19.9 cm.)

On the invitation that has come to Eliot through Robert Giroux to read his poems in Texas.

G791 To William Turner Levy 3 Kensington Court Gardens, London, W.8 9 September 1957

T. Air Letter s. "Tom" 1 p. (24.4 × 19.9 cm.)

Thanking Levy for another first edition of Pogo.

G792 To Charles Norman FABER AND FABER, LTD., 24 RUSSELL SQUARE, LONDON, W.C.1 13 September 1957

T. Air Letter s. (24.2 × 19.8 cm.)

On E. E. Cummings.

G793 To Henry Sherek FABER AND FABER, LTD., 24 RUSSELL SQUARE, LONDON, W.C.1 24 October 1957

T. L. s. "Tom" 1 p. (20.3 × 17.6 cm.)

On extending Act II of *The Elder Statesman* and planning to begin Act III.

G794 To Henry Sherek   FABER AND FABER, LTD., 24 RUSSELL SQUARE, LONDON, W.C.1   22 November 1957

T. L. s. "Tom" 1 p. (20.3 × 17.6 cm.)

Of working on Act III for *The Elder Statesman.*

G795 To J. Donald Adams   FABER AND FABER, LTD., 24 RUSSELL SQUARE, LONDON, W.C.1   27 November 1957

T. Air Letter s. with autograph changes 1 p. (24 × 19.7 cm.)

On Copeland and "English 12" at Harvard, in which Eliot was a student. Cited in *Copey of Harvard* by J. Donald Adams (Boston, 1960), pp. 153–4.

G796 To George Barker   FABER AND FABER, LTD., 24 RUSSELL SQUARE, LONDON, W.C.1   4 December 1957

T. L. s. "Tom" with autograph postscript 1 p. (25.4 × 20.3 cm.)

Accepting the title *Two Plays,* though it seems dull and does not give due prominence to *The Seraphina.*

G797 To Henry Sherek   FABER AND FABER, LTD., 24 RUSSELL SQUARE, LONDON, W.C.1   4 December 1957

T. L. s. "Tom" with autograph postscript 1 p. (25.5 × 20.3 cm.)

On Eliot's having completed eighteen typed pages of Act III, with about eighteen to go.

G798 To Henry Sherek   3 KENSINGTON COURT GARDENS, LONDON, W.8 29 December 1957

T. L. s. "Tom" 1 p. (22.7 × 17.9 cm.)

Questioning whether *The Elder Statesman* is marketable, and if so whether a final revised text may be completed in time for the Edinburgh Festival.

G799 To Henry Sherek 3 KENSINGTON COURT GARDENS, LONDON, W.8
9 January 1958

T. L. s. "Tom" 1 p. (22.7 × 17.9 cm.)

On the question of the title for Eliot's still unnamed play.

G800 To William Turner Levy 3 Kensington Court Gardens, London,
W.8 11 January 1958

T. Air Letter s. "Tom" 1 p. (24.4 × 20 cm.)

On having finished the first draft of his new play which is different,
Eliot feels, for having been written in part since his marriage. Cited in
Affectionately, T. S. Eliot, pp. 100–101.

G801 To William Turner Levy 3 Kensington Court Gardens, London,
W.8 12 January 1958

T. Air Letter s. "Tom" 1 p. (24.5 × 20.1 cm.)

Thanking Levy for the recording of Prokofieff's "Peter and the Wolf,"
with Mrs. Roosevelt reading the text.

G802 To Colin Wilson FABER AND FABER, LTD., 24 RUSSELL SQUARE,
LONDON, W.C.1 15 February 1958

T. L. s. 2 pp. (25.4 × 20.3 cm.)

On Wilson's interest in writing a book on Eliot and Eliot's objection.

G803 To J. Donald Adams FABER AND FABER, LTD., 24 RUSSELL SQUARE,
LONDON, W.C.1 18 March 1958

T. Air Letter s. with autograph correction 1 p. (24 × 19.7 cm.)

Acknowledging receipt in photocopy of an essay on Kipling which Eliot
wrote for Professor Copeland at Harvard; and giving permission to
quote from it. Passages from the essay are quoted in *Copey of Harvard*,
pp. 158–64.

G804 To William Turner Levy 3 Kensington Gardens, London, W.8
21 March 1958

T. Air Letter s. "Tom" 2 pp. (24.5 × 20 cm.)

Encouraging Levy to develop his lecture-essay on Eliot's work into a book. But Eliot would not write a prefatory note to a book about himself. Cited in *Affectionately, T. S. Eliot*, p. 101.

G805 To Henry Sherek HOTEL CONTINENTAL, CAMBRIDGE, MASSACHUSETTS 5 May 1958

A. L. s. "Tom" 1 p. (26.7 × 18.5 cm.)

On casting the role of Lord Claverton.

G806 To William Turner Levy c/o Mrs. H. W. Eliot, 84 Prescott Street, Cambridge, Massachusetts 6 May 1958

T. L. s. "Tom" with autograph postscript 1 p. (28 × 21.6 cm.)

Explaining how fully Eliot is engaged—a dinner in his honor at Eliot House, a party planned by the Signet Society for May 16th, a prospective meeting with Robert Frost, and dinner with Conrad Aiken.

G807 To Henry Sherek Cambridge, Massachusetts 9 May 1958

Cablegram from "Eliot Hotel Continental"

Requesting two tickets for the Edinburgh Festival, preferably on the first night.

G808 To Henry Sherek FABER AND FABER, LTD., 24 RUSSELL SQUARE, LONDON, W.C.1 11 June 1958

T. L. s. "Tom" 1 p (20.2 × 17.6 cm.)

Acknowledging receipt of Sherek's letter describing the cast.

G809 To [William Turner] Levy London 4 July 1958 [stamped date of receipt]

Telegram in photocopy from "Tom and Valerie"

Condolence on death of Jacob Levy, father of William Turner Levy. Cited in *Affectionately, T. S. Eliot*, p. 111.

G810 To Mrs. [Jacob] Levy and William [Turner] Levy 3 Kensington Court Gardens, London, W.8 6 July 1958

T. Air Letter s. "Tom" with autograph postscript by Valerie Eliot signed "Valerie" 1 p. (24.3 × 19.8 cm.)

On the death of Jacob Levy. Cited in *Affectionately, T. S. Eliot*, p. 111.

G811 To [William Turner Levy?]   2 September 1958

A. N. s. 1 p. (8.5 × 13.5 cm.)

Apologizing for overlooking a previous request. On the verso of the card is the phrase "Nobel Prize in Literature, 1948."

G812 To Henry Sherek   3 Kensington Court Gardens, [London, W.8] 7 September 1958

T. L. s. "Tom" with autograph revision 2 pp. (25.4 × 20.3 cm.)

Discussing criticism of certain words in the dialogue of *The Elder Statesman*.

G813 To Henry Sherek   FABER AND FABER, LTD., 24 RUSSELL SQUARE, LONDON, W.C.1   17 September 1958

T. L. s. "Tom" with autograph postscript 1 p. (25.4 × 20.3 cm.)

On Eliot's interest in a letter which Sherek has written to Sir Ian Jacob.

G814 To Henry Sherek   3 Kensington Court Gardens, London, W.8 20 September 1958

T. L. s. "Tom" 1 p. (22.8 × 17.8 cm.)

About certain words and possible revisions in the text of *The Elder Statesman*.

G815 To Mrs. [E.] McKnight Kauffer   FABER AND FABER, LTD., 24 RUSSELL SQUARE, LONDON, W.C.1   12 November 1958   TSE/AM

T. Air Letter s. "Tom" 1 p. (24 × 19.7 cm.)

On Mrs. Kauffer's going to Mexico; and on Marianne Moore's special gifts in a public performance.

G816 To Henry [Sherek]   24 RUSSELL SQUARE, [LONDON,] W.C.1   25 November 1958

A. L. s. "Tom" 2 pp. (17.7 × 11.4 cm.)

Thanking Sherek for the pictures from *Life* magazine reporting on *The Elder Statesman*.

G817 To Henry Sherek FABER AND FABER, LTD., 24 RUSSELL SQUARE, LONDON, W.C.1 3 December 1958 TSE/AM

T. L. s. "Tom" 1 p. (25.3 × 20.3 cm.)

On Eliot's hope of seeing his play again before it closes in London.

G818 To Henry Sherek FABER AND FABER, LTD., 24 RUSSELL SQUARE, LONDON, W.C.1 9 December 1958 TSE/AM

T. L. s. "Tom" 1 p. (25.4 × 20.3 cm.)

On Mr. O'Higgins of University College, Dublin, who says that Eliot gave him permission to produce any of his plays.

G819 To William Turner Levy 3 Kensington Court Gardens, London, W.8 3 January 1959

T. Air Letter s. "Tom" 1 p. (24.5 × 20 cm.)

Thanking Levy for a gift of cake.

G820 To Geoffry Barry FABER AND FABER, LTD., 24 RUSSELL SQUARE, LONDON, W.C.1 9 January 1959 TSE/AM

T. L. s. 1 p. (25.4 × 20.3 cm.)

Agreeing to meet Miss Jennings, whose poetry Eliot already knows.

G821 To Charles Norman FABER AND FABER, LTD., 24 RUSSELL SQUARE, LONDON, W.C.1 27 January 1959

T. Air Letter s. "Ann Macfadyen Secretary to Mr. Eliot" 1 p. (24.2 × 19.3 cm.)

Acknowledging receipt of a letter which will be shown to Mr. Eliot when he returns from abroad.

G822 To Neville Braybrooke FABER AND FABER, LTD., 24 RUSSELL SQUARE, LONDON, W.C.1 29 April 1959 TSE/AM

T. L. s. 1 p. (20.3 × 17.6 cm.)

On Braybrooke's using *The Cultivation of Christmas Trees* for an anthology.

G823 To J. P. Sullivan FABER AND FABER, LTD., 24 RUSSELL SQUARE, LONDON, W.C.1 4 June 1959 TSE/AM

T. L. s. 1 p. (25.3 × 20.3 cm.)

Encouraging Sullivan to continue his study of Pound's use of Propertius.

G824 To Charles Norman FABER AND FABER, LTD., 24 RUSSELL SQUARE, LONDON, W.C.1 10 June 1959 TSE/AM

T. Air Letter s. 1 p. (24.1 × 19.2 cm.)

On Eliot's memory of how he first met Ezra Pound.

G825 To J. P. Sullivan FABER AND FABER, LTD., 24 RUSSELL SQUARE, LONDON, W.C.1 11 June 1959 TSE/AM

T. L. s. 1 p. (25.3 × 20.3 cm.)

Suggesting that Sullivan's commentary on Pound's *Propertius* could be more readily considered for publication if an American publisher agreed to take some of the printed sheets from Faber and Faber.

G826 To Mrs. [E.] McKnight Kauffer FABER AND FABER, LTD., 24 RUSSELL SQUARE, LONDON, W.C.1 18 June 1959 TSE/AM

T. Air Letter s. "Tom" 2 pp. (24 × 19.6 cm.)

Expressing the hope that Edward Kauffer's work can be collected and preserved in London where it made such a deep impression.

G827 To William Turner Levy FABER AND FABER, LTD., 24 RUSSELL SQUARE, LONDON, W.C.1 18 June 1959 TSE/AM

T. Air Letter s. "Tom" with autograph correction 1 p. (24.2 × 19.6 cm.)

Acknowledging receipt of a bound proof copy of Levy's book on William Barnes, whom Eliot compares with Thomas Hardy. Cited in *Affectionately, T. S. Eliot*, p. 114.

G828 To J. P. Sullivan FABER AND FABER, LTD., 24 RUSSELL SQUARE, LONDON, W.C.1 26 June 1959 TSE/AM

T. L. s. 1 p. (20.3 × 17.6 cm.)

Expressing the hope of seeing Sullivan's manuscript draft at the end of the year.

G829 To Charles Norman FABER AND FABER, LTD., 24 RUSSELL SQUARE, LONDON, W.C.1 29 June 1959

T. Air Letter s. "Ann Macfadyen Secretary to Mr. T. S. Eliot" 1 p. (23.9 × 19.6 cm.)

Expressing thanks, in Eliot's absence, for the book on E. E. Cummings.

G830 To Ronald Duncan FABER AND FABER, LTD., 24 RUSSELL SQUARE, LONDON, W.C.1 4 August 1959 TSE/AM

T. L. s. 1 p. (20.3 × 17.2 cm.)

Expressing interest in seeing "Solitudes" revised, and other poems which Duncan has written since.

G831 To [J.] Donald Adams FABER AND FABER., LTD., 24 RUSSELL SQUARE, LONDON, W.C.1 21 August 1959 TSE/AM

T. Air Letter s. 1 p. (24.1 × 19.7 cm.)

On the use and ownership of the essay which Eliot wrote for Professor Copeland at Harvard.

G832 To Ronald Duncan FABER AND FABER, LTD., 24 RUSSELL SQUARE, LONDON, W.C.1 10 September 1959 TSE/MDG

T. L. s. "Tom" 1 p. (20.3 × 17.6 cm.)

Acknowledging receipt of Duncan's letter with his revised poems.

G833 To [J.] Donald Adams FABER AND FABER, LTD., 24 RUSSELL SQUARE, LONDON, W.C.1 23 September 1959 TSE/AM

T. Air Letter s. with autograph correction 1 p. (23.9 × 19.6 cm.)

On Eliot's approval of printing extracts only from his essay written for Professor Copeland at Harvard.

G834 To Ronald Duncan   FABER AND FABER, LTD., 24 RUSSELL SQUARE, LONDON, W.C.1   23 September 1959   TSE/AM

T. L. s. "Tom" 1 p. (25.3 × 20.3 cm.)

Expressing pleasure with the text of Duncan's poems in their revised form.

G835 To William Turner Levy   FABER AND FABER, LTD., 24 RUSSELL SQUARE, LONDON, W.C.1   1 October 1959   TSE/AM

T. Air Letter s. "Tom" 1 p. (24 × 19.6 cm.)

Thanking Levy for the birthday gift of a tie.

G836 To Ronald Duncan   FABER AND FABER, LTD., 24 RUSSELL SQUARE, LONDON, W.C.1   1 October 1959   TSE/AM

T. L. s. "Tom" 1 p. (25.4 × 20.3 cm.)

Expressing concern that certain lines of Duncan's text are possibly libelous.

G837 To Ronald Duncan   FABER AND FABER, LTD., 24 RUSSELL SQUARE, LONDON, W.C.1   6 October 1959

T. L. s. "Tom" with autograph postscript 1 p. (20.3 × 17.7 cm.); with enclosure 1 p. (25.5 × 20.3 cm)

Accepting Duncan's assurance that there is no danger of libel; and enclosing the draft of a blurb for *The Solitudes and Other Poems* for approval.

G838 To [J.] Donald Adams   Cambridge, Massachusetts   31 October 1959

T. L. s. 1 p. (20.4 × 12.7 cm.)

Declining with regret the invitation to be a guest at the Dinner of the Academy of American Poets.

G839 To Philip Mairet   FABER AND FABER, LTD., 24 RUSSELL SQUARE, LONDON, W.C.1   8 December 1959   TSE/AM

T. L. s. "T.S.E." 1 p. (25.4 × 20.3 cm.)

Promising to try to write a message for Basil Hembry by December 14th.

G840 To William Turner Levy   3 Kensington Court Gardens [London] W.8   28 December 1959

T. Air Letter s. "Tom" 1 p. (24.6 × 20 cm.) with autograph note on verso signed "Valerie."

Thanking Levy for the addition to Eliot's Pogo collection; and expressing the hope that Levy's sermon on Dr. Johnson may be developed in print. Cited in *Affectionately, T. S. Eliot*, p. 115.

G841 To Ronald Duncan   FABER AND FABER, LTD., 24 RUSSELL SQUARE, LONDON, W.C.1   5 January 1960   TSE/AM

T. L. s. 1 p. (25.3 × 20.3 cm.)

Reporting on having read Mrs. Brennan's sonnets.

G842 To Charles Norman   FABER AND FABER, LTD., 24 RUSSELL SQUARE, LONDON, W.C.1   16 February 1960

T. Air Letter s. "Ann Macfadyen Secretary to Mr. T. S. Eliot" 1 p. (24 × 19.6 cm.)

Withholding permission, in Eliot's absence, to use the essay on Ezra Pound published in *Poetry*, and two letters to Julien Cornell.

G843 To Richard Cobden-Sanderson   FABER AND FABER, LTD., 24 RUSSELL SQUARE, LONDON, W.C.1   24 March 1960   TSE/AM

T. L. s. "Tom" 1 p. (20.3 × 17.8 cm.)

Expressing the hope, like theirs, that Eliot may see the Cobden-Sandersons again, possibly at Margot Coker's.

G844 To Charles Norman   FABER AND FABER, LTD., 24 RUSSELL SQUARE, LONDON, W.C.1   28 March 1960

T. Air Letter s. "Ann Macfadyen Secretary to Mr. T. S. Eliot" 1 p. (24 × 19.7 cm.)

Asking more information about passages which Norman wishes to quote.

G845 To Charles Norman FABER AND FABER, LTD., 24 RUSSELL SQUARE, LONDON, W.C.1 7 April 1960 TSE/AM

T. Air Letter s. 1 p. (24.2 × 19.7 cm.)

On permission to print, if Norman has the Pounds' consent, Eliot's letters to Julien Cornell or other correspondence about Ezra Pound.

G846 To J. P. Sullivan FABER AND FABER, LTD., 24 RUSSELL SQUARE, LONDON, W.C.1 20 April 1960 TSE/AM

T. L. s. 1 p. (20.3 × 17.7 cm.)

Concerning Eliot's evaluation of Sullivan's book on Pound and *Propertius*.

G847 To Charles Norman FABER AND FABER, LTD., 24 RUSSELL SQUARE, LONDON, W.C.1 21 April 1960 TSE/AM

T. Air Letter s. 1 p. (24 × 20 cm.)

On the question of printing certain letters concerning Ezra Pound.

G848 To Charles Norman FABER AND FABER, LTD., 24 RUSSELL SQUARE, LONDON, W.C.1 10 May 1960 TSE/AM

T. Air Letter s. 1 p. (24.2 × 19.7 cm.)

On having received Mrs. Pound's permission for Norman to publish Eliot's letter of 24 November 1948 to Julien Cornell.

G849 To Charles Norman FABER AND FABER, LTD., 24 RUSSELL SQUARE, W.C.1 19 May 1960

T. Air Letter s. "Angela Miles Secretary to Mr. T. S. Eliot" 1 p. (24.3 × 19.6 cm.)

Expressing Eliot's thanks for the assurance that Norman will use the letter to Cornell only in accordance with Mrs. Pound's wishes.

G850 To Mrs. Jacob Levy and William Turner Levy FABER AND FABER, LTD., 24 RUSSELL SQUARE, LONDON, W.C.1 7 October 1960 TSE/AM

T. Air Letter s. "Tom" 1 p. (24.1 × 19.6 cm.)

Thanking the Levys for their birthday greetings. And suggesting names of English periodicals which may review Levy's book on William Barnes.

G851 To Marion [van] Dorn [Mrs. E. McKnight Kauffer] FABER AND FABER, LTD., 24 RUSSELL SQUARE, LONDON, W.C.1 7 October 1960 TSE/AM

T. L. s. "Tom" 2 pp. (26.3 × 20.7 cm.)

On *The View of Fuji*, a manuscript on Japan which Eliot has read at Marion Dorn's request.

G852 To Ronald Bottrall FABER AND FABER, LTD., 24 RUSSELL SQUARE, LONDON, W.C.1 30 November 1960 TSE/AM

T. Air Letter s. "Tom" 1 p. (24 × 19.4 cm.)

Expressing Eliot's pleasure in the forthcoming publication of Bottrall's *Collected Poems* by Sidwick and Jackson. But Eliot is unable to agree to write an introduction.

G853 To F. W[arren]. Roberts FABER AND FABER, LTD., 24 RUSSELL SQUARE, LONDON, W.C.1 24 April 1961

T. Air Letter s. "Angela Miles Secretary to Mr. Eliot" 2 pp. (23.9 × 19.4 cm.)

On the quotations and illustrations to be printed in the catalogue of a forthcoming Eliot exhibition at the University of Texas.

G854 To F. W[arren]. Roberts FABER AND FABER, LTD., 24 RUSSELL SQUARE, LONDON, W.C.1 26 April 1961 TSE/AM

T. L. s. 1 p. (26.4 × 20.3 cm.)

Expressing no objection to printing a photograph of the Eliot bust by Jacob Epstein.

G855 To J. P. Sullivan FABER AND FABER, LTD., 24 RUSSELL SQUARE, LONDON, W.C.1 2 May 1961 TSE/AM

T. L. s. 1 p. (25.5 × 20.4 cm.)

On Sullivan's Pound book, now to be published at the University of Texas; and on Pound's criticism of the original manuscript of *The Waste Land*.

G856 To Mrs. Ann Bowden FABER AND FABER, LTD., 24 RUSSELL SQUARE, LONDON, W.C.1 11 May 1961

T. L. s. 2 pp. (26.4 × 20.7 cm.) with envelope

On the manuscript of *The Waste Land* at the University of Texas (F2).

G857 To F. W[arren]. Roberts FABER AND FABER, LTD., 24 RUSSELL SQUARE, LONDON, W.C.1 12 May 1961 TSE/AM

T. Air Letter s. 1 p. (23.8 × 19.4 cm.)

On Eliot's inability to attend the forthcoming exhibition of his work at the University of Texas.

G858 To Mrs. Ann Bowden FABER AND FABER, LTD., 24 RUSSELL SQUARE, LONDON, W.C.1 25 May 1961

T. L. s. "Angela Miles Secretary to Mr. T. S. Eliot" 1 p. (26.3 ×20.6 cm.)

Concerning Eliot's original typescript on George Herbert at the University of Texas (F28).

G859 To J. P. Sullivan FABER AND FABER, LTD., 24 RUSSELL SQUARE, LONDON, W.C.1 14 June 1961 TSE/AM

T. L. s. 1 p. (25.5 × 20.3 cm.)

Thanking Sullivan for his offprint from *Essays in Criticism*, and commenting on modern studies in Latin and Greek literature.

G860 To Mrs. Ann Bowden FABER AND FABER, LTD., 24 RUSSELL SQUARE, LONDON, W.C.1 26 June 1961

T. L. s. "Angela Miles Secretary to Mr. T. S. Eliot" 1 p. (23.9 × 19.6 cm.)

Acknowledging receipt of the catalogue for the Eliot exhibition at the University of Texas (Bl21).

G861 To Mrs. Ann Bowden FABER AND FABER, LTD., 24 RUSSELL SQUARE, LONDON, W.C.1   13 July 1961   TSE/AM

T. Air Letter s. 2 pp. (23.9 × 19.5 cm.)

Inquiring about certain groups of Eliot letters at the University of Texas.

G862 To Mrs. Ann Bowden FABER AND FABER, LTD., 24 RUSSELL SQUARE, LONDON, W.C.1   2 August 1961   TSE/AM

T. Air Letter s. 1 p. (24 × 19.6 cm.)

On Eliot's attitude toward the publication of his correspondence during his lifetime.

G863 To F. W[arren]. Roberts FABER AND FABER, LTD., 24 RUSSELL SQUARE, LONDON, W.C.1   3 October 1961   TSE/JM

T. Air Letter s. 1 p. (24 × 19.6 cm.)

Granting permission to quote from a letter which Eliot wrote to Christopher Morley in 1950.

G864 To William Turner Levy FABER AND FABER, LTD., 24 RUSSELL SQUARE, LONDON, W.C.1   12 October 1961   TSE/JM

T. Air Letter s. "Tom" with autograph postscript 1 p. (24 × 19.6 cm.)

Thanking Levy for the birthday gift of the hymnal.

G865 To F. W[arren]. Roberts FABER AND FABER, LTD., 24 RUSSELL SQUARE, LONDON, W.C.1   13 October 1961   TSE/JM

T. Air Letter s. 1 p. (24 × 19.6 cm.)

On the letters by Eliot at the University of Texas.

G866 To Charles Wrey Gardiner FABER AND FABER, LTD., 24 RUSSELL SQUARE, LONDON, W.C.1   30 May 1962   TSE/JM

T. L. s. 1 p. (20.2 × 17.8 cm.)

On Eliot's inability to contribute to a volume which is to honor John Gawsworth [T. I. F. Armstrong].

G867 To Ronald [Bottrall] 24 RUSSELL SQUARE, LONDON, W.C.1 20 June 1962

A. L. s. 2 pp. (17.6 × 20.5 cm.)

On Eliot's sense of new financial responsibility since marriage.

G868 To Richard [Church] FABER AND FABER, LTD., 24 RUSSELL SQUARE, LONDON, W.C.1 6 September 1962

T. L. s. "Tom" 2 pp. (20.3 × 17.8 cm.)

Introducing two friends, Canon and Mrs. V. A. Demant.

G869 To [Leo F. Hamilton] the Acquisitions Assistant, University of Texas FABER AND FABER, LTD., 24 RUSSELL SQUARE, LONDON, W.C.1 19 September 1962 TSE/PB

T. Air Letter s. 1 p. (24 × 19.6 cm.)

On a volume which Eliot had sent anonymously to the University of Texas (D 66).

G870 To William Turner Levy FABER AND FABER, LTD., 24 RUSSELL SQUARE, LONDON, W.C.1 5 October 1962 TSE/PB

T. Air Letter s. "Tom" 1 p. (24.1 × 19.6 cm.)

Thanking Levy for acting to have Eliot invited to City College, but he is unable to accept more engagements on this visit.

G871 To William Turner Levy FABER AND FABER, LTD., 24 RUSSELL SQUARE, LONDON, W.C.1 10 October 1962 TSE/PB

T. Air Letter s. "Tom" 1 p. (24.2 × 19.6 cm.)

Expressing pleasure in Levy's piece about Robinson Jeffers, who like Conrad Aiken and Djuna Barnes seems inadequately appreciated. Cited in *Affectionately, T. S. Eliot*, p. 131.

G872 To Richard Church FABER AND FABER, LTD., 24 RUSSELL SQUARE, LONDON, W.C.1 2 August 1963 TSE/AB

T. L. s. "Tom" 1 p. (25.4 × 20.3 cm.)

On Eliot's agreement to write what he can about Richard Aldington in response to a request from Frédéric-Jacques Temple. Church added and initialed the autograph note: "Temple is Professor of English at Montpellier." Temple and Alister Kershaw edited *Richard Aldington An Intimate Portrait* (Carbondale and Edwardsville, Illinois, 1965).

G873 To F. W[arren]. Roberts FABER AND FABER, LTD., 24 RUSSELL SQUARE, LONDON, W.C.1   6 August 1963

T. Air Letter s. "Pamela Barker Secretary to Mr. Eliot" 1 p. (24 × 19.6 cm.)

Acknowledging receipt of an advance copy of *Bottom on Shakespeare* by Louis Zukofsky.

G874 To the Reverend Sister Marie-Bernarde, O. P.   FABER AND FABER, LTD., 24 RUSSELL SQUARE, LONDON, W.C.1   15 August 1963

T. L. s. in photocopy 1 p. (28 × 21.6 cm.)

Returning a thesis on Eliot's work.

G875 To Richard Church FABER AND FABER, LTD., 24 RUSSELL SQUARE, LONDON, W.C.1   16 August 1963   TSE/PB

T. L. s. "Tom" 1 p. (25.3 × 20.2 cm.)

Questioning Richard Church for joining Masefield and Sandburg in praise of Amado Yuzon, author of the *Citizen's Poems*; with allusions to the Scottish poets, McGonigal and Hugh MacDiarmid. Church added and initialed the autograph note: "McGonigal was a 'Sunday' poet whose banality has immortalized him." Eliot had received a copy of Yuzon's book with the author's inscription dated 2 June 1963. Inscribed by Eliot "for Richard Church with T. S. Eliot's compliments!" This copy was listed for sale in Catalogue 548 (1968) by Goodspeed's Book Shop, Boston.

G876 To Richard Church FABER AND FABER, LTD., 24 RUSSELL SQUARE, LONDON, W.C.1   21 August 1963   TSE/PB

T. L. s "T. S. E." 1 p. (25.3 × 20.2 cm.)

On Hugh MacDiarmid and other modern versifiers in Lallans.

G877 To Richard Church FABER AND FABER, LTD., 24 RUSSELL SQUARE, LONDON, W.C.1   28 August 1963   TSE/PB

T. L. s. "Tom" 1 p. (25.3 × 20.2 cm.)

On Amado Yuzon's unwarranted use of Church's praise; Eliot is reminded of his experience in praising an Indian author. *Hali* by G. V. Desani was published in 1950 with a "Foreword by T. S. Eliot and E. M. Forster" (B*l* 8).

G878 To Mrs. [E.] McKnight Kauffer FABER AND FABER, LTD., 24 RUSSELL SQUARE, LONDON, W.C.1   29 August 1963   TSE/PB

T. Air Letter s. "Tom" 2 pp. (24 × 19.6 cm.)

On Eliot's health and well-being in marriage.

G879 To Constantine FitzGibbon FABER AND FABER, LTD., 24 RUSSELL SQUARE, LONDON, W.C.1   18 September 1963

T. L. s. 2 pp. (25.3 × 20.3 cm.)

On the work of Dylan Thomas.

G880 To William Turner Levy FABER AND FABER, LTD., 24 RUSSELL SQUARE, LONDON, W.C.1   12 October 1963   TSE/PB

T. Air Letter s. "Tom" 1 p. (24.1 × 19.1 cm.)

Thanking Levy for the gift of a scarf. Cited in *Affectionately, T. S. Eliot,* p. 132.

G881 To J. V. Healy FABER AND FABER, LTD., 24 RUSSELL SQUARE, LONDON, W.C.1   15 October 1963

T. Air Letter s. "Pamela Barker, Secretary to Mr. Eliot" 1 p. (23.7 × 19.6 cm.)

Replying to a letter, and recalling that he did read the *Satyricon* of Petronius with E. K. Rand at Harvard. Some of its words may have unconsciously suggested some of his own.

G882 To Ronald Bottrall FABER AND FABER, LTD., 24 RUSSELL SQUARE, LONDON, W.C.1   15 November 1963   TSE/PB

T. L. s. "Tom/T. S. Eliot" 1 p. (25.2 × 20.1 cm.)

Acknowledging receipt of Bottrall's translation from the *Inferno*, and discussing the question of publishing a new translation of the *Divine Comedy.*

G883 To Ronald Bottrall   FABER AND FABER, LTD., 24 RUSSELL SQUARE, LONDON, W.C.1   22 November 1963   TSE/PB

T. L. s. 1 p. (25.2 × 20.1 cm.)

Reporting Fabers' unwillingness to publish a new translation of the *Divine Comedy.*

G884 To [M. J. Thurairajah] Tambimuttu   FABER AND FABER, LTD., 24 RUSSELL SQUARE, LONDON, W.C.1   31 July 1964

T. Air Letter s. 1 p. (24 × 19.6 cm.)

On Eliot's inability with short notice to write anything for Marianne Moore's seventy-seventh birthday; but he sends warmest regards to her.

G885 To Mrs. Jacob Levy and William Turner Levy   FABER AND FABER, LTD., 24 RUSSELL SQUARE, LONDON, W.C.1   2 October 1964

T. Air Letter s. "pp. T. S. Eliot (Dictated by Mr. Eliot and signed in his absence)" 1 p. (23.8 × 19.6 cm.)

Thanking the Levys for a birthday telegram.

APPENDIX TO G:

ALPHABETICAL LIST
OF ELIOT'S CORRESPONDENTS

Adams, Donald: 795, 803, 831, 833, 838

Aldington, Richard: 2–3, 5, 7–25, 27, 31–2, 36–8, 40–1, 51–7, 60, 62–3, 65, 68, 74–8, 80, 86–7, 90, 94, 98–9, 101, 106–10, 115, 117–18, 123–4, 126, 134, 137, 142, 146–7, 152

Anonymous: 33, 267

ApIvor, Denis: 548

Armstrong, T. I. F.: 472

Bagley, Robert H.: 639

Barker, George: 207, 209, 212–14, 216–19, 221, 225, 227–9, 231–2, 234, 239, 241, 244, 251–3, 275–7, 279, 281–2, 284, 291–3, 303, 315, 324, 326, 330, 407–8, 410–11, 446, 449, 463, 494, 556, 560, 562, 628–9, 654, 724, 745, 759, 763–4, 796

Barry, Geoffrey: 574–5, 584, 599, 635, 663, 677, 747, 820

Bax, Clifford: 26

Blakeney, E. H.: 338–9

Bottrall, Ronald: 170, 180, 189, 191, 194–5, 198–201, 204–5, 254, 268, 280, 287, 294, 297, 301, 311, 319–20, 322–3, 337, 355–7, 366, 373, 376, 384, 404, 416, 418, 421, 435, 449, 489, 496, 508, 510, 520, 592–3, 613, 631, 650, 852, 867, 882–3

Bowden, Mrs. Ann: 856, 858, 860–2

Braybrooke, Neville: 822

Breit, Harvey: 790

Carpenter, Maurice: 712

Carrington, C. E.: 680, 683

Chambers, Maria Christina: 158, 554

Green, Russell: 6

Grigson, Geoffrey: 240, 260, 283, 289, 312, 317

Hamilton, Leo: 869

Healy, J. V.: 332–4, 881

Heppenstall, Rayner: 211, 223, 236–8, 245–7, 255, 257–8, 262–3, 269, 271, 273–4, 285–6, 288, 290, 295, 298–300, 302, 304–7, 309–10, 313–14, 316, 318, 321, 427, 579, 583, 586, 777

Hughes, Glenn: 154–7, 159, 163

Hynes, Samuel L.: 682

Johnson, R. J. G.: 242–3, 265

Jonas, Klaus W.: 570

Kauffer, Marion van Dorn [Mrs. Edward McKnight]: 447, 465, 470, 506–7, 705–6, 713, 717, 750, 815, 826, 851, 878

Knight, G. Wilson: 190, 535, 568, 607–8

Knight, W. F. Jackson: 398, 425, 431–2, 464, 471, 497–8, 543

Knights, L. C.: 203

Leavis, F. R.: 178, 181, 187, 208, 256, 278, 348, 372, 380, 383, 457, 477, 533

Lehmann, John: 222, 250, 261, 270, 272, 335, 342–3, 368, 413, 426, 618

Lehmann, Wilhelm: 69, 73, 79

Levy, Mrs. Jacob: 646, 657, 660, 671, 675, 740

Levy, Mrs. Jacob and William Turner: 810, 850, 885

Levy, William Turner: 469, 513–14, 524, 529, 547, 550, 572, 576–7, 581, 588, 611, 617, 627, 633, 641, 644, 665, 674, 687–8, 700, 704, 708, 711, 719, 721–2, 725, 728, 751, 754, 757, 761, 768, 770, 781–2, 786, 789, 791, 800–1, 804, 806, 809, 811, 819, 827, 835, 840, 864, 870–1, 880

MacNeice, Louis: 370, 377, 386

MacQuarrie, Hector: 679

Mairet, Philip: 325, 340, 344–7, 359, 388, 393, 424, 436, 452, 466, 473, 475, 478, 486, 492–3, 499–500, 511, 519, 523, 528, 530–2, 536, 542, 544, 564, 605–6, 621, 640, 645, 667, 690, 697, 702–3, 710, 714–15, 718, 720,

Scott, Tom: 664, 695, 701, 780

Scott-James, R.A.: 787

Sherek, Henry: 539, 551–2, 555, 558, 563, 567, 569, 578, 582, 585, 587, 598, 600, 610, 620, 638, 643, 651–2, 655–6, 659, 661–2, 666, 668–70, 672, 678, 684, 694, 696, 699, 737, 742, 744, 752, 755, 758, 762, 765–6, 769, 771–2, 775–6, 779, 784, 793–4, 797–9, 805, 807–8, 812–14, 816–18

Sitwell, Edith: 381, 414, 423, 430, 434, 441–2, 534, 537–8, 540–1, 553, 571, 573, 590, 602–3, 642, 648, 689, 692, 730, 773

Sitwell, Osbert: 387, 390

Smith, Ronald Gregor: 363, 365, 428

Spender, Stephen, and Cyril Connolly: 331

Squire, John C.: 1

Strong, L. A. G.: 71, 96–7, 111, 483

Sullivan, John P.: 823, 825, 828, 846, 855, 859

Tambimuttu, [M. J. Thurairajah]: 884

Tiller, Terrence: 589

Titus, Edward W.: 174

Tonks, Henry: 182–3

Treece, Henry: 328, 349–54, 360–1, 367, 369, 371, 374–5, 378–9, 382, 385, 391–2, 394–7, 399–400, 402–3, 405–6, 409, 412, 415, 433, 438, 440, 443, 448, 451, 453, 455, 459, 467–8, 474, 476, 481, 485, 491, 503, 505, 512, 522, 546, 549, 557, 565–6, 591, 594, 596–7, 609, 612, 614, 622, 624–5, 630, 731, 735

Trevelyan, Mary: 458, 545

Ussher, Arland: 461

West, Geoffrey: 179, 185

Woolf, Virginia: 82–3, 85, 88, 92–3, 102–3, 119

Wilson, Colin: 802

Zukofsky, Louis: 169, 192–3, 595, 601, 604, 619, 785

H

MANUSCRIPTS: LETTERS TO T. S. ELIOT

With few exceptions these are typed carbon copies, or autograph draft copies, which were kept by the writer. Usually unsigned and without address of origin, they are described in chronological sequence in a form similar to that used for letters by T. S. Eliot. Reference to Eliot's letters by date or number is to the collection at Texas.

H1 From [Harold Monro]   25 June 1920

T. L.   carbon copy   1 p. (25.9 × 20.4 cm.)

Asking for a first refusal of literary articles that Eliot may write. Monro was editor of *The Chapbook*.

H2 From T. Sturge Moore   [November 1926]

A. L. s.   draft copy with revisions   1 p. (25.5 × 20.3 cm.)

Enclosing two detachable stanzas which Eliot may offer to *Commerce*. Moore's wife could translate them into French. Written on back of Eliot's letter, 15 November 1926 (G112).

H3 From T. Sturge Moore   [November 1926]

A. L.   draft copy with revisions   1 p. (25.6 × 20.4 cm.)

Offering two poems for *The Criterion*. Written on back of Eliot's letter, 18 November 1926 (G113).

H4 From T. Sturge Moore   [July 1927]

A. L.   draft copy with revisions   2 pp. (18.2 × 11.5 cm.)

Concerning Moore's uneasiness about Eliot's poetry. Written on back of Eliot's letter, 9 July 1927 (G127).

H5 From T. Sturge Moore   [December 1927]

A. L. s.   draft copy with revisions   1 p. (25.2 × 20.2 cm.)

Expressing disappointment that Eliot has had to return the manuscript "In Defense of Beauty," and promising to sent the Blake review for *The Criterion*. Written on back of Eliot's letter, 30 December 1927 (G144).

H6 From [Harold Monro]   London   [29 May 1929]

T. L.   carbon copy   1 p. (25.6 × 20.4 cm.)

On certain poems by Eliot which Monro wants for his anthology (*Twentieth Century Poetry*). Eliot replied 4 June 1929 (G164).

H7 From Harold Monro   London   17 June 1929

T. L.   carbon copy   1 p. (25.6 × 20.5 cm.)

Expressing disappointment in Eliot's letter of June 4th on what poems Monro may use in his anthology.

H8 From [Ernest Rhys]   [October 1930]

A. L.   draft copy   1 p. (25.4 × 20.6 cm.)

Assuring Eliot that he is destined to write on Pascal and that Rhys will await Eliot's inspiration. Written in the margin of Eliot's letter to Rhys, 16 October 1930.

H9 From Ezra Pound   S. Luigi Gonzaga   21 June [1931]

T. P. C. with typed signature "E. P." (9 ×14 cm.)

Replying to Eliot; the "MORAL [:] And a little cheeyeild shall lead them."

H10 From [Harold Monro]   8 September [1931]

T. L.   carbon copy   1 p. (25.6 × 20.5 cm.)

On Monro's understanding last spring that Eliot would be willing to give a "Reading or a Talk" like the one he gave a few years ago on Whitman and Tennyson. Eliot replied 10 September 1931 (G176).

H11 From George Barker   Danegelts, Geldeston, Norfolk   23 May 1934

T. L. s.   "George B." draft copy with autograph corrections   1 p. (25.3 × 20.2 cm.)

Thanking Eliot for the improved advance payment.

H12 From Giovanni Papini   Palazzo di Parte Guelfa, Firenze   4 January 1939

T. L.   copy made by T. S. Eliot   1 p. (25.4 × 20.2 cm.)

Inviting Eliot to participate in a conference. Eliot sent a copy to Bottrall on January 13th (G322) to ask for information and advice.

H13 From J. V. Healy   Cape Cottage Woods, Maine   15 March 1940

T. L. s.   carbon copy   1 p. (28 × 21.6 cm.)

Concerning the attribution of anti-Semitism to Benjamin Franklin in Ezra Pound's *Cantos LII–LXXI* (London: Faber & Faber, 1940).

H14 From E[zra]. P[ound].   Rapallo   13 April 1940

T. L.   "signed E. P." "copy"   1 p. (28.4 × 22.2 cm.)

Replying to J. V. Healy's question about Benjamin Franklin and the Jews.

H15 From J. V. Healy   Cape Cottage Woods, Maine   16 April 1940

T. L. s.   carbon copy   1 p. (28 × 21.6 cm.)

About what appears to be anti-Semitism in the work of Eliot as well as in the recently published *Cantos* of Ezra Pound.

H16 From J. V. Healy   Cape Cottage Woods, Maine   31 May 1940

T. L. s.   carbon copy   2 pp. (28 × 21.6 cm.)

On Pound's and Eliot's defenses in recent letters against the charge of anti-Semitism.

H17 From [John Lehmann]   5 July 1940

T. L.   carbon copy   1 p. (25.5 × 20.3 cm.)

Requesting Faber and Faber's permission to include poems by Spender, Auden, and MacNeice in *Penguin New Writing*.

H18 From [John Lehmann]   12 July 1940

T. L.   carbon copy   1 p. (25.5 × 20.5 cm.)

Suggesting the fee Lehmann would pay for each poem he wishes to include in his anthology.

H19 From [John Lehmann]   Fieldhead, Bourne End, Buckingham-
shire   27 January 1941

T. L.   carbon copy   1 p. (25.4 × 20.3 cm.)

On the special case of reprinting poems by Auden which had been
published originally in *Penguin New Writing*.

H20 From [John Lehmann]   "as from Fieldhead, Bourne End, Bucks."
12 February 1941

T. L.   carbon copy   1 p. (25.4 × 20.3 cm.)

On W. H. Auden's *New Year Letter* which has been received in proof.

H21 From Henry Treece   [1942]

A. L.   draft copy   1 p. (25 × 20.1 cm.)

On Treece's volume *Invitation and Warning* (Faber and Faber, 1942).

H22 from [John Lehmann]   23 August 1944

T. L.   carbon copy   1 p. (12.5 × 20.4 cm.)

On *Four Quartets*, and in reply to Eliot's letter concerning his attitude
toward writing more poetry (G413).

H23 From [Arthur V. Moore]   6 January 1945

T. L.   carbon copy   1 p. (25.5 × 20.3 cm.)

Thanking Eliot for a copy of Pound's *Jefferson and/or Mussolini*. Replying to Eliot's letter of 3 January (G419).

H24 From J[ames]. L[aughlin].   New Directions, Norfolk, Connecticut   23 December [1945]

T. L.   1 p. (26.4 × 20.1 cm.)

On the cheerful acceptance by Ezra Pound of the plea of insanity. He
was declared "insane and mentally unfit for trial" on 21 December 1945
(Julien Cornell, *The Trial of Ezra Pound*, p. 37).

H25 From James Laughlin   New Directions, Norfolk, Connecticut

15 February 1946

T. L.   carbon copy   2 pp. (33.3 × 20.3 cm.)

On Laughlin's pleasure that Eliot will write an essay on Pound for the special number of *Poetry* (September 1946); and on the progress of Pound's trial.

H26 From [Ronald Duncan]   14 East Heath Rd., Hampstead, [London,] N.W.3   8 April 1946

T. L.   carbon copy   1 p. (20.3 × 12.7 cm.)

Suggesting that John Piper, who designed sets for *The Rape of Lucretia*, might also design the dustwrapper of the book.

H27 From J. H. Oldham   THE BRITISH COUNCIL OF CHURCHES. COMMISSION ON THE ERA OF ATOMIC POWER. 20 BALCOMBE STREET, DORSET SQUARE, LONDON, N. W. 1   26 April 1946

T. L. s.   1 p. (26 × 20.2 cm.)

Gratefully acknowledging the help given by Eliot in preparing the report of the Commission, and hoping that Eliot will like it in its final form better than he did in earlier drafts.

H28 From Ronald [Bottrall]   Palazzo Borghese, Rome   21 February 1948

A. L. s.   "Ronald"   draft copy   2 pp. (32.5 × 20.5 cm.)

Concerning Eliot's comments on Bottrall's poetic language, and on the "bareness" that Bottrall feels can be sustained only "if you are a Dante or Eliot."

H29 From [Ronald Bottrall]   Palazzo Borghese, Rome   4 April 1948

A. L.   draft copy   2 pp. (32.4 × 20.3 cm.)

On Bottrall's difficulty in finding an American publisher for his poems.

H30 From the "Secretary to Mr. John Lehmann"   6 April 1948

T. L.   carbon copy   1 p. (25.5 × 20.4 cm.)

Requesting Eliot's permission to reprint "Cultural Diversity and European Unity" in an issue of *Prisma* which Lehmann is to edit.

H31 From [Ronald Duncan]   30 August 1948

T. L.   carbon copy   1 p. (25.3 × 20.3 cm.)

Sending letters received from John Drummond and Dorothy Pound that may help size up the situation of Ezra Pound in Washington before Eliot goes there.

H32 From Peter Russell   43 Duke St., [London] W. 1   13 September 1948

T. L. s. "P. R."   carbon copy   2 pp. (25.5 × 20.4 cm.)

Thanking Eliot for two pamphlets, "Impact" and "Alf Venison."

H33 From Peter Russell   43 Duke St., London, W. 1   7 December 1948

T. L.   carbon copy   4 pp. (33.7 × 20.3 cm.)

Asking Eliot if he would be willing to be president of the Ezra Pound Circle.

H34 From [Roy Campbell]   [1947–48]

A. L.   draft copy   1 p. (26.1 × 16 cm.)

Asking if Faber and Faber may be interested in the publication in England of five verse plays which Campbell has translated from Spanish. They were used with success on the Third Programme.

H35 From [Peter Russell]   43 Duke St., London, W. 1   22 May 1949

T. L.   carbon copy   2 pp. (33.7 × 20.3 cm.)

Inquiring what aspect of Pound's work Eliot may want to write about in the volume planned for Pound's sixty-fifth birthday. And on seeing in Italy Santayana reading *Four Quartets* "evidently under instruction from Robert Lowell!"

H36 From Peter Russell   43 Duke St., London, W. 1   7 June 1949

T. L. s.   carbon copy   2 pp. (33.7 × 20.3 cm.)

On Russell's activity as Pound's agent and on a book which is to be written on Pound's total achievement.

H37 From [Henry Sherek]   HENRY SHEREK LTD., 40 PALL MALL, LONDON, S.W.1   19 September 1949

T. L.   autograph copy by Sherek   2 pp. (33.2 × 20.4 cm.)

On having heard from Martin Browne Eliot's reaction to Sherek's thought that *The Cocktail Party* should open in New York before London.

H38 From [Henry Sherek]   10 January 1950

T.   copy of telegram   (15.6 × 20.2 cm.)

Asking if Eliot would "give Crainford authority" to negotiate terms with Decca for recording extracts from *The Cocktail Party*.

H39 From [Henry Sherek]   11 January 1950

T.   copy of telegram   (7.1 × 20.3 cm.)

Asking radio reply to the question about Decca recordings.

H40 From [Henry] Sherek   4 February 1950

T.   copy of telegram   (17.9 × 21.5 cm.)

Asking approval of recording contract with Decca.

H41   From [Henry Sherek]   2 March 1950

T. L.   carbon copy   1 p. (25.4 × 20.3 cm.)

Sending advance payment for recording of *The Cocktail Party*.

H42 From [Henry Sherek]   8 March 1950

T. L.   carbon copy   1 p. (25.4 × 20.3 cm.)

Commenting on Eliot's remark that the money sent to him on March 2nd should go to Faber and Faber.

H43 From H[enry] S[herek]   22 March 1950

T. L.   carbon copy   1 p. (25.4 × 20.3 cm.)

Enclosing a letter from the drama critic John Chapman praising the New York performance of *The Cocktail Party.*

H44 From H[enry] S[herek]   30 March 1950

T. L.   carbon copy   1 p. (25.4 × 20.3 cm.)

Inviting Eliot to meet the company that will begin rehearsing next Monday morning at the New Theatre.

H45 From H[enry] S[herek]   5 April 1950

T. L.   carbon copy   1 p. (25.5 × 20.3 cm.)

On the company rehearsing *The Cocktail Party* being rather despondent at not having met Eliot.

H46 From H[enry] S[herek]   10 July 1950

T. L.   carbon copy   2 pp. (25.4 × 20.3 cm.)

Thanking Eliot for a copy of the German translation of *The Cocktail Party.* Sherek is critical of the translation and expresses disappointment that he was not allowed to have an interest in the continental rights in their native languages.

H47 From H[enry] S[herek]   14 July 1950

T. L.   carbon copy   1 p. (25.4 × 20.4 cm.)

Inviting Eliot to a party "to celebrate our having passed the hundredth performance in London, and over two hundred in New York, and to say 'Goodbye' to Rex Harrison."

H48 From [Henry Sherek]   9 November 1950

T. L.   carbon copy   2 pp. (32.3 × 20.3 cm.)

On the acute dropping off of attendance at the New Theatre, and Sherek's determination not "to raise the flag of surrender." "We would have liked to have had the Bard with us in these trying times."

H49 From [Henry Sherek]   11 January 1951

T. L.   carbon copy   1 p. (25.4 × 20.4 cm.)

On the plan to close *The Cocktail Party* at the New Theatre February 10th, and hoping that Eliot will join a party planned for the night of the three hundredth performance, January 19th.

H50 From [Henry Sherek]   16 February 1951

T. L.   carbon copy   1 p. (25.4 × 20.4 cm.)

Listing dates and places where the London company will play *The Cocktail Party*.

H51 From H[enry] S[herek]   21 February 1951

T. L.   carbon copy   1 p. (25.4 × 20.4 cm.)

Forwarding a request for an interview by Ward Morehouse of *The New York World-Telegram and Sun*, "who states that he has written more about *The Cocktail Party* in New York than anybody."

H52 From Basil Bunting   Lido di Camaiore [Italy]   2 May 1951

T. L.   carbon copy   2 pp. (28.3 × 22.2 cm.)

Recommending Louis Zukofsky.

H53 From Dylan Thomas   The Boat House, Langhorne, Carmenhenshire   28 May 1951

A. L. s.   1 p. (18 × 13.6 cm.)

Gratefully acknowledging Eliot's gift of a check.

H54 From [Henry Sherek]   21 August 1951

T. L.   carbon copy   1 p. (25.4 × 20.4 cm.)

Inviting Eliot and John Hayward to lunch.

H55 From the "Secretary to Mr. [Henry] Sherek."   20 September 1951

T. L.   carbon copy   1 p. (25.4 × 20.4 cm.)

Forwarding press notices of the South African production of *The Cocktail Party*.

H56 From [Henry Sherek]   1 October 1951

T. L.   carbon copy   1 p. (25.5 × 20.4 cm.)

Inviting Eliot and John Hayward to lunch.

H57 From [Henry Sherek]   3 October 1951

T. L.   carbon copy   1 p. (25.5 × 20.4 cm.)

Enclosing a "tour list of *The Cocktail Party* in South Africa."

H58 From [Henry Sherek]   5 October 1951

T. L.   carbon copy   1 p. (25.5 × 20.4 cm.)

". . . still grasping a very crumpled ten shilling note . . . waiting to hear when you and John can lunch."

H59 From [Henry Sherek]   11 October 1951

T. L.   carbon copy   1 p. (25.5 × 20.4 cm.)

Listing places where *The Cocktail Party* is being shown in South Africa, and announcing the beginning of tour in San Francisco October 15th, "should you wish to send the company a cable."

H60 From [Henry Sherek]   22 October 1951

T. L.   carbon copy, with autograph additions   1 p. (25.5 × 20.4 cm.)

Forwarding a press notice of the performance in San Francisco.

H61 From [Henry Sherek]   9 November 1951

T. L.   carbon copy   1 p. (25.5 × 20.4 cm.)

Expressing the hope that "when you are fit again I will be allowed to wait upon you. Ian Hunter and Alec Guinness have been allowed into the presence. . . ."

H62 From [Henry Sherek]   15 January 1952

T. L.   carbon copy   1 p. (25.5 × 20.4 cm.)

On Sherek's desire to tell Eliot about "the adventures of *The Cocktail Party* in those United States."

H63 From [Henry Sherek]   23 January 1952

T. L.   carbon copy   1 p. (25.5 × 20.4 cm.)

Of the letter received from the National Theatre Organisation asking Sherek to thank Eliot for his assistance regarding the South African tour.

H64 From John Lehmann   1 April 1952

T. L.   carbon copy   1 p. (25.5 × 20.4 cm.)

Asking if Eliot will contribute a piece for the B. B. C. *New Soundings* programme about his experience as editor of an avant-garde magazine —either *The Egoist* or *The Criterion*. Eliot replied on April 7th.

H65 From [Henry Sherek]   30 April 1952

T. L.   carbon copy with autograph addition   1 p. (25.6 × 20.4 cm.)

Asking if the enclosed report from *The Daily Mail* about a film of *The Cocktail Party* has any truth.

H66 From [Christopher Morley] Rostyn, Long Island, New York   6 May 1952

T. L.   2 carbon copies   incomplete   1 p. (28.1 × 21.7 cm.)

Inviting Eliot to meet at 3 P.M. and "drive home with me."

H67 From [Henry Sherek]   2 July 1952

T. L.   carbon copy   1 p. (25.5 × 20.4 cm.)

Sending a copy of an address given at Harvard "by a certain Mr. Bluestone" on "Ezra Pound and the Bollingen Award."

H68 From [Henry Sherek]   9 September 1952

T. L.   carbon copy   1 p. (25.5 × 20.4 cm.)

Sending a copy of "the German version of your Cat Book." Sherek recently bought it in Berlin.

H69   From [Henry Sherek]   13 October 1952

T. L.   carbon copy   1 p. (25.5 × 20.4 cm.)

Asking Eliot what he thinks of the suggestion from the Edinburgh Festival Society that Sherek put on, in repertory, *The Family Reunion, The Cocktail Party*, and Eliot's new play, at the Festival of 1953. Eliot replied on October 28th.

H70 From [Henry Sherek]   10 December 1952

T. L.   carbon copy   2 pp. (25.5 × 20.4 cm.)

On Sherek's reading the first two acts of *The Confidential Clerk*.

H71 From [Henry Sherek]   17 December 1952

T. L.   carbon copy   1 p. (25.5 × 20.4 cm.)

Arranging to meet Eliot with Martin Browne, the director, on December 30th.

H72 From [Henry Sherek]   2 January 1953

T. L.   carbon copy   1 p. (25.6 × 20.4 cm.)

On casting *The Confidential Clerk*, and Sherek's intention to communicate periodically with Eliot.

H73 From [Henry Sherek]   13 January 1953

T. L.   carbon copy   1 p. (25.5 × 20.4 cm.)

On progress being made in casting.

H74 From H[enry] S[herek]   4 February 1953

T. L.   carbon copy   1 p. (25.5 × 20.4 cm.)

On the difficulty of both Martin Browne and Sherek in understanding how Eliot sees the character of B. Kaghan.

H75 From [Henry Sherek]   18 March 1953

T. L.   carbon copy   1 p. (25.5 × 20.4 cm.)

Asking Eliot about the advisability of changing the name of the heroine Lucasta, because an all-Negro cast is soon to open a play entitled *Anna Lucasta*; and also asking Eliot's opinion about a forty-minute extract to be produced on television.

H76 From [Henry Sherek]   20 March 1953

T. L.   carbon copy   1 p. (25.5 × 20.4 cm.)

Thanking Eliot for the newspaper clipping on Arthur Miller's conflict with the legal profession; but Sherek does not think they will be "assailed by the Bar Association."

H77 From [Henry Sherek]   30 March 1953

T. L.   carbon copy   2 pp. (25.5 × 20.4 cm.)

More on the inadvisability of using the name Lucasta. Eliot replied on April 8th.

H78 From [Henry Sherek]   7 April 1953

T. L.   carbon copy   1 p. (25.5 × 20.4 cm.)

More on the choice of an extract for the television performance of *The Confidential Clerk*, and more on the name Lucasta.

H79 From [Henry Sherek]   10 April 1953

T. L.   carbon copy   1 p. (25.5 × 20.4 cm.)

More on Lucasta; the American manager, who threatened legal action, had never heard of Richard Lovelace, as Eliot guessed.

H80 From Charles Allen   STANFORD UNIVERSITY PRESS, STANFORD, CALIFORNIA   7 May 1953

T. L.   carbon copy   1 p. (28 × 21.6 cm.)

Inviting Eliot to contribute to a volume being planned to celebrate the centennial of *Leaves of Grass*.

H81 From [Henry Sherek]   29 May 1953

T. L.   carbon copy   1 p. (25.5 × 20.3 cm.)

On Sherek's having completed the casting for *The Confidential Clerk*.

H82 From H[enry] S[herek]   9 July 1953

T. L.   carbon copy   1 p. (25.4 × 20.3 cm.)

Reporting that Sherek has engaged a London theatre.

H83 From H[enry] S[herek]   22 July 1953

T. L.   carbon copy   1 p. (25.4 × 20.3 cm.)

Reporting that the first reading of *The Confidential Clerk* is scheduled for July 22nd, and (in confidence) that the theatre engaged in London is the Lyric.

H84 From H[enry] S[herek]   23 July 1953

T. L.   carbon copy   1 p. (25.4 × 20.3 cm.)

On a request from the B.B.C. which Sherek says does not affect him since he does not have the continental rights.

H85 From H[enry] S[herek]   30 July 1953

T. L.   carbon copy   1 p. (25.4 × 20.3 cm.)

On postponing a recording until after the Edinburgh Festival and on Eliot's question concerning the United Nations Association.

H86 From H[enry] S[herek]   5 August 1953

T. L.   carbon copy   1 p. (25.4 × 20.2 cm.)

Asking Eliot to study the enclosed *Report on Omnibus 1952–1953*, because Sherek has been in correspondence with the Ford Foundation about televising part of *The Confidential Clerk* in New York.

H87 From H[enry] S[herek]   17 September 1953

T. L.   carbon copy   1 p. (25.4 × 20.3 cm.)

Congratulating Eliot on the successful opening of *The Confidential Clerk* in London, and asking for a meeting to discuss the New York production.

H88 From H[enry] S[herek]   23 September 1953

T. L.   carbon copy   1 p. (25.4 × 20.4 cm.)

Asking Eliot to set a time "and I will wait upon you."

H89 From H[enry] S[herek]   7 October 1953

T. L.   carbon copy   1 p. (25.4 × 20.3 cm.)

Expressing pleasure in Sherek's hour meeting with Eliot yesterday, and Sherek's sense of having reached full agreement.

H90 From H[enry] S[herek]   20 October 1953

T. L.   carbon copy   1 p. (25.4 × 20.4 cm.)

On the problem of taking an English cast to New York.

H91 From H[enry] S[herek]   22 October 1953

T. L.   carbon copy   1 p. (25.5 × 20.4 cm.)

Requesting an interview with Eliot for Anthony Havelock-Allan and Anthony Asquith.

H92 From M[arianne] M[oore]   260 Cumberland St., Brooklyn 5, New York   9 December 1953

T. L.   carbon copy   1 p. (28.1 × 21.8 cm.)

On Gertrude Flynn, an actress who has written to Marianne Moore about the role of Lucasta.

H93 From [Marianne Moore]   260 Cumberland Street, Brooklyn 5, New York   20 January 1954

T. L.   carbon copy   draft with autograph additions and revisions 1 p. (27.8 × 21.5 cm.)

Acknowledging receipt of an inscribed copy of *The Three Voices of Poetry.*

H94 From [Henry Sherek]   9 March 1954

T. L.   carbon copy   1 p. (25.4 × 20.1 cm.)

On Sherek's desire to tell Eliot "all about the American adventure."

H95 From [Henry Sherek]   16 March 1954

T. L.   carbon copy   1 p. (25.4 × 20.1 cm.)

Reporting an American associate's view (with which Ina Clair, the actress, and Sherek agree) that cuts are desirable, especially in the first act, but also in the third.

H96 From [Henry Sherek]   22 March 1954

T. L.   carbon copy   1 p. (25.4 × 20.1 cm.)

On the difficulty of communicating directly with Eliot, Sherek's General Manager being informed that "you were not to be bothered."

H97 From [Henry Sherek]   23 March 1954

T. L.   carbon copy   1 p. (25.4 × 20 cm.)

Enclosing a letter from "some other people in Johannesburg, which we could perhaps discuss."

H98 From [Henry Sherek]   29 March 1954

T. L.   carbon copy   1 p. (25.4 × 20 cm.)

On Eliot's gesture toward reducing his royalties "whilst the play is at the Duke of York's Theatre."

H99 From [Marianne Moore]   30 March 1954

T. L.   carbon copy with autograph corrections   2 pp. (28.1 × 21.8 cm.)

Discussing *The Confidential Clerk*—"the best of your plays not excepting *Murder in the Cathedral*."

H100 From Hector MacQuarrie   South African Broadcasting Corporation, 48 Bloomsbury Street Bedford Square, London, W.C. 1 [March 1954]

T. L. s.   1 p. (25.5 × 20.4 cm.)

Asking permission to broadcast *The Confidential Clerk* in South Africa between May and July. Eliot replied on March 17th.

H101   From [Henry Sherek]   7 April 1954

T. L.   carbon copy   1 p. (25.3 × 20.1 cm.)

Suggesting that *The Confidential Clerk* be closed May 1st, and that they try later to get a company together for a tour.

H102   From the Secretary to Henry Sherek   10 April 1954

T. L.   carbon copy   1 p. (25.4 × 20.2 cm.)

Asking for Eliot's comment on a letter enclosed (not identified).

H103   From [Marianne Moore]   18 April 1954

T. N.   carbon copy with autograph revisions   3 pp. (28.1 × 21.3 cm.)

About their mutual friends Edward and Marion McKnight Kauffer. Written to be sent with the letter of this date.

H104   From Marianne [Moore]   260 Cumberland Street, Brooklyn 5, New York   18 April 1954

T. L. s. "Marianne"   carbon copy   with autograph revisions 1 p. (28.1 x 21.8 cm.)

On receiving "a very beautiful present"—an inscribed copy of *The Confidential Clerk*. And on her own choice of *The Fables of La Fontaine* which in her translation seem best.

H105   From Marianne [Moore]   23 April 1954

T. L. s. "Marianne" copy partly in carbon   with autograph addition 1 p. (28.1 × 21.8 cm.)

Expressing concern for Eliot's health.

H106   From Marianne [Moore]   30 May 1954

T. Air Letter s. "Marianne"   draft copy   with autograph revisions

1 p. (17.6 × 18 cm.)

Thanking Eliot and John Hayward for Hayward's reassuring letter about Eliot's health (I22).

H107 From H[enry]. S[herek].   3 June 1954

T. L.   carbon copy   1 p. (25.4 × 20.2 cm.)

Enclosing two letters from Henry Hewes of the *Saturday Review*, and asking if Eliot would care to reply himself or instruct Sherek to reply.

H108 From H[enry]. S[herek].   25 June 1954

T. L.   carbon copy   1 p. (25.4 × 20.2 cm.)

On having completed casting of *The Confidential Clerk* for the Paris Festival and for the English tour afterwards.

H109 From [Marianne Moore]   260 Cumberland Street, Brooklyn 5, New York   25 July 1954

T. L.   carbon copy   1 p. (28.1 × 21.8 cm.)

Concerning the forthcoming publication of *The Fables of La Fontaine* in Marianne Moore's translation.

H110 From [Henry Sherek]   29 July 1954

T. L.   carbon copy   1 p. (25.5 × 20.4 cm.)

On the dates for the English tour of *The Confidential Clerk*. "The 'Times' was, as usual, very unfair, and I enclose four notices which bear out what I say."

H111   From [Henry Sherek]   3 August 1954

T. L.   carbon copy   1 p. (25.5 × 20.4 cm.)

Asking for Eliot's opinion of the play, *Un Nomme Judas*. Eliot replied on August 18th.

H112 From [Marianne Moore]   5 August 1954

T. L.   carbon copy   1 p. (28 × 21.5 cm.)

Concerning mutual friends Edward and Marion McKnight Kauffer.

H113 From H[enry] S[herek]   25 August 1954

T. L.   carbon copy   1 p. (25.5 × 20.4 cm.)

Thanking Eliot for his gesture as regards royalties. "Heaven knows we need it, because I am afraid the tour is not doing well."

H114 From [Henry Sherek]   6 October 1955

T. L.   carbon copy   1p. (25.7 × 20.5 cm.)

Inviting Eliot to lunch on October 18th, or any other Tuesday, "our roast beef day."

H115 From [Henry Sherek]   2 December 1955

T. L.   carbon copy   1 p. (25.6 × 20.4 cm.)

Inviting Eliot "to lunch in company with Miss Greenwood" on December 13th.

H116 From [Henry Sherek]   6 December 1955

T. L.   carbon copy   1 p. (25.6 × 20.5 cm.)

". . . so you have succumbed to the lure of personal publicity. . . ." Eliot replied on December 7th to explain why he gave an interview to Sue Cardozo.

H117 From [Henry Sherek]   12 January 1956

T. L.   carbon copy   1 p. (25.4 × 20.4 cm.)

Replying to Eliot's letter of December 9th, and thanking Eliot for sending the Spanish play.

H118 From H[enry]. S[herek].   29 February 1956

T. L.   carbon copy   1 p. (25.4 × 20.4 cm.)

Returning the play *Elena Ossorio*, for which Sherek cannot suggest a production. Replying to Eliot's letter of January 9th (G744).

H119 From Sheri Martinelli c/o e.p., St. Elizabeth's, Washington, D.C. 24 June 1956

T. L. s. "SM" 2 pp. (28.1 × 21.6 cm.) with envelope stamped with Chinese ideogram, probably Ezra Pound's.

Expressing gratitude for *Four Quartets*—"they have kept me alive"— and offering a painting which has been made for Eliot. The envelope also contains two photographs taken in St. Elizabeth's Hospital.

H120 From [Henry Sherek] 19 July 1956

T. L. carbon copy with autograph note added later 1 p. (25.4 × 20.4 cm.)

Asking if Eliot is still against selling film rights to *The Confidential Clerk*. Eliot replied on July 23rd.

H121 From H[enry]. S[herek]. 13 August 1956

T. L. carbon copy 1 p. (25.4 × 20.4 cm.)

Wishing Eliot "a lovely time in Switzerland."

H122 From H[enry]. S[herek]. 8 October 1956

T. L. carbon copy 1 p. (25.3 × 20.4 cm.)

Replying to the letter of October 1st, and asking Eliot to forward the letter which he received from Ft. Wayne, Indiana.

H123 From Assistant Secretary to Mr. [Henry] Sherek 20 October 1956

T. L. carbon copy 1 p. (25.3 × 20.4 cm.)

Replying to Eliot's letter of October 17th. Sherek "has never heard of The Foundation Theatre Society either."

H124 From H[enry]. S[herek]. 8 November 1956

T. L. carbon copy 1 p. (25.4 × 20.4 cm.)

On casting the role of Lord Claverton in *The Confidential Clerk*. Eliot replied on November 12th.

H125 From H[enry]. S[herek].   15 November 1956

T. L.   carbon copy   1 p. (25.5 × 20.3 cm.)

On Sherek's plan to entertain at lunch on November 27th. "You like your roast beef well done, and John [Hayward] likes his roast beef underdone."

H126 From H[enry]. S[herek].   3 December 1956

T. L.   carbon copy   1 p. (25.4 × 20.3 cm.)

On the invitation of the Berliner Festwochen to send over a production of *The Elder Statesman* after the Edinburgh Festival. Eliot replied on December 5th.

H127 From H[enry] S[herek].   19 December 1956

T. L.   carbon copy   1 p. (25.3 × 20.4 cm.)

On the letter received by Sherek from Robert Ponsonby of the Edinburgh Festival who expresses concern that *The Elder Statesman* is still incomplete. Eliot replied on December 22nd.

H128 From H[enry]. S[herek].   6 February 1957

T. L.   carbon copy   1 p. (25.4 × 20.5 cm.)

On the inquiry from Robert Ponsonby whether Eliot would "hold the first performance of his new play until the opening of the 1958 Festival." Eliot replied on February 7th sending a copy to Ponsonby.

H129 From H[enry]. S[herek].   12 February 1957

T. L.   carbon copy   1 p. (25.4 × 20.5 cm.)

Inviting Eliot to lunch "any Tuesday."

H130 From H[enry]. S[herek].   29 April 1957

T. L.   carbon copy   2 pp. (25.5 × 20.4 cm.)

Acknowledging receipt of Eliot's article in *Maske and Kothurn*; and commenting on the relations of author and director, and on George Bernard Shaw's stage directions. Eliot replied on May 3rd.

H131 From H[enry]. S[herek]. 1 October 1957

T. L. carbon copy 1 p. (25.1 × 20.5 cm.)

Enclosing and commenting on a piece in *Time* magazine of September 23rd. Eliot replied on October 24th.

H132 From H[enry]. S[herek]. 24 October 1957

T. L. carbon copy 1 p. (25.1 × 20.5 cm.)

On questions which Sherek is pressed to answer about the Edinburgh Festival, and Eliot's silence.

H133 From H[enry]. S[herek]. 28 October 1957

T. L. carbon copy 1 p. (25.1 × 20.5 cm.)

Acknowledging Eliot's letter of October 24th. Illness explains his not replying to Sherek's questions.

H134 From H[enry]. S[herek]. 25 November 1957

T. L. carbon copy 1 p. (25.4 × 20.3 cm.)

Inquiry whether Sherek can tell the people at Edinburgh that Eliot's play will be completed in time for the Festival in 1958. Eliot replied on December 4th.

H135 From H[enry]. S[herek]. 6 December 1957

T. L. carbon copy 1 p. (25.4 × 20.3 cm.)

Expressing delight with Eliot's report of progress with *The Elder Statesman*, and annoyance with Edinburgh "because they will not give me two weeks but only one."

H136 From H[enry]. S[herek]. 20 December 1957

T. L. carbon copy 1 p. (25.4 × 20.3 cm.)

On Edinburgh's agreement "to wait even unto the eleventh hour," which for them is mid-January. Eliot replied on December 29th.

H137 From H[enry]. S[herek]. 31 December 1957

T. L.   carbon copy   1 p. (25.5 × 20.4 cm.)

Asking Eliot to send Acts I and II, "and what you have done of Act III."

H138 From H[enry]. S[herek].   7 January 1958

T. L.   carbon copy   1 p. (25.5 × 20.4 cm.)

On Sherek's objection to *The Rest Cure* as the title of Eliot's play (finally called *The Elder Statesman*). Eliot replied on January 9th.

H139 From [Henry Sherek]   13 January 1958

T. L.   carbon copy   1 p. (25.6 × 20.4 cm.)

On Sherek's attitude to Eliot's title.

H140 From H[enry]. S[herek].   17 January 1958

T. L.   carbon copy   1 p. (25.6 × 20.4 cm.)

On Martin Browne as director for Eliot's play.

H141 From H[enry]. S[herek].   8 May 1958

T. L.   carbon copy   2 pp. (25.5 × 20.4 cm.)

On the early need of the Edinburgh Festival for names of the cast.

H142 From [Henry] S[herek].   10 June 1958

T. L.   carbon copy   1 p. (25.6 × 20.5 cm.)

Inviting Eliot to see models of the stage sets for *The Elder Statesman*.

H143 From H[enry]. S[herek].   14 July 1958

T. L.   carbon copy   1 p. (25.5 × 20.4 cm.)

On plans to start the reading of the play on July 21st at The Criterion Theatre.

H144 From H[enry] S[herek]   16 July 1958

T. L.   carbon copy   1 p. (25.5 × 20.4 cm.)

Replying to Eliot's letter about press representatives at the Edinburgh Festival.

H145 From H[enry]. S[herek].   29 July 1958

T. L.   carbon copy   1 p. (25.5 × 20.4 cm.)

On the desire of the B. B. C. that "this company of the present play would enact a short scene from this and your two previous plays," to be presented on the programme called "Monitor."

H146 From H[enry] S[herek]   5 September 1958

T. L.   carbon copy   2 pp. (25.4 × 20.3 cm.)

Inviting the Eliots to share a box with the Shereks on the opening night of *The Elder Statesman* at the Cambridge Theatre, September 25th. Eliot replied on September 7th.

H147 From H[enry] S[herek]   11 September 1958

T. L.   carbon copy   2 pp. (25.4 × 20.3 cm.)

On the performance of *The Elder Statesman* at Brighton which Sherek thought was improved considerably because of the cuts Eliot made at Edinburgh.

H148 From Executive Secretary for Henry Sherek   18 September 1958

T. L.   carbon copy   1 p. (25.4 × 20.4 cm.)

On Sherek's request for an appointment to discuss a letter received from the B. B. C.

H149 From H[enry] S[herek]   19 September 1958

T. L.   carbon copy   1 p. (25.5 × 20.3 cm.)

Replying to Eliot's letter of September 7th on the character of Culverwell.

H150 From [Henry Sherek]   19 September 1958

T. L.   carbon copy   1 p. (25.5 × 20.3 cm.)

Sending tickets for "*your* box, and Pamela and I are delighted that you will allow us to sit in it."

H151 From H[enry] S[herek]   22 September 1958

T. L.   carbon copy   1 p. (25.5 × 20.3 cm.)

Expressing Sherek's desire "not to alter any lines for any member of the company at this stage before the opening."

H152 From [Henry Sherek]   2 October 1958

T. L.   carbon copy   1 p. (25.5 × 20.4 cm.)

On Sherek's having received a letter saying that *The Elder Statesman* "will have a wider appeal than either *The Cocktail Party* or *The Confidential Clerk.*"

H153 From H[enry] S[herek]   24 November 1958

T. L.   carbon copy   1 p. (25.5 × 20.4 cm.)

Sending pages from *Life* magazine with pictures related to Eliot's new play.

H154 From H[enry] S[herek]   26 November 1958

T. L.   carbon copy   1 p. (25.5 × 20.4 cm.)

Rejecting Eliot's description of *The Elder Statesman* as a "distinguished failure." Sherek calls it a success "considering that it was in a very large theatre."

H155 From H[enry] S[herek]   4 December 1958

T. L.   carbon copy   1 p. (25.5 × 20.4 cm.)

On the problem of taking *The Elder Statesman* to Dublin and to New York.

H156 From H[enry] S[herek]   10 December 1958

T. L.   carbon copy   1 p. (25.5 × 20.4 cm.)

Replying to Eliot's letter of December 9th. Sherek prefers a professional production in Dublin, if they can get it, to the possibility of one at University College.

H157 From Charles Norman   47 Perry Street, New York 14, N.Y. 13 May 1960

T. L. s.   carbon copy   1 p. (28 × 21.7 cm.)

Thanking Eliot for the report that Mrs. Pound has given "clearance" to use a letter concerning Ezra Pound. Replying to Eliot's letter of May 10th.

H158 From [Ronald Bottrall]   Villa Cornubia, Via Miramare, Albano Laziale, Rome, Italy   10 November 1963

T. L.   carbon copy   1 p. (28.1 × 22.1 cm.)

Asking Eliot's judgment on the translation of certain cantos from the *Inferno* which Bottrall has done for the B. B. C. And on the need for a new English translation of the *Divine Comedy*. Eliot replied on November 22nd.

H159 From Ronald Bottrall   Villa Cornubia, Via Miramare, Albano Laziale, Rome, Italy   1 December 1963

T. L.   carbon copy   1 p. (27.9 × 22.1 cm.)

Replying to Eliot's letter of November 22nd. With further comment on the English versions available and further question on Eliot's decision.

I

LETTERS REFERRING TO

T. S. ELIOT OR HIS WORK

Arranged chronologically, these letters represent a selection of those at Texas containing the more significant allusions to Eliot.

LETTERS REFERRING TO T. S. ELIOT

I1 Vivien Eliot to Richard Aldington 9 Clarence Gate Gardens, [London,] N.W.1 "Saturday morning" [1922]

A. L. s. 7 pp. (17.9× 13.6 and 21.4 × 13.6 cm.)

Complaining of an "unkind" and "not friendly" letter (unidentified) from Aldington to Eliot. And hoping that "Tom will soon get out" of England; Ezra "is lucky and wise to have got out."

I2 Ottoline Morrell to [Richard] Aldington THE MANOR HOUSE, GARSINGTON, OXFORD 17 July 1922

A. L. s. 4 pp. (19.4 × 12.1 cm.)

Replying to the appeal for the Bel Esprit Fund.

I3 T. Sturge Moore to [Osbert] Burdett [7 December 1927]

A. L. s. "T. S. Moore" draft copy with revisions 1 p. (25.3 × 20.2 cm.)

Expressing deep personal concern that *The Criterion* is to suspend publication. Written in back of a letter from I. P. Fassett, Secretary to T. S. Eliot, to Moore, 5 December 1927.

I4 Siegfred Sassoon to Edmund Blunden "Fitzhouse" 18 September 1932

A. L. s. "S. S." 3 pp. (18.1 × 11.6 cm.)

On Eliot's "throwing his shadow over all these youngish minds."

I5 Henry Eliot to Christopher [Morley] 315 EAST 68TH STREET, NEW YORK CITY 3 May 1933

T. L. s. 1 p. (28 × 21.5 cm.)

On *The Hoogus Mystery* by Henry Eliot, which he says is both humorous and serious and much influenced by his brother "Tom's critical writing."

I6 Henry Eliot to [Christopher] Morley   315 East 68th Street, New York City   28 June 1933

T. L. s.   1 p. (28 × 21.5 cm.)

On Tom Eliot—"a most lovable person"—and Tom's reaction to Henry's book.

I7 F. V. Morley to R. J. G. Johnson   Faber and Faber, Ltd., 24 Russell Square, London, W.C.1   6 November 1933

T. L. s.   1 p. (25.4 × 20.2 cm.)

On the purchase of two manuscripts of T. S. Eliot by Johnson, through the bookseller Bumpus.

I8 [Edith Sitwell] to the Editor of *The New Statesman*   13 December 1934

A. L.   draft copy   4 pp. (31.9 × 19.8 cm.)

Defending her treatment of Eliot in *Aspects of Modern Poetry* (1934). Written in a large notebook. Draft copy of the essay on Eliot is J31.

I9 Ashley Dukes to [Anthony] Bertram   The Mercury Theatre, 2 Ladbroke Road, Notting Hill Gate [London] W. 11

T. L. s.   with autograph postscript   1 p. (25.4 × 20.2 cm.)

On "commercial successes" of plays like *Murder in the Cathedral.*

I10 [Lord] Alfred [Bruce] Douglas to Mr. [Sidney Wentworth] Carroll   1, St. Ann's Court, Nizells Avenue, Hove 2, Sussex.   15 December 1939

A. L. s.   2 pp. (22.8 × 17.7 cm.)

Complaining of Hugh Walpole's repeated boosts for the "nonpoet T. S. Eliot." Carroll was literary editor of the *Daily Sketch* (1938–42).

I11 Edith Sitwell to the Editor of *The New Statesman*   [1943]

A. L.   draft copy   1 p. (31.9 × 19.8 cm.)

Protesting a review of *Four Quartets.* Written in a large notebook.

I12 Sherek Players Ltd. to Valerie Fletcher   6 March 1950

T. L.   carbon copy   1 p. (25.4 × 20.3 cm.)

Addresses of fifteen persons who may have a role in *The Cocktail Party*, sent at the request of Martin Browne to T. S. Eliot's secretary.

I13 [Henry Sherek] to V[alerie]. Fletcher   19 November 1950

T. L.   carbon copy   1 p. (25.4 × 20.2 cm.)

Asking whether Eliot would like *The Cocktail Party* to be done at the University of Capetown's Little Theatre.

I14 [Tennessee Williams] to his mother and grandfather   24 August 1951

T. L. s.   "Tom"   1 p. (28.1 × 21.4 cm.)

On having lunch with the "greatest living poet" and being given an inscribed copy of *The Cocktail Party*.

I15 [Henry Sherek] to V[alerie]. Fletcher   5 November 1951

T. L.   carbon copy   1 p. (25.5 × 20.4 cm.)

Asking if Miss Fletcher has received for Eliot the abridged version of *The Cocktail Party* which is to be broadcast in New York by the Theatre Guild.

I16 Peter du Sautoy to Henry Treece   FABER AND FABER, LTD. 24 RUSSELL SQUARE, LONDON, W.C.1   14 November 1951

T. L. s.   1 p. (25.4 × 20.3 cm.)

On the blurb written by Eliot for the dustwrapper of *The Exiles* by Henry Treece. Eliot's typescript is F 29.

I17 [Henry Sherek] to V[alerie]. Fletcher   5 May 1953

T. L.   carbon copy   1 p. (25.4 × 20.2 cm.)

On Eliot's wish to be reminded to send "a wire for the opening of Paul Rogers at the Old Vic tomorrow, and Margaret Leighton at the Haymarket Theatre on Thursday."

I18 [Henry Sherek] to [Valerie] Fletcher   20 August 1953

T. L.   carbon copy   1 p. (25.3 × 20.2 cm.)

Sending a ticket for Eliot's trip to Edinburgh "on the 10 a.m. train on Saturday."

I19 Ashley Dukes to [Samuel] Hynes   MERCURY THEATRE, 2 LADBROKE ROAD, LONDON, W.11   14 January 1954

T. L. s., with autograph corrections   1 p. (25.4 × 20.3 cm.)

On T. S. Eliot's bust by Jacob Epstein (K8), which will be placed in the Mercury Theatre.

I20 S. B. to [Valerie Fletcher]   20 January 1954

T. L.   carbon copy   1 p. (25.4 × 20.4 cm.)

Sending the Boston notices of *The Confidential Clerk*. "S.B." was General Manager of Henry Sherek, Ltd.

I21 Leonard Schach to [Henry] Sherek   HASHOMER, WORCESTER ROAD, SEA POINT, CAPETOWN   26 February [1954]

T. L. s.   1 p. (25.4 × 20.2 cm.)

Asking for rights to produce *The Confidential Clerk* in Capetown and Johannesburg. Schach, a theatrical producer, has just seen Eliot, and claims to have his strong approval.

I22 John Hayward to [Marianne] Moore   19 Carlyle Mansions, Cheyne Walk, London, S.W. 3   29 April 1954

T. Air Letter   s.   1 p. (24.5 × 20.1 cm.)

On false rumors spread in the newspapers about Eliot's health. "Tom's pulse became normal again over a week ago."

I23 Babette Deutsch to [Tom] Scott   300 West 108 Street, New York 25   23 February 1955

T. Air Letter   s.   1 p. (30.2 × 18.9 cm.)

Along with Eliot and others, Babette Deutsch can be counted on as an admirer of Scott's work.

I24 J[ohn]. Lehmann to [Valerie]. Fletcher THE LEAGUE OF DRAMA-
TISTS, 84 DRAYTON GARDENS, London, S.W. 10   30 June 1955

T. L. s. with autograph note by Eliot addressed to Peter du Sautoy
1 p. (17.7 × 20.2 cm.)

On the proposed television performance of *The Confidential Clerk*, and
the broadcasting of *The Cocktail Party* from records.

I25 [Henry Sherek] to Valerie Fletcher   5 July 1955

T. L. carbon copy   1 p. (25.5 × 20.3 cm.)

On the need to write Decca in New York "to make quite sure what the
position is regarding the broadcasting of these records."

I26 [Henry Sherek] to V[alerie]. Fletcher   18 July 1955

T. L. carbon copy   1 p. (25.6 × 20.4 cm.)

On the promise from Gilbert Miller's office in New York "to inquire
from Decca about the use of *The Cocktail Party* recording."

I27 [Henry Sherek] to V[alerie]. Fletcher   22 October 1956

T. L. carbon copy   1 p. (25.2 × 20.3 cm.)

Enclosing a letter from Decca on Eliot's right to accede to the request
from Station WOWO, Ft. Wayne, Indiana. Replying to Eliot's letter of
October 1st.

I28 Hugh [Dinwiddy] to Neville [Braybrooke] MAKERERE COLLEGE,
KAMPALA, UGANDA   15 November 1956

A. Air Letter s.   2 pp. (24 × 19.6 cm.)

Accepting invitation to write on his experience of teaching Eliot's work
for the *Symposium* to be edited by Braybrooke, and published in 1958.

I29 W. F. J[ackson]. Knight to Neville [Braybrooke] CAROLINE
HOUSE, STREATHAM RISE, EXETER   26 February 1957

A. L. s.   1 p. (17.7 × 13.7 cm.)

Accepting invitation to write on Eliot as a classical scholar, for the
Symposium to be edited by Braybrooke.

I30 Colin Wilson to Ronald Duncan "Old Walls" 12 February 1958

T. L. s. "Colin" 2 pp. (25.4 × 20.2 cm.)

On having written a letter to Eliot, "asking if he will sign or not" (a petition that is to help free Ezra Pound).

I31 Isabella [Massey] to Frances [M. Barbour] 22 Elers Road, London, W. 13 20 March 1958

A. L. s. "Isabella" photocopy 2 pp. (20.4 × 12.8 cm.)

On Eliot's recent marriage and his appearance with his new wife. Isabella Massey was Professor of German at Bedford College, University of London.

I32 From Valerie Eliot to William Turner Levy 3 Kensington Gardens, London, W. 8 30 March 1958

T. Air Letter s. "Valerie" 2 pp. (24.5 × 19.9 cm.)

On the recent visit to Rome where Eliot received an honorary degree, and where the Eliots met Pizzetti, the Italian composer who has set *Murder in the Cathedral* as an opera.

I33 [Henry Sherek, Ltd.] to John Reid 12 May 1958

T. L. carbon copy 1 p. (25.5 × 20.5 cm.)

Asking Reid of the Edinburgh Festival Society whether two seats may be reserved for the first night of *The Elder Statesman*. Eliot has requested them (G807) for his cousins the Misses Lamb.

I34 Executive Secretary [of Henry Sherek, Ltd.] to Kenneth Corden 19 July 1958

T. L. carbon copy 1 p. (25.5 × 20.5 cm.)

Forwarding a special request from Eileen Peel for "two seats for the opening night of *The Elder Statesman*."

I35 [Henry Sherek] to M. E[lizabeth]. Barber 23 July 1958

T. L. carbon copy with autograph corrections 1 p. (25.5 × 20.4 cm.)

Asking Miss Barber of the League of Dramatists to write to Eamonn O'Higgins. If the League does not object neither Eliot nor Sherek objects to O'Higgins' producing *The Elder Statesman* at University College, Dublin. Sherek raised a further question about this in a letter to Eliot, December 4th (H155), and Eliot replied on December 9th (G819).

I36 M. Elizabeth Barber to Henry Sherek THE LEAGUE OF DRAMATISTS, 84 DRAYTON GARDENS, LONDON, S.W.10 24 July 1958

T. L. s. 1 p. (17.5 × 20.2 cm.)

Reporting that the League has written to Eamonn O'Higgins about producing *The Elder Statesman*.

I37 [Sherek Players, Ltd.] to Susan MacEwen 12 September 1958

T. L. carbon copy with autograph corrections 1 p. (25.5 × 20.2 cm.)

Acknowledging Eliot's request to reserve seats for several persons listed at performances of *The Elder Statesman*.

I38 Ronald Bottrall to Hugh Kenner British Embassy, Tokyo, Japan 4 June 1961

T. L. carbon copy 1 p. (33.1 × 20.2 cm.)

Quoting conversations between Eliot and himself, and between Eliot and Paul Elmer More, in 1931–32, on the American people, and on "The Hippopotamus."

I39 Valerie Eliot to Florence [Mrs. Jacob] and William [Turner Levy] 3 Kensington Court Gardens, London W.8 27 August 1961

T. L. s. "Valerie" 4 pp. (17.8 × 13.9 cm.)

On Eliot's visits and travelling. "Tom will not let me leave him more than one day." Also on Gerald Kelly's portraits of Mr. and Mrs. Eliot. Eliot's portrait is K9.

I40 Valerie Eliot to William Turner Levy 3 Kensington Court Gardens, London W. 8 18 June 1962

T. Air Letter s. "Valerie" 2 pp. (24.5 × 20 cm.)

On Gerald Kelly's portrait of Eliot (K9).

I41 Valerie Eliot to Mrs. Jacob Levy and W[illiam]. Turner Levy
3 Kensington Court Gardens, London, W. 8   11 February 1963

T. L. s.   "Valerie"   1 p. (24.4 × 19.9 cm.)

On Eliot's "five weeks in the Brompton Hospital," and Mrs. Eliot's care
of him at home.

I42 Valerie Eliot to Mrs. Jacob Levy and W[illiam]. T[urner]. Levy
Bermuda   25 April 1963

A. P. C. s.   "Valerie" (9 × 14 cm.)

On a recent vacation in Bermuda.

I43 Valerie Eliot to Mrs. Jacob Levy and W[illiam]. Turner Levy
Emerald Beach Hotel [Bahamas]   19 January 1964

A. P. C. s.   "Valerie"   (8.9 × 14 cm.)

On Eliot's health and on a recent visit with Margie Cohn.

I44 Osbert Sitwell to [Horace] Liveright   2 Castle Square, Chelsea,
London

A. L. s.   "copy"   4 pp. (17.6 × 11.3 cm.)

On Sitwell's sense of his own independence and difference from Eliot
as poet.

J

MANUSCRIPTS: POEMS, ESSAYS, AND NOTES ON T. S. ELIOT OR HIS WORK

These writings, arranged alphabetically by the name of the author, are held in an original script of some kind. When given, the date is usually from the manuscript.

POEMS, ESSAYS, AND NOTES

ON T. S. ELIOT

J1a Richard Aldington   EZRA POUND AND T. S. ELIOT   A LEC-
TURE   1954

Typescript with autograph corrections signed   24 pp. (27.2 × 20.5 cm.)

The "Author's Note," dated "Christmas 1953," describes the "ensuing
pages" as "part of a series given at an Eastern American University" in
1939. The date at the end, "U.S.A. 1939," is followed by a "Postscript
1954."

J1b Richard Aldington   EZRA POUND & T. S. ELIOT   A LEC-
TURE   1954

Seven sheets of galley proof (56.8 × 18 cm.) plus one (39 × 18 cm.)
for the title; with autograph revisions by Aldington.

The "Postscript 1954," which had already been revised, is deleted.
Published by The Peacock Press (Hurst, Berkshire, 1954) in a signed
edition of 10 and a regular edition of 350. Number 9 of the signed edition and a copy of the regular edition are at The University of Texas at
Austin.

J2 George Barker   VERSES FOR THE 60TH BIRTHDAY OF
THOMAS STEARNS ELIOT   1948

Autograph manuscript with revisions signed   4 pp. (26.8 × 20.9 cm.)

A poem (40 lines) published in *T. S. Eliot, A Symposium* (London,
1948). In line 10 ("taming Apollyon with a pen") "taming" is emended
to "tame," as it appears when published. Other revisions in diction:
"whistle" for "sing" (l. 20); "seen" for "heard" (l. 29).

J3 [George Barker]   [ON T. S. ELIOT'S *POETRY AND DRAMA*]
1951

Autograph manuscript with revisions   draft copy   12 pp. (19.8 × 12.5
cm.) torn from a notebook.

A review of *Poetry and Drama* (Cambridge, Massachusetts, 1951), the Theodore Spencer Memorial Lecture delivered at Harvard in 1950.

J4a Ronald Bottrall DEAD ENDS (*HOMAGE TO T. S. ELIOT*) 1948

Typescript with autograph revision 2 pp. (26.7 × 20.4 cm.)

In a typescript of the poems collected for publication with the title poem *Palisades of Fear* (1949). The poem on Eliot had first appeared in *T. S. Eliot, A Symposium* (1948). L. 24 of the typescript, "And we fall back among clashing swords," is emended to read, "And we fall back among withered words."

J4b Ronald Bottrall DEAD ENDS (*HOMAGE TO T. S. ELIOT*) 1948

Typescript with autograph revision 2 pp. (26.7 × 20.4 cm.)

A later typescript than J4a. in the collection *Palisades of Fear*. "Dead Ends" is typed as in J4a., with the same autograph revision.

J5a Neville Braybrooke [T. S. ELIOT'S PURSUIT OF THE WHALE] 1963

Typescript with autograph revisions 3 pp. (25.4 × 20.4 cm.)

"First draft" of an article written for Eliot's seventy-fifth birthday, first published in *The Chicago Herald Tribune* (September, 1963).

J5b Neville Braybrooke T. S. ELIOT'S PURSUIT OF THE WHALE 1963

Typescript with autograph revisions 4 pp. (25.4 × 20.4 cm.)

"Final draft."

J6a Neville Braybrooke T. S. ELIOT'S EARLIEST WRITINGS 1964

Typescript with autograph revisions 7 pp. (25.6 × 20.3 cm.)

"First draft and notes" for the article "accepted by *The Sunday Times* (October, 1964)."

J6b [Neville Braybrooke] [T. S. ELIOT'S EARLIEST WRITINGS] 1964

Typescript incomplete with autograph corrections   2 pp. (26.7 × 20.3 cm.)

A revision of pp. 6–7 of the first draft.

J6c [Neville Braybrooke] [T. S. ELIOT'S EARLIEST WRITINGS] 1964

Typescript   carbon copy   with autograph corrections   7 pp. (25.6 × 20.3 cm.)

"Final Version 1964."

J7a Neville Braybrooke   LES ÉCRITS DE JEUNESSE DE T. S. ELIOT   Un aperçu de ses poèmes et contes écrits à l'âge de 16 ans 1965

Typescript with autograph corrections signed   9 pp. (32.5 × 20.3 cm.)

"Final draft" of article published in Belgium in *Synthéses* (September, 1965).

J7b Neville Braybrooke   LES ÉCRITS DE JEUNESSE DE T. S. ELIOT   Un aperçu de ses poèmes et contes écrits à l'âge de 16 ans 1965

Page proof with autograph corrections by the author   6 pp. (23.9 × 16 cm.)

J8 Neville Braybrooke   T. S. ELIOT   1888–1965   1965

Typescript with autograph corrections   3 pp. (25.5 × 20.4 cm.)

"Final draft" of the obituary published in the *Catholic Herald* (January, 1965).

J9a Neville Braybrooke   T. S. ELIOT IN THE SOUTH SEAS   A Look at the Short Stories and Poems that he wrote in 1905 as a schoolboy 1966

Typescript with autograph corrections   6 pp. (25.4 × 20.4 cm.)

"Final draft" of the article published in *Sewanee Review*, LXXIV (Winter 1966).

J9b Neville Braybrooke   T. S. ELIOT IN THE SOUTH SEAS   1966

Typescript   carbon copy   with autograph corrections   6 pp. (25.4 × 20.4 cm.)

"Final corrected draft" of the article published in *T. S. Eliot: The Man and His Work*, edited by Allen Tate (New York, 1966).

J10a Neville Braybrooke   [T. S. ELIOT]   1966–67

Typescript with autograph corrections   49 pp. (25.5 × 20.3 cm.)

First draft of an essay for the "Christian Perspective Series."

J10b Neville Braybrooke   [T. S. ELIOT]   1967

Typescript with autograph corrections   55 pp. (25.4 × 20.3 cm.)

"Final draft" of *T. S. Eliot: A Critical Essay*, published in the series "Contemporary Writing in Christian Perspective," edited by Roderick Jellema (Grand Rapids, Michigan: William B. Eerdmans, 1967).

J11a [Harvey Breit]   FOUR QUARTETS [a review]   1943

Autograph manuscript   draft copy   9 pp. (31.9 × 20.2 cm.) including 2 pp. cut short.

J11b [Harvey] Breit   FOUR QUARTETS [a review]   1943

Typescript   8 pp. (28 × 21.6 cm.)

J12 David Daiches   ON POETRY AND POETS [a review]

Corrected typescript in carbon with autograph inscription signed 2 pp. (33 × 20.2 cm.)

"Published in *The Listener*."

J13 Una Ellis-Fermor   T. S. ELIOT   THE DEVELOPING DRAMA-TIST   1939

Autograph notes   1 p. (26 × 17 cm.)

Inserted loosely in a copy of *The Family Reunion* (London, 1939) A 33 a. (6)

J14 V. H. F[riedlander]. COLLECTED POEMS 1909–1935 BY T. S. ELIOT [a review]

Typescript   carbon copy   2 pp. (26.8 × 20.2 cm.)

With an autograph note on page one, signed H[erbert]. E. P[almer].: "Excellent short article on Eliot by Miss Friedlander. I believe this review was printed in Country Life but I am not sure."

J15a G. Wilson Knight   T. S. ELIOT   SOME PERSONAL IMPRES-SIONS

Autograph manuscript   draft copy with revisions   12 pp. (3 pp. 32.4 × 20.4; 9 pp. 25.4 × 20.3 cm.)

An early draft of the article in the *Sewanee Review*

J15b G. Wilson Knight   T. S. ELIOT   SOME LITERARY IMPRES-SIONS

Autograph manuscript with revisions signed 26 pp. and a title page (32.5 × 20.3 cm.)

A note in autograph on the title page: "For the Sewanee Review com-missioned."

J16 [John Lehmann]   T. S. ELIOT   1947

Typescript mimeograph copy for radio broadcast with inscription signed 5 pp. (32.9 × 20.4 cm.)

The text of a B.B.C. broadcast in the series, "Studies in English Litera-ture." The date of recording is given as 23 September 1947. It was broadcast in the Far Eastern Programme 28 October 1947.

J17 John Lehmann   ENGLISH LITERATURE   1936–1946 February 1947

Typescript   signed   26 pp. (25.4 × 20.2 cm.)

Includes references to Eliot under "II. The Poets" (pp. 2–8).

J18 [Frank V. Morley]   WEEK-END GUESTS   [1934–35]

Typescript carbon copy with autograph revision 3 pp. (25.6 × 20.4 cm.)

Fictionalized narrative of an event near Pike's Farm, Morley's home in Surrey: "Uncle Tom," arriving by car, has a collision with Frank Morley's son, Donald, riding on his bicycle. After a quick visit to the hospital Uncle Tom, Donald, and others arrive happily at the house for lunch. Frank V. Morley, younger brother of Christopher Morley and a colleague of Eliot's at Faber and Faber, published memoirs of Eliot in *T. S. Eliot: The Man and His Work* (1966). There he mentions "Uncle Tom's" visits to Pike's Farm, as well as his son Donald (age 9 in 1935), but not this particular incident.

J19a Herbert E. Palmer   THE CHASTE WAND

Typescript   carbon copy (1 p.) and autograph manuscript (5 pp.) with autograph revisions and miscellaneous notes 6 pp. (varied sizes, approximately 25 × 20 cm.)

An early draft.

J19b Herbert E. Palmer   THE CHASTE WAND

Typescript with autograph revisions signed 6 pp. (25.4 × 20.1 cm.)

Autograph footnote added on page 1: "The framework of this conception was published in *New Britain,* two years ago. Since then I have revised and more than doubled it, and now present it in its final form."

J20 Herbert E. Palmer   [ON THE POETRY OF T. S. ELIOT]

Autograph manuscript with revisions   25 pp. (25.4 × 20.3 cm.)

J21a Herbert E. Palmer   THE HOAX AND EARNEST OF *THE WASTE LAND*   1932–33

Typescript with autograph revisions   signed 14 pp. (25.6 × 20.5 cm.)

The 14 pages include two versions of pages 10 and 11: an earlier version of page 10 in autograph, and an earlier version of the conclusion, page 11, in typescript, signed.

J21b Herbert E. Palmer   THE HOAX AND EARNEST OF *THE WASTE LAND*   1933

Galley proof with autograph revisions   3 pp. (68 × 21.3 cm.)

Stamped on first galley "9 Feb 1933." The article was published in *The Dublin Magazine*, VIII. 2 (April–June 1933) 11–19. A footnote on p. 11 indicates that the article was written in 1931.

J22a Herbert E. Palmer   THE SAHARA (*WITH APOLOGIES TO T. S. ELIOT AND SOME OTHERS*)

Autograph manuscript with revisions signed   5 pp. (25.5 × 20.2 cm.)

An early draft, with an earlier title "New Year Illuminations" cancelled, and many variant readings from the published text in *Cinder Thursday* (London, 1931). This poem was omitted from *Cinder Thursday* in *The Collected Poems of Herbert Edward Palmer* (London, 1933[1932]).

J22b Herbert E. Palmer   THE SAHARA (*WITH APOLOGIES TO P.* [sic] *S. ELIOT*)

Typescript in carbon with autograph revisions signed   3 pp. (25.5 × 20.7 cm.)

A later draft than J22a. With variant readings from the text in *Cinder Thursday*.

J22c Herbert E. Palmer   [THE SAHARA]

Autograph manuscript with revisions signed   5pp. (25.4 × 20.3 cm.)

A later draft than J22b, but with variant readings from the published version.

J22d Herbert E. Palmer   [THE SAHARA]

Autograph manuscript incomplete with a few revisions   3 pp. (25.4 × 20.3 cm.)

Early drafts of certain pages.

J22e Herbert E. Palmer   THE SAHARA (*WITH APOLOGIES TO T. S. ELIOT*)

Autograph manuscript with revisions signed   5 pp. (25.5 × 20.3 cm.)

A late draft with instruction on p. 1, "Two carbons."

J23a Brigit Patmore   MEMOIRS OF T. S. ELIOT

Autograph note   3pp. (16×13.7 cm.)

On two sheets, with notes concerning Mrs. St. John H[utchinson]. on verso of one. Mrs. Hutchinson and Brigit Patmore were friends of Vivien and T. S. Eliot at the time of their marriage in 1915.

J23b Brigit Patmore   T. S. ELIOT   SOME EARLY MEMORIES

Autograph manuscript   signed   31 pp. (22.8×17.7 cm.) in a spiral bound notebook.

Develops and extends the brief notes in J23a especially about Vivien and T. S. Eliot together. "There seemed to be nothing that she & Tom did not take with a terrible seriousness. It was slightly exhausting, and it explained why Vivien said once, with a sigh: 'The frightful time I have with Tom.' How was it she could make him gay at times—even with a schoolboy sense of humour. . . ."

J23c Brigit Patmore   T. S. ELIOT   SOME EARLY MEMORIES

Typescript   two carbon copies   10 pp. each (28×21.6 cm.)

A transcript of J23b.

J24 [George Santayana]   [THE THOUGHT OF T. S. ELIOT]

Autograph manuscript with revision   1 p. (25.4×20.3 cm.)

"The thought . . . is subterranean without being profound . . . peep and run intuition appears in his leading ideas as well as in the detail of his appreciations . . . he hopes to set up barriers of taste, to keep mankind from touching the bottom or from quite seeing the light."

J25 George Santayana   TRAGIC PHILOSOPHY   1936

Autograph manuscript   23 pp. (27.5×21.1 cm.)

Written to comment on certain allusions to his work (*Scrutiny* IV. 3 [December 1935]), particularly to his view of T. S. Eliot's contrast between Shakespeare and Dante. Published in *Scrutiny* IV. 4 (March 1936) 365–76.

J26 [Henry Sherek]   T. S. ELIOT

Typescript   carbon   copy   with   autograph   revisions   4 pp. (25.3 ×
20.2 cm.)

A memoir of their first meeting ("after I had decided to do *The Cocktail Party*"), and their subsequent personal relations.

J27 [Edith Sitwell]   FIRST MEETING WITH TOM

Autograph manuscript draft copy with revisions   2 pp. (38.3 ×
24.5 cm.)

In a large notebook (Number 308).

J28 [Edith Sitwell]   SOME NOTES ON THE TECHNIQUE OF
T. S. ELIOT'S EARLY POEMS

Typescript   carbon copy   5 pp. (26 × 20.2 cm.)

J29 [Edith Sitwell]   T. S. ELIOT

Autograph manuscript with revisions   8 pp. (33 × 20.7 cm.)

J30 Edith Sitwell   [ON *THE COCKTAIL PARTY* IN THE THEA-
TRE]   1950

Autograph note with revisions   1 p. (32 × 19.5 cm.)

In a large notebook (Number 231).

J31 Edith Sitwell   T. S. ELIOT

Autograph manuscript with revisions   draft copy   33 pp. (31.9 ×
19.8 cm.)

In a large notebook (Number 235), signed on p. 1. Published in *Aspects
of Modern Poetry* (London, 1934).

J32 [Ruthven Todd]   [MEMOIR OF T. S. ELIOT]   1965

Autograph manuscript with revisions   5 pp. (30.5 × 21.2 cm.)

J33 M[ary]. T[revelyan].   [ON T. S. ELIOT]

Autograph note signed "M. T." on flyleaf of *The Art of T. S. Eliot* by

Helen Gardner (London, 1949), given to her by T. S. Eliot. Mary Trevelyan writes below Eliot's signature: "T. S. Eliot thought this the best book written about him."

J34 M[ary]. T[revelyan].   [ON T. S. ELIOT]   1947

Autograph note on flyleaf of *The Complete Nonsense of Edward Lear* (1947): "M. Trevelyan from T. S. E. Christmas 1947. One of T. S. E.'s favorite authors M.T."

J35 Mary [Trevelyan]   [ON *THE CONFIDENTIAL CLERK*]

Autograph notes signed "Mary"   3 pp. (32.4 × 20.4 cm.)

Lines of the play are quoted with critical notes addressed to Eliot.

J36 [Rex Warner]   T. S. ELIOT *SELECTED PROSE*   EDITED BY JOHN HAYWARD [a review]

Autograph manuscript with revisions   4 pp. (32.4 × 20.2 cm.)

K

MUSICAL SETTINGS, FOREIGN

TRANSLATION, AND ICONOGRAPHY

Manuscripts and other original materials are arranged under each heading in approximate chronological order.

MUSICAL SETTINGS

K1 Denis ApIvor   THE HOLLOW MEN   (Words by T. S. Eliot)
1939

Autograph manuscript of the musical score signed 50 pp. (35 × 26 cm.)
In decorated gray paper boards and cloth spine.

With autograph note by the composer on verso of flyleaf: "Composed
in 1939   Original orchestral version destroyed and work was re-orches-
trated in 1949   First Performance   BBC Concert Hall London   Conductor Constant Lambert   1950   Published Oxford University Press
1951" (E4e). With autograph notes and markings in the score by the
conductor. He does not want the words, "A penny for the Old Guy"
and "Mistah Kurtz—he dead," to be spoken, as the composer planned.
These and other changes were incorporated in the printed text. The
composer contributed an essay, "Setting *The Hollow Men* to Music,"
to *T. S. Eliot: A Symposium for his Seventieth Birthday* (New York,
1958).

K2 Denis ApIvor   LANDSCAPES (Words by T. S. Eliot)   1950

Autograph manuscript of the musical score signed 76 pp. (30 × 23 cm.)
1953

Five poems—*New Hampshire, Virginia, Usk, Rannoch by Glencoe,
Cape Ann*—are set for tenor voice, flute, clarinet, horn, and a string trio
(violin, viola, cello). Composed in 1950, and first performed in 1953.

K3 Camillo Togni   OPUS 34.   CORO DI T. S. ELIOT   (Da 'Assassinio nella Cattedrale'; Parte II, Coro IV). A chorus from *Murder in
the Cathedral,* translated by Alberto Castelli, set for five voices.

Autograph manuscript of the musical score   24 pp. (34.8 × 25 cm.)

In paper covers, wire-stitched. Published in 1962 (E4u).

FOREIGN TRANSLATION

K4 FOUR QUARTETS   [in German translation]

Typescript carbon copy, with autograph correction 17 pp. (33 ×
21.5 cm.)

The translation is unidentified. Note in autograph at the top of page 1:
"Juli-version 3. kopie." The translation differs from the published version by Nora Wydenbruck.

ICONOGRAPHY

K5 Wyndham Lewis STUDY OF T. S. ELIOT [1920–25?]

Pencil drawing on paper signed matted and framed (10 13/16″ ×
8 9/16″ inside mat, and 17 1/2″ × 15 1/4″ overall)

K6 Wyndham Lewis HEAD OF T. S. ELIOT 1925

Pencil drawing on paper signed matted and framed (11 9/16″ ×
9 11/16″ inside mat, and 21″ × 18 5/8″ overall)

K7 Wyndham Lewis PORTRAIT OF T. S. ELIOT 1949

Charcoal drawing on paper signed matted and framed (21 1/2″ ×
12 1/2″ inside mat, and 33 3/4″ × 23 3/4″ overall)

K8 Jacob Epstein T. S. ELIOT PORTRAIT BUST 1953

Cast Bronze signed "Epstein" (19″ × 18″ × 10″)

Eliot wrote to Ashley Dukes, 2 April 1953 (G658) of having gone "last
Saturday [28 March] to look at the completed bronze." For a public
showing, scheduled for 14 May, Eliot agreed to say a few words ("I
should like to do this to please Epstein, as I have taken such a great
liking to him"). Dukes acquired the bust in 1953 and kept it at the
Mercury Theatre with T. E. Hulme's bust by Epstein (Ashley Dukes
to Samuel Hines, I19, 14 January 1954). The bust of Eliot is illustrated
in profile on the back cover of An Exhibition . . . of T. S. Eliot (University of Texas at Austin, 1961).

K9 R[obert]. S[tewart]. Sheriffs PORTRAIT OF T. S. ELIOT (a
profile)

Watercolor and ink drawing on paper   signed "S"   matted and framed (7 3/4″ × 6 7/8″ inside mat).

Sheriffs (1906–60) published caricatures in *Punch,* where an obituary appeared 4 January 1961.

K10 Feliks Topolski   HONORIS CAUSA [Portrait of T. S. Eliot in academic robe] 1961

Oil on canvas   signed   "Feliks Topolski 61"   framed (45″ × 37″ inside frame, and 52 1/2″ × 41″ overall).

Topolski was an official war artist in Poland (1940–45) before making London his residence.

K11 Gerald Kelly   T. S. ELIOT IN MY STUDIO   1965

Oil on canvas   signed "Kelly '65."   Under glass in a gilt frame (45″ × 34 1/2″ inside frame, and 52 1/2″ × 41 1/2″ overall)

Gerald Kelly, president of the Royal Academy 1949–54, had painted state portraits of King George VI and Queen Elizabeth. Though dated 1965 on the canvas, Eliot's portrait was begun long before. Mrs. Eliot wrote in a letter, 27 August 1961 (I39): "Sir Gerald Kelly, who asked Tom and me to sit for him, is painting hard to complete our portraits before we go away as he wants to exhibit them in next year's Royal Academy." On 18 June 1962 (I40) she wrote: "Gerald Kelly's portrait of Tom wearing a raincoat hangs in this year's summer exhibition at the Royal Academy, and will eventually rest (if we can prevent the artist from tinkering with it—no easy thing) in our drawing room. It has been much admired, and rightly so, as Sir Gerald has caught Tom's spiritual nobility..."

Fifteen hundred copies of this book have been printed by the
Printing Division of The University of Texas at Austin.
The title page is hand-set Palatino Italic designed by Hermann Zapf,
with the text set in Caledonia on Creme Blanc Laid paper
with Columbia Bayside cloth used for binding.
Design and typography by William R. Holman